DIFFUSION
IN BODY-CENTERED
CUBIC METALS

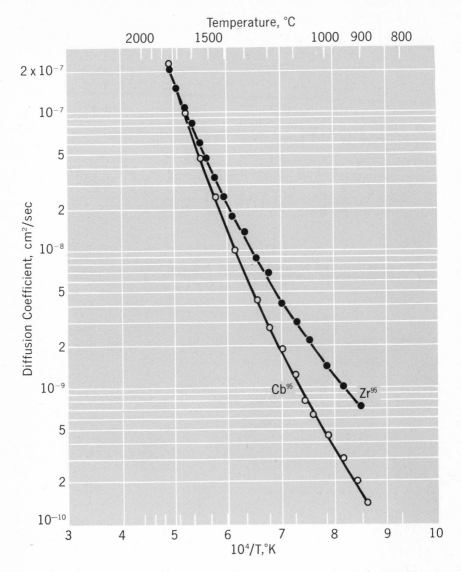

Temperature Dependence of Diffusion of Zr^{95} and Cb^{95} in bcc Zr

Recent studies have shown that the diffusion behavior of some bcc metals, when viewed over a broad temperature range, deviates from the Arrhenius law for the linear temperature dependence of the diffusivity. These curves, taken from Chapter 3, p 35, are typical of the curves found experimentally for the so-called anomalous bcc metals. In an attempt to compile the most recent findings on diffusion in bcc metals, this book examines the experimental verification of the anomaly and sets forth various attempts to explain it on a theoretical basis.

DIFFUSION
IN BODY-CENTERED
CUBIC METALS

Papers presented
at the International
Conference on Diffusion
in Body-Centered Cubic Materials
Gatlinburg, Tennessee
September 16 to 18, 1964

 AMERICAN SOCIETY FOR METALS
Metals Park, Ohio

Preface

In view of the increasing importance of bcc metals in nuclear, space, and other high-temperature applications, it was thought appropriate that a conference be held on the subject of Diffusion in Body-Centered Cubic Materials. Much work has appeared recently with but scant theoretical information with which to explain the results. The purpose of this conference was to assimilate these experimental data in order to get a clearer and more unified concept of the diffusion process in bcc metals and to provide a base for further theoretical treatments and experimental investigations.

The conference, held in Gatlinburg, Tennessee, at the Mountain View Hotel on September 16–18, 1964, was co-sponsored by the Oak Ridge Chapter of ASM and the Oak Ridge National Laboratory. The conference was attended by one hundred and fifty scientists from the United States, Canada, and Europe.

We are most grateful for additional financial support provided by the National Science Foundation and the National Aeronautics and Space Administration. To their representatives, Michael Gaus at NSF and R. R. Nash at NASA, we are most appreciative for their assistance in these matters. We thank the Union Carbide Corporation for being such generous hosts at the reception prior to the conference dinner and Professor Henry Eyring, University of Utah, the speaker at the conference dinner.

The conference would not have been successful without the assistance of D. D. Cowen, who handled all the arrangements. We also wish to thank T. S. Lundy and M. S. Wechsler, who with one of us (F. R. W.) served as the program committee.

Oak Ridge National Laboratory   J. A. WHEELER, JR.
Oak Ridge, Tennessee   F. R. WINSLOW
April, 1965

Contents

Part 2. Lattice Dynamics

Part 3. Diffusion by Stress Relaxation Methods

8. The Measurement of Diffusion Coefficients by Internal Friction 131

R. GIBALA AND C. A. WERT

9. Diffusion of Interstitial Impurities in Body-Centered Cubic Metals 149

DANIEL N. BESHERS

Part 4. Chemical and Tracer Diffusion

10. Diffusion in Body-Centered Cubic Transition Metals—a Theoretical Critique...............................155

DAVID LAZARUS

Part 6. Discussion

PART 1

Introduction and Survey of Experimental Work

Chapter 1
Application of Diffusion Theory to the Body-Centered Cubic Structures

A. D. LE CLAIRE

There is a good deal of theoretical work on diffusion in metals—generally—and we believe we have a fair understanding of many of the processes involved. But there is, to my knowledge, no theoretical treatment that recognizes any established fundamental difference between diffusion in bcc metals and diffusion in metals of other structures—a difference, that is, that would be a genuine source of material for a paper under this title. This, of course, is simply because, until quite recently, there appeared to be no feature of diffusion in bcc metals sufficiently striking to warrant drawing any distinction from other structures. In fact it may be a little surprising that differences in structure reflect so little in differences in diffusion behavior. Even metals that are strongly anisotropic are often disappointingly near-isotropic in their diffusion behavior.

During the last few years, however, there has been considerable effort to measure diffusion in bcc metals, and this work has made it appear that the diffusion behavior of at least some of the bcc metals might differ fundamentally from that of other metals. These metals are γ-U (1–3), β-Ti (4), β-Zr (5–11) and maybe V (12, 13). What is particularly disturbing is that only these three or four are different—in experimental results reported so far anyway—and most bcc metals still show no unusual features in their diffusion behavior.

Consequently, if the results on these anomalous metals—as they have come to be called—really represent true lattice diffusion behavior, then we have, it seems, a major theoretical problem in trying to understand them and in trying to understand why only so few of the bcc metals behave in this way. If any diffusion theory is to be specifically applied to bcc structures, it is needed at this point. Thus, this paper will be concerned mainly with the situation presented by these results.

The author is with the Solid State Physics Division, Atomic Energy Research Establishment, Harwell, England.

3

It may be useful, first, to summarize briefly what we mean by "normal" behavior in metal diffusion so that we can show how the anomalous metals are anomalous.

"Normal" Diffusion

There are probably three essential features of the results of diffusion measurements—at least self-diffusion measurements—that may be said to characterize normal diffusion behavior:

1. The temperature dependence of D is almost always accurately described by the Arrhenius law

$$D = A \exp\left(-Q/RT\right) \tag{1}$$

It is generally found that the more carefully D is measured, the more accurately the law is obeyed, that is, the more closely the points lie on a straight line when $\log D$ is plotted against $1/T$. The terms Q and A are independent of temperature. Where departures from this law have been found, they have so very often been successfully accounted for as associated with some crystallographic or magnetic transformation or as due to simultaneous operation of two or more diffusion processes. Examples of the latter are lattice plus grain-boundary diffusion or lattice plus dislocation diffusion or, in the instance of ionic crystals like AgBr, vacancy plus interstitialcy diffusion, that is, two separate and distinguishable lattice mechanisms.

2. The activation energy Q is roughly proportional to the melting point. For self-diffusion in metals we have the relation

$$Q = 34T_m \tag{2}$$

which seems accurate to $\pm 20\%$. There are other correlations too, such as the one with the latent heat of melting.

$$Q = 16.5L_m \tag{3}$$

3. The pre-exponential factor A seems always to be within an order of magnitude of 0.5, that is, it is between 0.05 and 5.0 cm²/sec.

These three properties have come to be regarded as characterizing "normal" diffusion because they are common to self-diffusion in such a wide range of fcc, bcc, hcp and other structured metals. Any noticeable departures from them have usually meant that the validity of the results was seriously doubted. In a number of instances, later measurements have produced results showing normal behavior. Interesting and salutary examples are provided by Cr and Sn, which were, at one time, anomalous metals (14, 15) but are no longer (16–19)!

As to the theoretical understanding of these properties, I think the reasons for the temperature dependence being of this Arrhenius form are now quite clear. All theoretical discussions of diffusion processes lead to expressions of this form, at least in giving the exponential term as the dominant source of the temperature variation.

We know too, especially from thermal expansion and quenching experiments, that normal diffusion, in fcc metals at least, takes place by the vacancy mechanism. The quantity Q is then the sum of the enthalpies of movement H_m and of formation E_f of vacancies, and theoretical calculations of this sum, in the very few instances when they have been made, agree with values obtained in experiments.

One cannot say much about the relations given in Eq 2 and 3. Their physical basis has always been obscure. One accepts them because they work so well and because they are plausible expressions of the close relation there must be between atomic mobility and lattice binding.

The size of the pre-exponential term A is reasonably well understood, at least its order of magnitude. The usual expression for A is

$$A = \gamma \alpha^2 f \nu \exp \left[(S_f + S_m)/R \right] \tag{4}$$

where γ, a geometrical factor, is 1 for bcc and fcc metals; α is the lattice parameter and $\alpha^2 \sim 10^{-15}$; f, the correlation factor, is 0.78 for self-diffusion in fcc metals and 0.72 for self-diffusion in bcc metals; ν is a lattice vibration frequency that is not always well defined but will be somewhere around the Debye frequency, say $5 \cdot 10^{12}$; S_f and S_m are the formation entropy and activation entropy of movement of a vacancy. Thus

$$A \sim 5 \cdot 10^{-3} \exp \left[(S_f + S_m)/R \right] \tag{5}$$

If $S_f + S_m$ is positive and $\sim 5R$, we can account for the observed magnitude of A.

The only direct theoretical calculations of $S_f + S_m$ for a metal are those of Huntington, Shirn and Wajda (20), and these do yield a positive $S_f + S_m$ for vacancy diffusion, although less than $5R$—actually $\sim R$. Calculations of this type are difficult to do and results are very sensitive to the assumptions made, so this disagreement need not be taken too seriously. The important point is that normal metals evidently have appreciably positive values for $S_f + S_m$.

One can go a little further. For a few metals S_f has been measured and turns out to be $\sim R$. Thus

$$A \sim 1.5 \cdot 10^{-2} \exp (S_m/R)$$

So, we can say all normal metals have positive S_m, because in every instance $A > 10^{-2}$. It may be added that positive entropies of activation seem to be a general feature not only of self-diffusion in metals but of diffusion generally in all solids. The well-known Zener relation

$$S_m = -\lambda H_m \, \partial(\mu/\mu_0)/\partial T \tag{6}$$

also predicts a positive S_m. The term λ is the fraction of the activation energy H_m that goes into producing elastic-strain energy in the lattice, μ is a shear modulus and μ_0 its value at 0 K. The quantity S_m is always positive because $\partial\mu/\partial T$ is always negative.

This equation gives a remarkably good account of S_m for interstitial solute diffusion in metals with λ actually equal to one. A similar but rather more empirical expression relating the total entropy S to the total activation energy Q also gives a very good account of the observed values of S for self-diffusion in normal metals, with $\lambda \sim 0.55$ for fcc metals.

This is perhaps surprising because, as Huntington, Shirn and Wajda have emphasized, the Zener equation really represents only one of several contributions to the total S. Some of these can in fact be negative, but they do nevertheless add up to give a net positive result.

So it is not too clear why the Zener expression gives such a good account of things. It really should be accorded only the status of a semi-empirical correlation. Its virtue lies in the fact that it works rather than in the rigor of its derivation.

To sum up, the general features of normal diffusion are accurate obedience to the Arrhenius equation, Q's $\sim 34 T_m$ and A's $\sim 5 \cdot 10^{-2}$ to 5, corresponding to appreciably positive entropies of activation. It is against this background that we have to consider the results on the so-called anomalous metals. The more notorious ones, γ-U, β-Ti and β-Zr, appear to violate every one of these canons of normal behavior.

"Anomalous" Metals

Figure 1 shows Federer and Lundy's measurements of self-diffusion in β-Zr (10). The Arrhenius plot is very clearly *nonlinear*. So, if the results are to be represented by a single equation, A and Q must be markedly

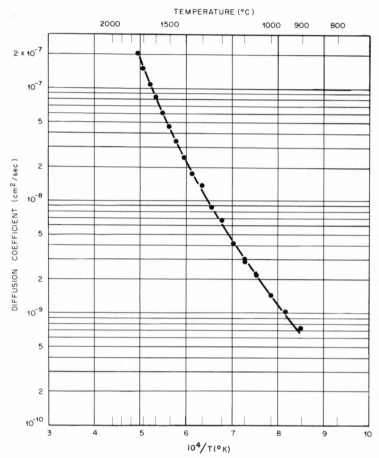

Fig. 1. Temperature dependence of diffusion of Zr^{95} in bcc Zr

temperature dependent. This is most unusual and unexpected, but equally unusual and unexpected is the fact that the values of A and Q derived from the plot cover ranges well *below* the normal values.

Murdock (4) has recently made some measurements of self-diffusion in β-Ti at Oak Ridge, and these give results very similar to these on Zr.

Figure 2 shows measurements made by Rothman and his group (3), Adda and Kirianenko (2), and Bochvar (1) for self-diffusion in γ-U. The results agree quite well. At least two of the plots—from the work of Rothman and of Bochvar—show some evidence of curvature, but there are too few measurements and the temperature range is unfortunately too restricted, to be sure about this. Again A and Q are well below normal. There are a number of measurements of tracer solute diffusion in these

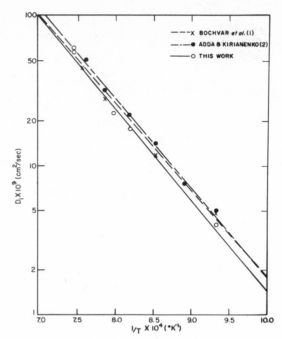

Fig. 2. Arrhenius plot for self-diffusion in γ-U

metals—in γ-U by Rothman and his group (21), in Ti by Tomlin and his group (22), and in Zr and Ti (less extensive measurements) by the Oak Ridge group (4, 12). Like the self-diffusion measurements, these measurements show both curvature and anomalously low values of A and Q.

There is a fourth metal, V, which also has some claims to be included among the anomalous, because its Arrhenius plot is not linear. Figure 3 shows Peart's measurements (13) on this metal. There seem to be two straight lines here rather than a continuous curve, but at least the Q's and A's are within the normal range, and so this metal is not as strikingly anomalous as the others.

Figure 4 shows all the known values of A for self-diffusion in metals (23) and exhibits the extent to which the behavior of U, Ti and Zr is abnormal. Note first that nearly all the values lie in the band 0.05 to 5.0. Most of the values not in this band are from measurements not noted for precision. Note also that *within* the band there is no discernible difference between the bcc and the other metals—no tendency for the bcc points to be higher or lower than the others. But the values for U, Ti and Zr fall well below it and do indeed appear to belong to quite a different class. They also all correspond to appreciably *negative* entropies of activation.

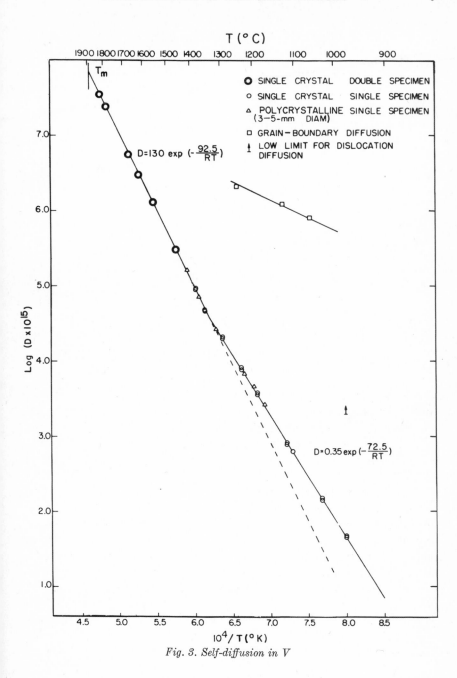

Fig. 3. Self-diffusion in V

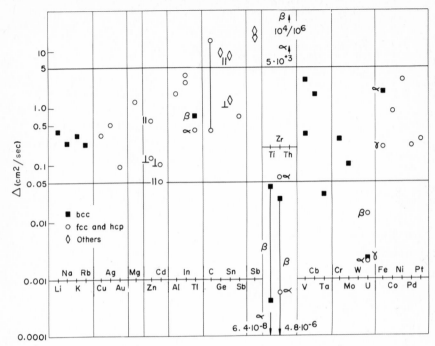

Fig. 4. Known values of A for self-diffusion in metals

Figure 5 shows an up-to-date plot of Q against the absolute melting point. A thick line is drawn for $Q = 34T_m$, corresponding to Eq 2. The points cluster quite well about the line. Once more it is important to note there is no very obvious difference between the disposition of the bcc points about the line and that of the other structures, except again for U, Ti and Zr, all of which fall very much *below* the 20% band, which contains most of the other points.

There is nevertheless quite a spread of points. This is not, of course, too surprising because it can hardly be expected that Q depends on T_m alone. And of course there have been attempts to find better correlations by taking other properties into account. One of the more recent is that of Sherby and Simnad (24). They divided the metals into structural groups and then sought a separate correlation for each group with T_m and with the valency. They worked from actual values of D and then assumed $A = 1$ for all metals, but if one works with the actual reported values of Q, one gets a slightly different correlation and maybe a slightly better fit. The result is

$$Q = RT_m(K + 1.5V) \tag{7}$$

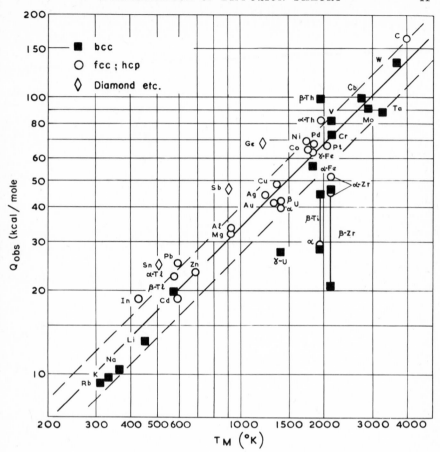

Fig. 5. Q versus absolute melting point. Q = 34 T_m

where the constant K is 13 for bcc metals, 15.5 for fcc and hcp metals and 20 for metals of more open structures, diamond, Sn, etc., and V is the normal chemical valency. For the transition metals a good fit seems to be achieved by taking V as the lowest valency commonly encountered in chemical combination. This seems less arbitrary than the practice of Sherby and Simnad who used $V = 0$ for U, Pd and Pt and $V = 3$ for all other transition metals.

Figure 6 shows this correlation. There is clearly a considerable improvement on the previous one (Fig. 5), and most points now lie within a 10% band. But it does nothing to bring γ-U, β-Ti and β-Zr into conformity. They still appear as exceptional metals, and perhaps even more so than

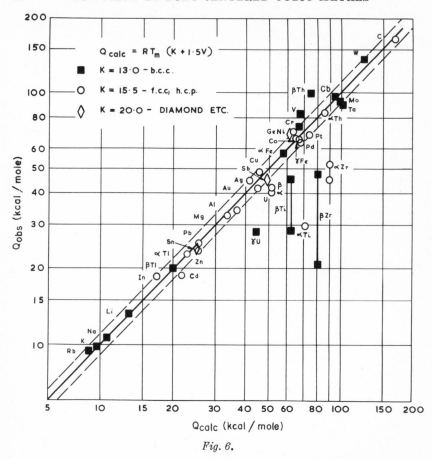

Fig. 6.

before. Refining the correlation does not alter the anomaly they appear to present.

Discussion

The big question that is getting a great deal of attention among persons interested in bcc metals is whether we are really faced here with some fundamentally new diffusion behavior—and many persons seem to be convinced that the results are sufficiently well established for this to be true—or whether there is a possible explanation along lines proved successful before, which would not therefore call for any fundamental departure from our present understanding of diffusion in metals.

Those who support the "surely-there's-a-simple-explanation" approach base their arguments on the hypothesis that there are two or more mechanisms operating in instances of so-called anomalous diffusion. Accordingly they begin by trying to fit the curved Arrhenius plots to a sum of two exponential terms

$$D = A_1 \exp\left(-Q_1/RT\right) + A_2 \exp\left(-Q_2/RT\right) \qquad (8)$$

It seems that a very good fit can be obtained, and some of the results are shown in Table 1. These values of A_1, Q_1, A_2 and Q_2 fit the measurements well within experimental error, although because of experimental uncertainties it is not possible to provide unique values.

These results certainly seem most encouraging. The values of A_1 and Q_1, which refer to the mechanism dominant at high temperatures, are perfectly "normal" values. The A_1 values shown for self-diffusion, 1.34 and 1.09, are well inside the commonly encountered range, and the activation energies are within the allowed limits of the melting-point correlation. Also, the fact that the activation energy of Zr is greater than that of Ti is consistent with the fact that the melting point of Zr is higher than that of Ti.

Furthermore, Q_1 for impurity diffusion in Ti decreases steadily as we go from Cb and Mo across the periodic table to Ni, just as present understanding of impurity diffusion would lead us to expect.

If then there are two mechanisms operating, one of them appears to have all the characteristics of normal diffusion behavior. This is most satisfactory because it removes a lot of the sting from the anomaly. The anomalous metals begin to look a lot less anomalous, and the problem is reduced to identifying the second component.

Table 1. Values of Coefficients in Exponential Terms Used by Some to Describe the Mechanisms Operating in Instances of Anomalous Diffusion

Metal	A_1	Q_1	A_2	Q_2
β-Zr.......	1.34	65.2	8.5×10^{-5}	27.7(a)
β-Ti.......	1.09	60.0	3.58×10^{-4}	31.2(b)
Cb in Ti...	20	73	5×10^{-3}	39.3(c)
Mo in Ti...	20	73	8×10^{-3}	43.0
Cr in Ti....	4.9	61	5×10^{-3}	35.3
Mn in Ti...	4.3	58	6.1×10^{-3}	33.7
Fe in Ti....	2.7	55	7.8×10^{-3}	31.6
Co in Ti....	2.0	52.5	1.2×10^{-3}	30.6
Ni in Ti....	2.0	52.5	9.2×10^{-3}	29.6

(a) Lundy and Federer (10), as fitted by Kidson (25).
(b) Murdock *et al.* (4).
(c) Gibbs, Graham and Tomlin (22).

Several possibilities have been suggested for this:

1. The second term may indicate the operation of some additional, intrinsic, lattice-diffusion mechanism in these metals, such as interstitial or interstitialcy diffusion or maybe divacancies or some as yet unrecognized mechanism. The major difficulty with this suggestion is the very small pre-exponential factor in the second term, corresponding to strongly *negative* activation entropies. As we have seen, all other materials in which diffusion has been studied show positive entropies, so one is disinclined to accept this suggestion for the second term, at least until all other possibilities have been eliminated.

2. The second term may represent a contribution from grain-boundary diffusion, a possibility that can be disposed of fairly quickly. Experiments on these anomalous metals have been done mostly with polycrystalline materials but usually the grain size has been large. All authors emphasize their certainty that there was no detectable grain-boundary contribution to their results. The evidence they adduce is the linearity of $\log C$ versus x^2 plots and the absence in autoradiographs of grain-boundary blackening beyond the lattice diffusion zone. One should bear in mind, though, that a sizable grain-boundary contribution may go undetected in a $\log C$ versus x^2 plot if there is much scatter in the points; sometimes in measurements on the anomalous metals there has been a great deal of scatter in the points. The results may not be altogether without objection for this reason. But it certainly seems unlikely that this is the major source of the second term.

3. The second term may reflect a contribution from dislocation diffusion, a more likely possibility. This is a little more difficult to gainsay because a dislocation contribution does not affect the linearity of the $\log C$ versus x^2 plots; it only decreases the slope and leads to an increased D value. Dislocation diffusion is believed to have an activation energy of around half the value for lattice diffusion, so this hypothesis would at least account for the observed values of Q_2. To get an estimate of the dislocation density that would be required to account for the values of A_2, we use the Hart-Mortlock equation (26, 27)

$$D = D_{\text{latt}} + f \frac{C_d}{C_0} D_{\text{disl}} \qquad (9)$$

where f is the fraction of sites on dislocations, C_d is the fractional concentration of diffusant on dislocations and C_0 is the concentration in the lattice. For self-diffusion $C_d/C_0 = 1$, and if we assume a pre-exponential factor of one for dislocation diffusion, then $f \sim 10^{-4}$ for Zr and Ti. This corresponds to a dislocation density of $\sim 10^{10}/\text{cm}^2$, if we take the effective dislocation cross section as ~ 10 atoms.

A_2 for solute diffusion in Ti is larger than that for self-diffusion in Zr and Ti, by a factor of about 10 to 100. This is rather satisfactory because it is in the direction expected. C_d/C_0 for solute diffusion could well be of the order of 10 to 100 because this corresponds to the quite reasonable value of a few tenths electron volt for the solute atom-dislocation binding energy.

However, a dislocation density of 10^{10} per cm^2 is rather high and a little difficult to accept. It is usually assumed that well-annealed metals have a density of 10^5 to 10^6 per cm^2. But this estimate is based on studies of fcc metals; unfortunately there seem to be very few measurements of dislocation densities in bcc metals, and it would be interesting to know if these were characterized by a dislocation density in the annealed condition that is generally higher than that found in fcc metals.

It is relevant to note at this point that the three anomalous metals have in common a phase change to bcc for the diffusion anneal. One might then argue that the transformation could well introduce extra dislocations and bring the density up to the required level of 10^{10}. But this argument is not too easy to sustain because in one or two instances, samples have been given their diffusion anneal only after a lengthy pre-anneal of the sample in the bcc phase and without then letting the temperature fall below the change point. One would imagine that this would remove any excess dislocations before the diffusion began, but when this procedure has been followed, no significant effect on the resulting values of D has occurred.

Perhaps it is particularly difficult to anneal dislocations out of bcc metals, and the pre-anneals were not long enough or carried out at a sufficiently high temperature. Perhaps dislocations are particularly strongly locked in by impurities in these metals or form particularly stable low-angle boundary arrays. We know little about either possibility. We do know, though, that the dislocation structure and other physical properties of a metal can be profoundly influenced by impurity content (28, 30), and we know that the materials used in the experiments on U, Ti and Zr were not free of impurities. It would be interesting to see measurements on very much purer materials annealed under far more stringent vacuum conditions than those usually used, and perhaps to study the effect of much more extensive pre-annealing and of varying the pre-anneal treatment.

4. The second term may result from a strong attraction between vacancies and some impurity in the metal, a possibility suggested by Kidson (25). This means there will be extra vacancies in the metal in

addition to the normal intrinsic vacancy concentration. These will be present as associated vacancy–impurity-atom pairs, and it is the diffusion of these pairs that gives rise to the second term in Eq 8. If we assume a fairly tight binding of the pair so that we can ignore the effects of dissociation, the first and second terms of Eq 8 may be written as the first and second terms in the equation

$$D = a^2 w_0 c_v f_0 + g a^2 w_1 c \left[1 + \frac{1}{z} \exp\left(\frac{E_f - B}{RT} \right) \right]^{-1} f\left(\frac{w_1}{w_2} \right) \qquad (10)$$

where a is the lattice constant, w_0 the vacancy jump rate in pure metal, c_v the free vacancy concentration and f_0 the self-diffusion correlation factor. In the second term, g is a geometrical factor, w_1 is the jump rate for exchange of an associated vacancy with a solvent atom, c is the impurity concentration and $f(w_1/w_2)$ is the correlation factor for diffusion by associated vacancies. This is a function of w_1/w_2, w_2 being the impurity jump rate. The bracketed term is the degree of association, z being the coordination number, E_f the free energy to form a vacancy and B its binding energy to an impurity.

Kidson assumed for simplicity that $g = 1$, $w_1 = w_0$, $f = f_0$ and finally that the binding energy was so large that the bracketed term was near unity, that is, that nearly every impurity atom had a vacancy associated with it. Under these conditions

$$D = a^2 w_0 c_v f_0 + a^2 w_0 c f_0 \qquad (11)$$

so that $A_1 = a^2 \nu_0 f_0 \exp\left[(S_m^{(0)} + S_f)/R \right]$ $A_2 = a^2 \nu_0 c f_0 \exp\left(S_m^{(0)}/R \right)$
$Q_1 = H_m^{(0)} + E_f$ $Q_2 = H_m^{(0)}$

and to account for the observed values of A_1 and A_2 we require a concentration of impurity given by

$$c = (A_2/A_1) \exp\left(S_f/R \right) \qquad (12)$$

Taking a reasonable value for S_f based on experimental and theoretical estimates gives $c \sim 4 \cdot 10^{-4}$ for Zr and $c \sim 2 \cdot 10^{-3}$ for Ti. This argument gives a satisfactory account of Q_2, and the values of c are just the order of magnitude of the impurity content of the Zr and Ti used in the experiments. The idea is then a very appealing one and worth pursuing in more detail. Let us comment then on some of the assumptions.

The factor g need not detain us because it is likely to be about *unity* anyway. Its magnitude will depend on whether we are dealing with interstitial or substitutional impurities and on the assumptions we care to make about the allowed jumps of the complex.

Secondly, w_1 may not equal w_0. The presence of the impurity may seriously affect the solvent-atom jump rate in its neighborhood; in particular the activation $E_m{}^{(1)}$ for w_1 jumps may differ sizably from $E_m{}^{(0)}$.

The correlation factor $f(w_1/w_2)$ may play a very important part, that is, if w_2, the impurity jump rate, was $\ll w_1$, the associated vacancy would be relatively immobile and there would be very little contribution to D from vacancy-impurity pairs. This would correspond to a very small f. Also, f would be temperature dependent. At the other extreme, if $w_2 \gg w_1$, then f would tend to a limiting value and would be temperature independent. For interstitial impurities, f would in fact tend toward f_0, the self-diffusion value, and Kidson's assumption would be valid in this instance.

Finally, there is the assumption about the binding energy. If the degree of association really is ~ 1, then B must be at least nearly equal to E_f. If E_f has the conventional value of $\sim \frac{1}{2} Q_1$, then it is around 30 kcal/mole, and this would seem a rather large value for a binding energy. There is, however, some evidence for a binding energy as large as 10 kcal/mole for vacancy-C impurity pairs in α-Fe, from the work of Damask and his colleagues (31) on radiation-damage recovery in solutions of Fe and C, so maybe energies of ~ 30 kcal/mole are not altogether unreasonable. There is also the possibility that in bcc metals E_f is appreciably less than $\frac{1}{2} Q_1$. Sullivan and Weymouth (32, 33) have recently deduced, from the difference in their dilatometric and x-ray thermal-expansion measurements on Na, values of E_f for vacancies of 0.11 and 0.15 ev. These are approximately a quarter to a third of the activation energies for self-diffusion. So, if the same fraction were appropriate for all bcc metals, E_f for Zr and Ti would be in the range of 15 to 23 kcal/mole. Complete vacancy association with impurities in these metals would then require these much smaller binding energies.

It seems, however, more reasonable to suppose that $B < E_f$. The second term in Eq 10 then becomes

$$ga^2 w_1 czf(w_1/w_2) \exp\left[-(E_f - B)/RT\right] \qquad (13)$$

so that

$$A_2 = ga^2 v_1 \exp\left(S_m/R\right)cz\,f(w_1/w_2) \exp\left[(S_f - S_B)/R\right] \qquad (14)$$

and

$$Q_2 = H_m{}^{(1)} + E_f - B \qquad (15)$$

There may also be a contribution to Q_2 from the temperature dependence of f, but this is probably small.

Q_2 still can be satisfactorily accounted for by ascribing suitable values to $H_m^{(1)}$, E_f and B. The activation energy for w_1 jumps, $H_m^{(1)}$, must now be less than Q_2 because we have $B < E_f$.

Comparing A_1 and A_2 we now have for c

$$c = \frac{A_2 f_0 \exp\left(-S_B/R\right)}{A_1 gzf(w_1/w_2)} \tag{16}$$

if we assume $S_m^{(1)} \sim S_m^{(0)}$ and $\nu_1 \sim \nu_0$. Whatever the sign of S_B, the binding entropy, it is unlikely to be numerically greater than S_f. The value of gz could well be as large as 10. So, unless $f(w_1/w_2)$ is very small compared with f_0, it would appear that the values of c required to account for the observed values of A_2/A_1 may be even less than before (Eq 12) and possibly by as much as an order of magnitude. This puts c into the 10^{-5} range, that is, tens of parts per million atomic concentration, and at this level most of the impurities listed in analyses of the materials used in experiments on Zr and Ti become suspect as possibly responsible for the anomalous results obtained!

As to the nature of the impurity, Kidson originally suggested that this might be O in the instance of Zr, but this is in no way settled. It is not impossible that the operative impurity, whatever it might be, could be in solution in the metal in equilibrium with some precipitated compound, a compound either of the impurity with the metal or of the operative impurity with some other impurity. This would mean that changing the total amount of the impurity would not necessarily have any effect on the measured value of D because it would not alter the concentration of impurity in solution. It then might not be easy to identify the operative impurity simply by looking for the effect on D of varying the amounts of different impurities. This might account also for anomalous results from different laboratories, and therefore usually from different sorts of material being in agreement, as in the instance of γ-U, for example. The concentration in such an equilibrium solution might well be temperature dependent too, and this will contribute another term to Q_2.

One thing one can say about the impurity is that it must be rapidly diffusing, otherwise the extra vacancies will be comparatively immobile. This suggests an interstitial impurity, and the necessary large B values seem more likely in this instance, although one cannot rule out the possibility of it being substitutional.

Both Kidson's impurity enhancement model and the dislocation model provide for a possibility that different measurements of D might give

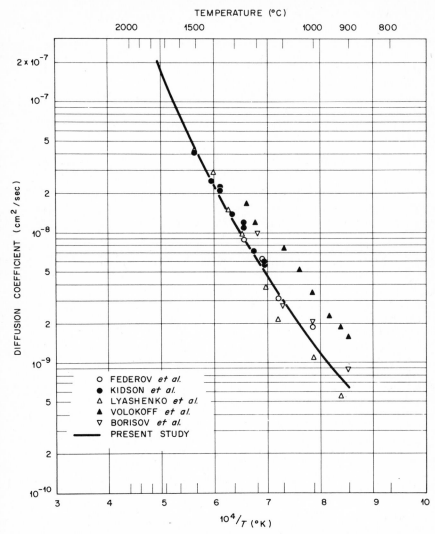

Fig. 7. Comparison of present results with results obtained by other investigators

different results because of differences in the dislocation or impurity content, especially at low temperatures. Any evidence of such behavior would certainly support either of these models. But there is very little data at present from which to draw a conclusion. There is only one measurement on Ti self-diffusion (4). The three measurements (1–3) on γ-U agree fairly well, but there are definite differences. The purer the

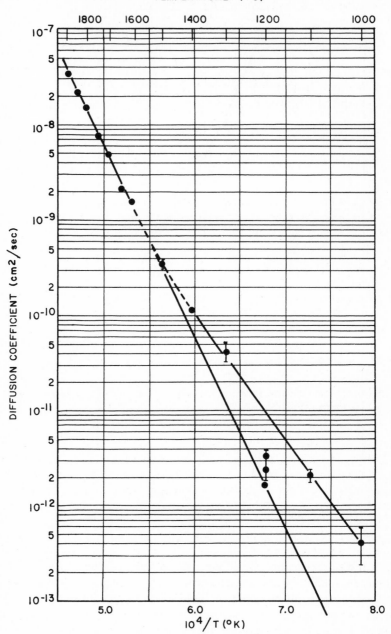

Fig. 8. Temperature dependence of diffusion of V^{48} in V

material, the lower D tends to be. For Zr there are six measurements (5–10), which are shown together in Fig. 7. There does seem to be some evidence here that agreement among them is better at high temperatures than at low, suggesting a possible part played by impurities or dislocations. And finally there is V, which is anomalous only in its showing nonlinear Arrhenius behavior. Figure 8 shows some recent Oak Ridge work on V self-diffusion (12), which is to be compared with the similar Illinois results (13) in Fig. 3. There is very good agreement at high temperatures, in marked contrast with the poor agreement at low temperatures. Here the Illinois results fall well below the Oak Ridge results (by a factor of about 3) and lie on a line about halfway between them and the line extrapolated from high temperatures. In other words, the Illinois results are markedly less "anomalous" than those of Oak Ridge.

Figure 9 is also interesting because of the rejected points. These were rejected because there had been some reaction between the samples and their containment materials. It is tempting to suggest that this reaction served to remove Kidson's impurities and so led to the lower values of D, which, be it noted, lie very close to the line extrapolated from high temperatures!

In summary we may say that these suggestions, proposed to explain the several instances of anomalous behavior, are indeed plausible and difficult at the present time to demolish. The work on V illustrates the fact that measurements in different laboratories can yield results with marked disparity between the degrees of anomaly they present. This must provide a considerable incentive for additional work on all the anomalous metals, with purer materials and more carefully controlled conditions, before it can be asserted with authority that anomalous diffusion is *not* due to either of the causes discussed in 3 and 4 above.

If it should prove possible to make such an assertion, then we shall indeed, it seems, be faced in γ-U, β-Ti and β-Zr with some fundamentally new type of diffusion process that is different from those in all other metals and that cannot be satisfactorily explained within the framework of our present understanding of diffusion.

Apart from providing an explanation of the anomalously low and varying A and Q values, it is worth emphasizing again that an important aspect of the problem will be that of accounting for why this anomalous behavior is found in only three of the bcc metals so far studied.

It has been suggested that there is no reason to be too surprised by a variable A and Q. There are no theoretical reasons why A and Q should be constant, and perhaps we should be surprised that they are as constant as they are in most instances. This is of course true. One might well expect some variation on account of thermal expansion. But a par-

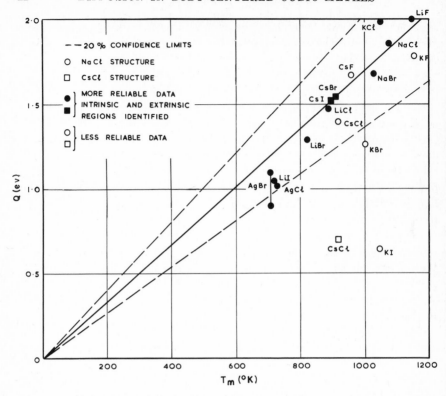

Fig. 9. Correlation between the intrinsic Q and T_m for ionic crystals.
$Q = 1.7 \times 10^{-3} T_m$ *ev; Q = 39 T_m kcal/mole*

ticularly disturbing feature of the present situation is the range of the variation. In Zr, for example, Q is more than doubled (21 to 47 kcal/mole) between the change point at 1136 K and the melting point at 2125 K. This is a very considerable change and is difficult to associate with a single mechanism.

An important and necessary step in providing an explanation would seem to be to establish the type of diffusion mechanism operating in bcc metals generally and in the anomalous ones in particular. Whereas it is now well established on good evidence that in fcc metals diffusion is by a vacancy mechanism, it is worth noting that similar evidence to support a vacancy or any other mechanism in metals of other structures is still wanting. It is usually assumed that the vacancy mechanism is general, but this assumption would appear to be based on the A values for other structures being similar to those for fcc metals and on the Q values for both following common correlations with T_m, etc. But it is very likely that adherence to a common correlation does not necessarily indicate a common mechanism. Figure 9, for which I am indebted to Dr. Barr, goes some way to confirming this. The activation energy for cation diffusion in a number of ionic crystals is shown plotted against their melting points. The correlation is seen to be as good as that for metals (see Fig. 5). The important point to note is that diffusion in the Ag halides is known to be largely by the interstitialcy mechanism and yet the points for AgBr and AgCl fall as well in the correlation band as those for the other crystals, in which there are good reasons to believe the vacancy mechanism alone operates.

A convincing conclusion on the mechanism of diffusion in bcc metals is therefore best sought from other evidence, but this at present is inadequate for the purpose. One fact that does seem established is that exchange or ring mechanisms seem most unlikely to play any major part. One reason for believing this is that the Kirkendall effect seems to be as evident in bcc metals as in fcc metals and in particular has been observed in systems for which the values of A and Q are anomalous, for example, Ti-Cr (34), U-Ti (35) and U-Zr (36). Also, in one or two instances, values of D determined by net-mass-transfer methods [in β-Zr by sintering (6) and in α-Fe by groove smoothing (37)] have been shown to agree well with those from tracer measurements. Such results, as also a recent demonstration (38) of a large Soret effect in β-Zr and β-Ti, would be very difficult to account for on a purely exchange or ring mechanism of diffusion.

The evidence is then strongly in favor of some defect mechanism, but only in Na is there any indication of what this is. Sullivan and Weymouth's expansion experiments (32) clearly indicate vacancies as the dominant defect, but they do not discount (33) the possibility of some interstitial defects too. Also, Barr and Mundy's isotope-effect measurements on Na suggest something more than a simple and straightforward type of vacancy mechanism. (See Chapter 11 in this volume.) In any case, the alkali metals and the transition metals are sufficiently different for there to be little justification of the assumption, based on the vacancy diffusion demonstrated in Na, that there is vacancy diffusion in general in bcc metals. Simmons-Balluffi-type expansion measurements on some other bcc metals would be of great interest and are probably as necessary for determining the nature of the defect in the bcc metals as they were in confirming it for fcc metals.

Historically, theoretical calculations of Q for the various possible mechanisms in Cu and comparison with the observed value provided the first positive indication of vacancy diffusion in close-packed metals. Apart from two conflicting calculations on Na (39, 40), there are no corresponding estimates of Q in bcc metals. Such calculations would naturally be of great value, although the complex electronic structures of the transition metals make such calculations for the metals of interest particularly difficult.

The nature of the defect mechanisms in bcc metals is then very much an open question at the present time. It may be vacancy diffusion. If so, it is likely that the considerable relaxation that may take place around a vacancy in the open bcc structure could alter in some important respect the details of the jump process in these metals. Such a possibility is discussed in Barr and Mundy's paper. It may be interstitialcy diffusion. If so, it is likely that two or more types of interstitialcy jump operate simultaneously. Given that these have different activation energies, we would then have a possible explanation for a variable A and Q. But with present understanding of jump processes, there would still be no means of accounting for the low values of A. Then, too, it may be some as yet unrecognized mechanism, the characteristics of which we can only hope may provide some clue to the origin of abnormally low values of A, should such low values be substantiated, and to the reason these occur only in the three presently supposed anomalous metals.

Acknowledgments. The benefit of numerous discussions I have had with Dr. L. W. Barr and Dr. J. Mundy is gratefully acknowledged.

References

1 A. A. Bochvar, V. G. Kuznetsova and V. S. Sergeev, Second Geneva Conference, Paper P/2306 (1958)
2 Y. Adda and A. Kirianenko, J Nucl Mater, 1, 120 (1959)
3 S. J. Rothman, L. T. Llovd, R. Weil and A. L. Harkness. Trans AIME, 218, 605 (1960)
4 J. F. Murdock, T. S. Lundy and E. E. Stansbury, Acta Met, 12, 1033 (1964)
5 G. B. Fedorov and V. D. Gulyakin, Met i Metalloved Christykh Metal Sb Nauchn Rabot, 1, 170–178 (1959)
6 G. Kidson and J. McGurn, Can J Phys, 39, 1146 (1961)
7 V. S. Lyashenko, V. N. Bykov and L. V. Pavlinov, Fiz Metal i Metalloved, VIII, 362 (1959)
8 D. Volkoff, S. May and Y. Adda, Compt Rend, 251, 2341 (1960)
9 E. V. Borisov, Y. G. Godin, P. L. Gruzin, A. E. Evstyukin and V. S. Ernelyanov, Metallurgy and Metallog, Moscow, 1958, p 291
10 J. I. Federer and T. S. Lundy, Trans AIME, 227, 592 (1963)
11 P. L. Gruzin and G. G. Ryabova, Metallurgy and Metallography of Pure Metals, Gordon and Breach, Science Publishers, Inc., New York, 1962, p 134
12 T. S. Lundy, Oak Ridge Report, ORNL 3617 (June 1964)
13 R. Peart, Chapter 16 in this volume
14 H. W. Paxton and E. G. Gondolf, Archiv Eisenhuettenw, 30, 55 (1959)
15 P. J. Fensham, Austrailian J Sci Res, 3, 91 (1950)
16 W. C. Hagel, Trans AIME, 224, 430 (1962)

17   J. Askill and D. Tomlin, Chapter 18 in this volume
18   J. D. Meakin and E. Klokholm, Trans AIME, **218**, 463 (1960)
19   W. Lange, A. Hässner and I. Berthold, Phys Status Solidi, **1**, 50 (1961)
20   H. B. Huntington, G. A. Shirn and E. S. Wajda, Phys Rev, **99**, 1085 (1955)
21   N. L. Peterson and S. J. Rothman, Chapter 12 in this volume
22   G. B. Gibbs, D. Graham and D. H. Tomlin, Phil Mag, **8**, 1269 (1963)
23   C. J. Smithells, Metals Reference Book, 4th edition, Butterworth, Washington (in press)
24   G. D. Sherby and M. T. Simnad, Trans ASM, **54**, 227 (1961)
25   G. V. Kidson, Can J Phys, **41**, 1563 (1963)
26   E. W. Hart, Acta Met, **5**, 597 (1957)
27   A. J. Mortlock, Acta Met, **8**, 132 (1960)
28   D. Hull, I. D. McIver and W. S. Owen, J Less-Common Metals, **4**, 409 (1962)
29   J. E. Bailey, J Nuclear Mater, **7**, 300 (1962)
30   J. A. Morrison and L. S. Salter, Phys Letters, **9**, 110 (1964)
31   A. C. Damask *et al.*, J Phys Chem Solids, **23**, 221 (1962); Acta Met, **12**, 331, 341 (1964)
32   G. A. Sullivan and J. W. Weymouth, Phys Letters, **9**, 89 (1964)
33   G. A. Sullivan and J. W. Weymouth, to be published in Phys Rev
34   R. F. Peart and D. H. Tomlin, Phys Chem Solids, **23**, 1169 (1962)
35   Y. Adda and J. Philibert, Compt Rend, **247**, 80 (1958)
36   Y. Adda, J. Philibert and H. Farrogi, Rev Met, **54**, 597
37   Young and H. Mykura, to be published
38   H. G. Feller and H. Wever, J Phys Chem Solids, **24**, 969 (1963)
39   S. Machlup, J Chem Phys, **24**, 169 (1956)
40   S. Machlup, TID 16526 (August 1962)

Chapter 2
A Summary of Impurity Diffusion in the
Beta Phase of Titanium

D. Graham

The temperature dependence of measured tracer self-diffusivities representing volume diffusion in a pure fcc metal can be represented by an Arrhenius relation having temperature-independent coefficients

$$D_T = D_0 \exp -(Q/kT)$$

The coefficients D_0 and Q can be interpreted in terms of exchanges between the tracer and the vacancies in thermal equilibrium with the lattice.

Recently much attention has been focused on diffusion in bcc structures, and in a number of these metals the same temperature dependence has been observed. Measurements of self-diffusion in Cr and Mo by Askill (1, 2) and in Cb by Peart (3) extend over ranges of 10^3 cm^2/sec in diffusivity and are adequately represented by an Arrhenius relation with temperature-independent coefficients. These coefficients are compatible with the melting-temperature rule for Q and Zener's theoretical analysis of D_0, and can be interpreted in terms of a vacancy diffusion model. In at least three bcc metals, however, β-Ti, β-Zr and γ-U, there is a significant departure from this "normal" diffusion behavior. Early work on β-Ti, at temperatures in the range of 900 to 1250 C (4), showed that impurity diffusion occurred with an activation energy approximately half that predicted by the melting-temperature rule and with a frequency factor three orders of magnitude below the minimum value predicted by Zener for a defect diffusion model.

The author is with the Lewis Propulsion Laboratory, National Aeronautics and Space Administration, Cleveland, Ohio. Paper describes work performed at the University of Reading, England.

27

Temperature Dependence of the
Diffusivity in Beta Titanium

The tracer diffusion coefficients for eleven impurities in β-Ti are shown in Fig. 1. In the temperature range of 900 to 1650 C, it is not possible to represent the diffusion of any impurity by a single rectilinear plot corresponding to an Arrhenius relation with temperature-independent

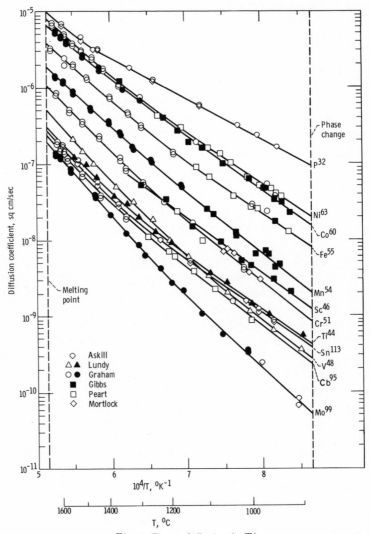

Fig. 1. Tracer diffusion in Ti

coefficients. This is also true of Murdock's data (5) for Ti[44] and V[48] diffusing in β-Ti, which have been included in Fig. 1.

From an examination of the data we can make the following observations:

1. For some of the impurities, that is, for P[32], Cb[95], V[48] and Ti[44], there is a range of temperatures in which the data can be represented by a rectilinear plot.

2. These rectilinear regions can occur at either extreme of the temperature range 900 to 1650 C.

3. A uniformly curving plot of the kind proposed by Lundy (6) for Zr[95] and Cb[95] diffusing in β-Zr does not give a good fit to the diffusion data for the impurities Cb[95] and P[32] diffusing in β-Ti.

If we assume that the basic nature of the temperature dependence is the same for all the impurities examined, we can propose two possible methods for interpreting the data, based on Arrhenius plots having temperature-independent coefficients:

1. There may be a normal diffusion process above and below T^*, at which temperature a discontinuity in the diffusion activation energy occurs (see Fig. 2a).

2. There may be two different processes, each having temperature-

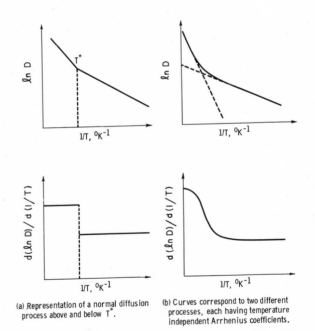

(a) Representation of a normal diffusion process above and below T*.

(b) Curves correspond to two different processes, each having temperature independent Arrhenius coefficients.

Fig. 2. Interpretation of temperature dependence of diffusivity

Table 1. Arrhenius Coefficients

| Solute | | Size factor, % | Method 1 (a) | | | | Method 2 (a) | |
| Element | Group | | 900–1250 C | | 1400–1650 C | | 1250–1650 C | |
			Q	D_0	Q	D_0	Q	D_0
			Period III					
P[32]	VA	−24	24.1	3.6×10^{-3}	...	...	...	...
			Period IV					
Sc[46]	IIIB	+9	32.7	2.1×10^{-3}	...	...	...	...
Ti[44]	IVB	0	31.2(b)	3.6×10^{-4}	~45	$\sim3 \times 10^{-2}$	~60	1.0
V[48]	VB	−7	32.2	3.1×10^{-4}	~45	$\sim6 \times 10^{-2}$	~57	1.5
Cr[51]	VIB	−12	35.3	5.0×10^{-3}	42.5	6.3×10^{-2}	61–66	5–14
Mn[54]	VIIB	−13	33.7	6.1×10^{-3}	39.6	5.9×10^{-2}	59–65	5–12
Fe[55]	VIII	−13	31.6	7.8×10^{-3}	38.0	7.3×10^{-2}	55–61	2–15
Co[60]	VIII	−15	30.6	1.2×10^{-2}	37.1	1.1×10^{-1}	53–61	2–16
Ni[63]	VIII	−15	29.6	9.2×10^{-3}	38.2	2.9×10^{-1}	53–60	2–20
			Period V					
Cb[95]	VB	0	34.9(b)	1.2×10^{-3}	57.2	7.8×10^{-1}	69–73	10–20
Mo[99]	VIB	−5	43.0	8.0×10^{-3}	47.0	4.0×10^{-2}	65–73	3–20
Sn[113]	IVA	+7	31.6(b)	3.8×10^{-4}	~45	$\sim3 \times 10^{-2}$	~60	~1.0

(a) Values for Q are given in kcal/g-atom; values for D_0, in cm²/sec.
(b) Self-diffusion on equivalent results.

independent Arrhenius coefficients. The measured diffusivity, then, would be the sum of the contributions from the two processes (see Fig. 2b). The solute data have been analyzed by both methods and the respective Arrhenius coefficients are shown in Table 1. When Method 1 is used, Q and D_0 for self-diffusion, both above and below T^*, are well below the empirical estimates of these parameters (65 to 75 kcal/g-atom and 10^{-1} to 10 cm²/sec). We obtain better agreement with the empirical data if we use Method 2. Then the coefficients for the low-temperature process correspond to the values given by Method 1 below T^*, but the predicted coefficients for the high-temperature mechanism are in excellent agreement with the empirical values usually associated with diffusion by a single vacancy mechanism. If this latter interpretation is correct, then self-diffusion and impurity diffusion in β-Ti can be considered "normal" bcc diffusion behavior accompanied by some other diffusion process that provides the major contribution to the measured diffusion coefficients at lower temperatures. It is stressed here that the experimental data support either of the proposed analyses equally well. The emphasis on Method 2 can be defended only on the grounds that it is a hypothesis, consistent with the experimental evidence, that can account for the temperature dependence of the diffusivity and relate diffusion in this metal to experimental observations in the "normal" bcc metals.

The Low-Temperature Diffusion Process

The temperature dependence of the diffusivity in β-Ti is similar, in some respects, to diffusion data obtained for polycrystalline materials, for which enhanced diffusion at the lower temperatures can be attributed to migration along short-circuit paths represented by the crystal grain boundaries. The specimens used in this work contained two to three grains 3 to 5 mm in diameter in the β phase, and no indications of enhanced diffusion along a grain boundary were observed in autoradiographs of the diffusion zones. However, it is conceivable that the short-circuit paths in this instance may be a high density of dislocations resulting from the cph to bcc phase change at 880 C. At least $10^{11}/cm^2$ would be required to account for the experimental diffusion coefficients measured at temperatures in the range of 900 to 1000 C. It must be assumed that the tracer atom executes a random walk along the dislocation network, to account for the rectilinear form of the plots of log (concentration) versus (penetration)² for all the specimens examined.

An alternative explanation, based on the concept of an extrinsic concentration of vacant lattice sites associated with the interstitial impurities present in β-Zr and β-Ti, has been proposed by Kidson. This explanation of the diffusion behavior is described in detail in Chapter 25 in this volume and will not be discussed here.

At present, no decision can be made as to the nature of the low-temperature diffusion process, and further work is being directed toward testing the validity of the proposed interpretations of the temperature dependence and the characteristics of the diffusion mechanism or mechanisms responsible.

Impurity Diffusion in Beta Titanium

Because of the unresolved problems associated with the temperature dependence of the diffusivity in this metal, even a summary of the results for impurity diffusion is difficult. However, the relative importance of the difference in size of the solute atom with respect to the solvent, as opposed to differences in their electronic configuration, can be examined, and the general features of the β-Ti data can be compared with impurity diffusion studies in two fcc noble metals.

The change in activation energy for a diffusing impurity compared with that for self-diffusion can be considered from two alternative viewpoints. The first assumes that differences in size between solute and solvent can be ignored and that only differences in the outer electron configurations are considered. This approach was used by Le Claire (7) in his analysis of impurity diffusion in Cu and Ag. The excellent agreement with experiment for nontransition impurities shows that, in these two systems, this is a reliable assumption. The second approach considers only the size difference between solute and solvent and does not give such satisfactory agreement with experiment in Cu and Ag, particularly for the slower diffusing impurities.

The uncertainties in the value of Q for the high-temperature process on the basis of either interpretation of the temperature dependence preclude an attempt to determine the relative importance of size effects, as opposed to differences in outer electron configuration. Therefore, we shall consider only the low-temperature mechanism and limit our examination to those tracers that are best represented by a rectilinear plot at the lower temperatures—Ti[44], Sn[113], Cb[95] and P[32]. The first three of these are shown in greater detail in Fig. 3.

As a first approximation for a solute atom that is small compared with the solvent, we expect the impurity activation energy to be less than that for self-diffusion. Thus the diffusion of P[32] agrees with this assumption. However, on this basis, we should expect that Q_{Cb} would be equal to Q_{Ti} and that Q_{Sn} would be greater than Q_{Ti}. Experiment shows the reverse to be true.

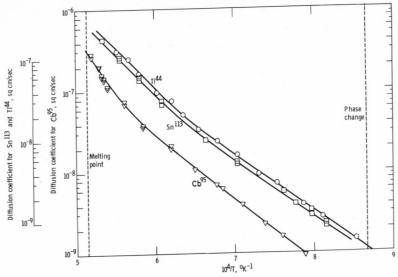

Fig. 3. Diffusion of Ti^{44}, Sn^{113} and Cb^{95} in β-Ti

Thus, for Cb and Sn, which do not differ greatly in size from Ti, electronic effects appear to be more significant than those related to size. The similarity in activation energy for Sn and Ti is interesting from this point of view because both elements exhibit a similar range of valence states. This suggests that Sn may have the same diffusion properties as the solvent atom, with the exception of its greater mass, which would account for the reduced diffusivity of this solute.

These observations tempt one to compare the data for impurity diffusion in β-Ti with that for impurity diffusion in Cu and Ag. For these systems impurities to the right of the solvent in the periodic table diffuse with an activation energy that decreases as the valence difference between solute and solvent increases. The reverse of this behavior occurs when moving to the left of the solvent. For solutes to the right of Cu and Ag, a valence difference can be determined on the basis of position in the periodic table because these solutes are nontransition metals. Unfortunately, in considering transition metals, position in the periodic table bears little relation to their valence difference, if one can even consider these metals to have a valence in the sense in which it is used for nontransition metals.

In view of these difficulties, it is not surprising that there is little similarity between impurity diffusion in β-Ti and Ag or Cu. This does not imply that electronic effects are unimportant or are complicated by size considerations, but rather it reflects our inability to assess the detailed differences in electron configuration between the solute and solvent when both are transition metals.

Conclusion

It has been shown that diffusion of an impurity at tracer concentration in β-Ti as a function of temperature cannot be represented by an Arrhenius relation with constant coefficients over the temperature range of 900 to 1650 C. Over smaller temperature ranges such a representation appears to provide a good fit to the data for some of the impurities examined. This suggests, as one possibility, an interpretation of the temperature dependence in terms of two competing mechanisms of diffusion where each is represented by an Arrhenius relation with constant coefficients. The higher activation energy process has characteristics that are usually associated with diffusion via vacancy defects, but there is no clear indication of the mechanism responsible for the diffusion process having the lower activation energy. A comparison of impurity diffusion in β-Ti with studies in the fcc noble metals, Cu and Ag, serves mainly to emphasize the difficulties in interpretation associated with impurity diffusion in transition metals. There is some indication that size differences between solute and solvent are not of primary importance if they do not exceed $\sim 10\%$. An attempt has been made to relate diffusion in β-Ti to the theoretical framework that has been used to describe diffusion phenomena in both fcc and bcc metals. The experimental evidence is consistent with, but cannot be considered to prove the proposed interpretation of the temperature dependence, and further experimental work must be directed toward establishing the exact nature of the diffusion processes in this metal.

References

1   J. Askill, private communication
2   J. Askill and D. H. Tomlin, Phil Mag, 8 (90), 997 (1963)
3   R. F. Peart, D. Graham and D. H. Tomlin, Acta Met, 10, 519 (1962)
4   R. F. Peart and D. H. Tomlin, Acta Met, 10, 132 (1962); G. B. Gibbs, D. Graham, and D. H. Tomlin, Phil Mag, 8 (92), 1269 (1963); D. Graham, PhD Thesis, 1963
5   J. F. Murdoch, ORNL 3616, 1964
6   J. I. Federer and T. S. Lundy, Trans AIME, 227, 562 (1963)
7   A. D. Le Claire, Phil Mag, 7 (75), 141 (1962)

Chapter 3

A Summary of ORNL Work on Diffusion in Beta Zirconium, Vanadium, Columbium and Tantalum

T. S. Lundy, J. I. Federer,
R. E. Pawel and F. R. Winslow

In this paper we will present the highlights of several Oak Ridge studies on diffusion in bcc metals. This particular aspect of our diffusion work was started approximately three years ago and is continuing. In all experiments we used radioactive-tracer methods combined with mechanical sectioning techniques, to determine activity profiles after the specimens had been subjected to isothermal diffusion-annealing treatments.

We first became interested in studying diffusion in bcc metals when we noted that there was an especially wide disagreement among previous investigators (1–5) on the experimental values of D_0 and Q in the Arrhenius-type equation describing self-diffusion in β-Zr. Experimental values of D_0 varied by nearly two orders of magnitude, and values of Q differed by as much as 14 kcal/mole. One possible explanation for these large discrepancies was that the different investigators had used Zr^{95} contaminated to different extents with the daughter Cb^{95}. Thus, because the decay gammas for these isotopes have identical energies, the experimentally determined values could have been different average values of the diffusion coefficients for Zr^{95} and Cb^{95}. We, therefore, decided to follow separately the diffusion of both isotopes to assess this possible explanation.

As for all other experiments to be described in this paper, we chose to study the diffusional properties of Zr by first depositing the isotope of interest onto the flat faces of cylindrical specimens. The subsequent redistribution of isotope for a given isothermal diffusion anneal was then followed by sectioning parallel to the initial plane source and counting the activities associated with the sections. If the thickness of the isotope layer is very small relative to the penetration depths, that is, if

The authors are with the Oak Ridge National Laboratory, Oak Ridge, Tenn.

$h < 0.1(Dt)^{1/2}$ where h is the isotope layer thickness, D is the diffusion coefficient and t is the time of the diffusion anneal, the applicable solution to Fick's second law indicates that

$$d \ln A(x)/dx^2 = -1/4\ Dt$$

where $A(x)$ is the specific activity at a distance x from the original isotope layer. Thus, plots of $\ln A(x)$ versus x^2 should yield straight lines with slopes equal to $-(4\ Dt)^{-1}$. If, on the other hand, the original isotope layer is too thick, that is, if $h > 0.1(Dt)^{1/2}$, plots of $\ln A(x)$ versus x^2 should not be linear but should be concave downward near $x = 0$.

Fortunately, for all of the experiments reported here the isotope layer could be considered a plane source. Possible exceptions are limited to a few of the diffusion experiments at low temperatures and short times in the Ta and Cb systems where sectioning was accomplished by anodizing and stripping.

Figure 1 shows four plots of $\ln A(x)$ versus x^2 for the diffusion of Cb[95] in β-Zr. For all temperatures, the data when plotted in this manner were linear. Such behavior is generally considered to indicate that atomic transport occurs primarily by some volume diffusion mechanism. Experimentally determining penetration plots such as these, we found diffusion coefficients of Cb[95] and Zr[95] in Zr over a temperature interval of almost 900 C, essentially covering the whole range of stability of the bcc β phase.

The Frontispiece of this book shows customary Arrhenius-type plots for describing the temperature dependence of diffusion coefficients for both Zr[95] and Cb[95] in β-Zr. At low temperatures the values of D for the two isotopes differ by a factor of about five, with Cb[95] being the slower diffusing species; at high temperatures the D values become almost identical. The presence of Cb[95] as a contaminant in Zr[95] isotope would, then, usually tend to lower the apparent self-diffusion coefficient for β-Zr.

Perhaps the most significant thing about these plots of the data is their marked curvature. If one considers the slopes of such plots at specified temperatures to be proportional to the activation energy, Q, of the diffusion process, then Q is found to vary from about 20.5 to 47.0 kcal/mole for Zr[95] and from about 26.0 to 56.0 kcal/mole for Cb[95]. Such a wide variation in the apparent activation energies was completely unexpected; but the presence of this variation does allow easy explanation of previous results on diffusion in β-Zr. Values of D_0 and Q obtained by any particular previous investigator simply depended on the temperature range emphasized during his work. Emphasis on the low-temperature range resulted in low D_0 and Q values; emphasis on higher temperatures gave higher D_0 and Q values.

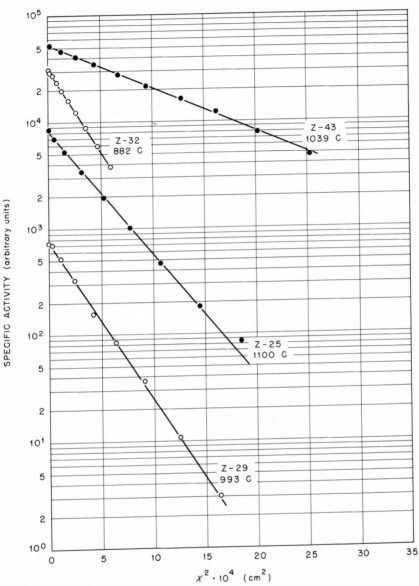

Fig. 1. Penetration profiles for diffusion of Cb⁹⁵ in β-Zr at 882, 993, 1039
and 1100 C (lathe method)

There are several possible explanations for this observed curvature.
The first and perhaps the best, is simply that it should not be unexpected
that the activation energy for a diffusion process varies with temperature.

Arrhenius (6) certainly made no claim that his equation should be applicable over more than a rather limited temperature interval. In fact, he did not attempt to apply his equation to diffusion data. Such application was first made in the early 1920's (7). The nearly universal acceptance of the Arrhenius expression as a "law" was based almost entirely on an empirical foundation generated by a considerable amount of data gathered over limited temperature ranges usually covering no more than 200 to 300 degrees. During the past several years instances of slight deviations from the relation were found (8) but were believed to be anomalous. It may be that there actually are good reasons for the activation energy of a given volume diffusion process to be constant with changing temperature. We feel that the question will be decided by obtaining precise experimental data over wide temperature intervals.

If one continues to subscribe to the idea that the Arrhenius concept must hold over wide temperature intervals for a given diffusion process, there exist other possible explanations for the "non-Arrhenius" behavior of the Zr data. These include the following:

1. Two mechanisms of volume diffusion may occur in this system, one dominating at high temperatures (possibly the vacancy mechanism) and the other at low temperatures (possibly the ring mechanism).

2. A temperature-independent vacancy concentration (9) that contributes significantly to low-temperature diffusional properties, but has little effect on diffusivities near the melting point, may exist.

3. Normal volume diffusion may occur by the vacancy mechanism near the melting point, and significant contributions from short-circuiting along boundaries and dislocation pipes may enhance the apparent volume diffusion coefficients determined at low temperatures.

For the Ta and Cb systems, we have observed this last effect and are inclined to accept it as the explanation. However, further experiments obviously need to be done.

After finding curvature in Arrhenius-type plots for diffusion in β-Zr, we decided to examine the Arrhenius behavior of other bcc systems. To avoid transformation problems and therefore have the opportunity of examining D over still larger temperature intervals with single crystals of the metal of interest, we then chose to study the self-diffusion of V. After using one batch of the V^{48} isotope ($t_{1/2} = 16.2$ days), we found that work on this system was also being done at the University of Illinois (10) and decided against further duplication of effort. With the few specimens that we did examine, however, we obtained reasonably accurate high-temperature data and established that deviations from normal Arrhenius behavior occur for self-diffusion in V. Figure 2 illustrates a typical

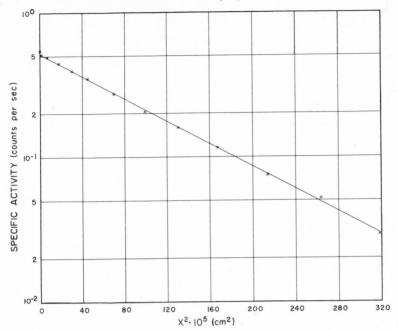

Fig. 2. Penetration profile for the diffusion of V^{48} in V at 1802 C (lathe method)

penetration plot for a lathe-sectioned V specimen and also the use of Winslow's computer code (11) in automatic calculation and plotting of diffusion data. The diffusion coefficient (1.54×10^{-8} cm²/sec), 90% confidence limits (2.1×10^{-10}), and other pertinent information (T = 1802 C and t = 18,120 sec) were plotted automatically.

Figure 3 summarizes our rather cursory study of this system. The data above 1600 C can be described by an Arrhenius-type expression with D_0 = 58 cm²/sec and Q = 91,500 cal/mole. This expression is in reasonable agreement with that obtained in the Illinois work (12). Our lower-temperature data deviate from this equation, but must be considered only qualitative. The points at 1200 C were markedly affected by a specimen reaction with quartz. It seems that Si lowers the diffusion rate of V^{48} in V.

The next system we examined was that of Cb^{95} in Cb. Resnick and Castleman (13) had previously determined diffusion coefficients in this system for temperatures of about 1600 to 2200 C. Peart, Graham and Tomlin (14) obtained five data points between about 1700 and 2330 C. In these works, the reported activation energies were 105 and 95 kcal/mole,

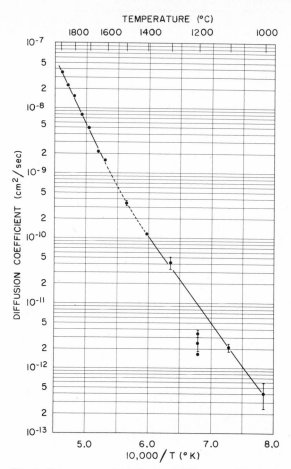

Fig. 3. Temperature dependence of diffusion of V^{48} in V

respectively. Corresponding D_0 values were 12.4 and 1.3 cm²/sec. We extended the temperature interval both to higher and, more particularly, to lower temperatures to more fully describe the Arrhenius-type behavior. In our study of this system, we used three sectioning techniques—lathe, grinding, and, more recently, anodizing and stripping (15). The first two of these techniques are rather standard, but the third is not so well known. Sectioning a specimen by this method involves the formation and subsequent mechanical stripping of an anodic film from a flat, electro-polished surface. Scotch Brand Magic Tape is used to strip the film and contain it during the counting operation. The newly exposed surface is then ready for repetition of the anodizing and stripping. Thickness of the

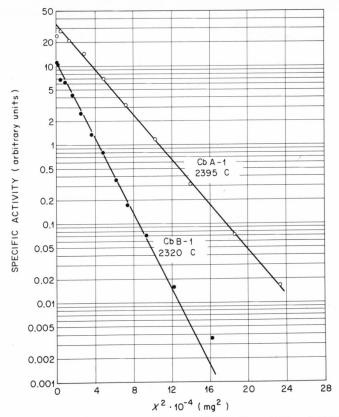

Fig. 4. Penetration profiles for diffusion of Cb[95] in Cb at 2320 and 2395 C (lathe method)

uniform anodic layer is, for all practical purposes, a unique function of the applied voltage. For Cb, the equivalent metal thickness can be varied from about 200 to 1000 A. Sections less than 100 A thick have been consecutively removed from single-crystal diffusion specimens of Ta by this method.

The penetration plots obtained when lathe-sectioning techniques were used are shown in Fig. 4 for Cb[95] in Cb specimens annealed at 2395 and 2320 C. Typical data obtained when a grinding technique was used are shown in Fig. 5. In this instance, we simultaneously followed the penetration of two isotopes—Cb[95] and Ta[182]. In Fig. 6 we see penetration plots obtained by anodizing and stripping a single specimen having, again, both Cb[95] and Ta[182] as diffusing species. Here the Cb[95] activity dropped by a factor of about five in the first micron of penetration, but the Ta[182]

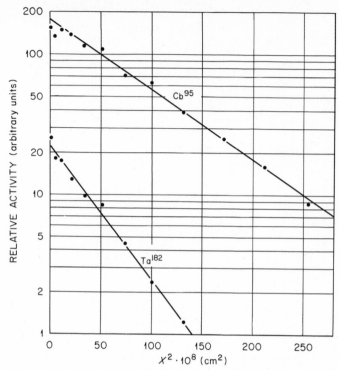

*Fig. 5. Penetration profiles for diffusion of Cb⁹⁵ and Ta¹⁸² in Cb at 1607 C
(grinding method)*

dropped more rapidly, indicating a smaller diffusion coefficient. Also, note that one micron of the specimen was divided into about 20 sections.

Figure 7 summarizes our data for self-diffusion in Cb. It is especially important that a straight line in this plot of ln D versus T^{-1} fits most of the data. Two additional data points at 878 C also lie on this line. Positive deviations from this line at 1500 to 1700 C and at 1000 to 1200 C can be explained by a combination of short-circuiting penetration of the isotope and limiting resolution of the sectioning procedures. Annealing times were simply too short and sectioning thicknesses too large for the whole picture to be seen adequately. This point will be clearer after we examine the data for diffusion in Ta. The equation for the line through these data is:

$$D = 1.94 \exp\left(-98{,}000/RT\right) \text{ cm}^2/\text{sec}$$

The values of D_0 and Q are quite close to those reported by Peart, Graham and Tomlin (14). The linearity of this plot over more than ten orders of

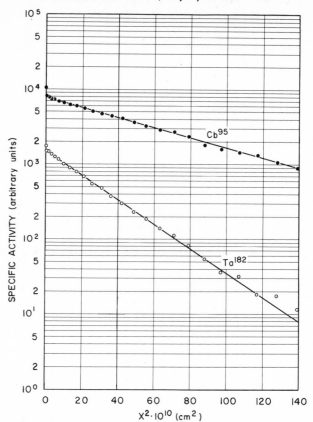

Fig. 6. Penetration profiles for diffusion of Cb⁹⁵ and Ta¹⁸² in Cb at 1408 C
(anodizing and stripping method)

magnitude of the diffusion coefficient from 2400 C down to about 875 C certainly supports the idea that the activation energy for a given volume diffusion mechanism does not necessarily vary with temperature.

Most of the initial experiments that we performed using the anodizing and stripping technique were on the system Cb^{95} in Ta. The type of penetration behavior first encountered is illustrated in Fig. 8. There are obviously two regions of the plot—one near the surface and one deeper into the specimen. Values of D determined from the slopes of the curves are considerably different for the two regions. In fact, the presence of multiple regions of diffusion makes one worry whether the usual boundary conditions applied to Fick's law are applicable in this instance. We compared values of D computed for both regions of such plots with the data of Gruzin and Meshkov (16) and concluded that the penetration behavior

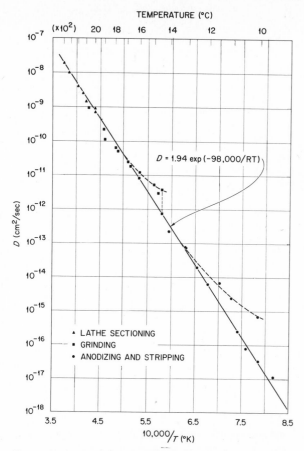

Fig. 7. *Temperature dependence of diffusion of Cb⁹⁵ in Cb*

deeper into the specimen was associated with volume diffusion. Thus, at first thought, it appeared that a near-surface effect similar to that now widely reported for diffusion in Al and in Ag was responsible for the vastly different near-surface characteristics. This interpretation was incorrect. We should have and now do consider the first region characteristic of volume diffusion in this system. The enhanced penetration deep into the specimen is probably caused by atomic migration along short-circuit paths. To reach this conclusion it was necessary to examine the data in terms of the experimental and analytical procedures, as well as their behavior as a function of several experimental variables.

Convincing evidence in this respect is seen when penetrations of Cb⁹⁵ into monocrystalline and polycrystalline Ta are compared. This is illus-

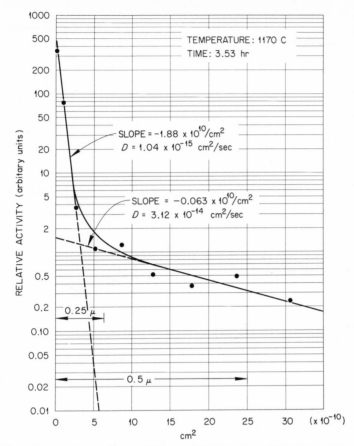

Fig. 8. Penetration profile for diffusion of Cb⁹⁵ in Ta at 1170 C (anodizing and stripping method) (15)

trated in Fig. 9 for specimens given identical annealing treatments. The greater relative importance of the second region in the polycrystalline specimen is obvious, although the slope of the first region tends to approach that for the single crystal at very small penetration distances. Thus, depending upon the sensitivity of the sectioning procedure, the presence of short-circuiting paths, such as grain boundaries, may contribute significantly to increasing the measured "bulk" diffusion coefficients. This effect is most pronounced at low temperatures. More complete penetration plots are shown in Fig. 10. It is obvious that if we had used coarser sectioning procedures, we could have easily masked the true picture and assigned volume diffusion to the wrong part of the penetration profile. It is also true that the slope near the surface of the

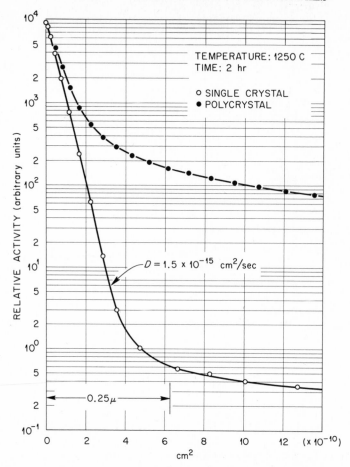

Fig. 9. Penetration profiles illustrating effect of crystalline perfection on diffusion of Cb^{95} in Ta at 1250 C (anodizing and stripping method)

polycrystalline specimen only approaches that of the single crystal. It is always on the side that would give an erroneously high volume diffusion coefficient.

From this plot for the polycrystalline specimen, it is apparent that the grain-boundary or short-circuit component is not well described by a straight line. It probably shouldn't be too surprising to find that it is also not linear when plotted as ln (activity) versus x. The latter plot, Fig. 11, is a check of the Fisher analysis for ideal grain-boundary diffusion. The nonlinearity of the plot shows that Fisher's model is an oversimplification of the real process.

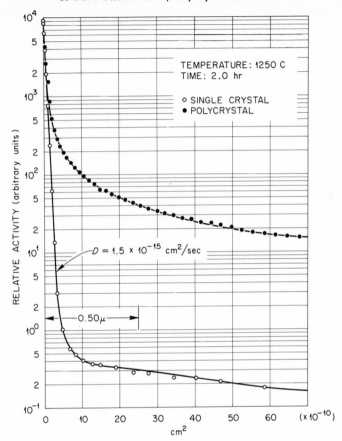

Fig. 10. More complete penetration profiles for specimens shown in Fig. 9

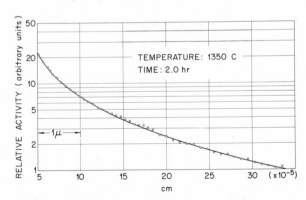

Fig. 11. Penetration profile for diffusion of Cb[95] in polycrystalline Ta for comparing data with Fisher's model of grain-boundary diffusion

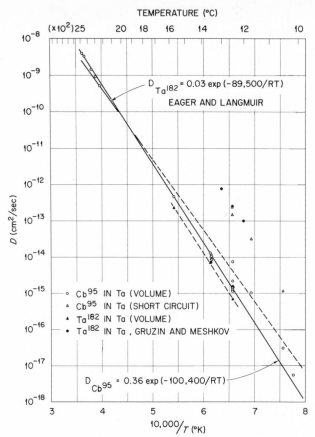

Fig. 12. Temperature dependence of diffusion of Cb^{95} and Ta^{182} in Ta

Figure 12 summarizes the data for diffusion in Ta. Here we see our data for diffusion of Cb^{95} and Ta^{182} in Ta and the data of Gruzin and Meshkov for Ta^{182} in Ta. Also included is the line representing high-temperature data of Eager and Langmuir and a dashed-line extrapolation to low temperatures. The equation of the line through our data for volume diffusion of Cb^{95} in Ta is

$$D = 0.36 \exp\left(-100,400/RT\right) \text{ cm}^2/\text{sec}$$

About nine orders of magnitude of the diffusion coefficient are included; the temperatures ranged from about 1000 to 2500 C. The points that lie above the straight line may be explained in terms of the effect of short-circuiting on the penetration plots. The same reason also explains some of the high points on the similar plot for diffusion in Cb.

One point is very clear from a consideration of these data. That is, one must be especially careful in interpreting low-temperature diffusion data because of the large structure-sensitive contributions to the over-all penetration plots. For example, in considering our data for diffusion in Ta, the region of pure lattice diffusion would have been missed entirely if we could not have characterized the first few tenths of a micron penetration. Even when single crystals were used, the contributions of subgrain boundaries and dislocation pipes were appreciable.

In summary, we have measured diffusion coefficients over wide ranges of temperature in β-Zr, V, Cb and Ta. We have found deviations from Arrhenius behavior in all instances. For Cb and Ta, at least, these deviations may be explained in terms of short-circuiting.

Acknowledgment. This work was sponsored by the U. S. Atomic Energy Commission under contract with the Union Carbide Corporation.

References

1 G. B. Federov and V. D. Gulyakin, Met i Metalloved Chistykh Metal Sb Nauchn Rabot, 1, 170 (1959)
2 G. Kidson and J. McGurn, Can J Phys, 39, 1146 (1961)
3 V. S. Lyashenko, V. N. Bykov and L. V. Pavlinov, Fiz Metal Metalloved, 8, 362 (1959)
4 D. Volokoff, S. May and Y. Adda, Compt Rend, 251, 2341 (1960)
5 Ye. V. Borisov et al., Metal i Metalloved, p 196 (1948)
6 S. Arrhenius, Z Physik Chem, 4, 226 (1889)
7 S. Dushman and I. Langmuir, Phys Rev, 20, 113 (1922)
8 C. A. Mackliet, Phys Rev, 109, 1964 (1958)
9 G. V. Kidson, Can J Phys, 41, 1563 (1963)
10 R. F. Peart, personal communication
11 F. R. Winslow, A FORTRAN Program for Calculating Diffusion Coefficients and Plotting Penetration Curves, ORNL-TM-726 (1963)
12 R. F. Peart, Chapter 16 in this volume
13 R. Resnick and L. S. Castleman, Trans AIME, 218, 307 (1960)
14 R. F. Peart, D. Graham and D. H. Tomlin, Acta Met, 10, 519 (1962)
15 R. E. Pawel and T. S. Lundy, J Appl Phys, 35, 435 (1964)
16 P. L. Gruzin and V. I. Meshkov, Probl Metalloved i Fiz Metal, 4, 570 (1955), as cited by N. L. Peterson, Diffusion in Refractory Metals, WADD-60-793 (March 1961)

Chapter 4

Binary Interdiffusion in Body-Centered Cubic Transition Metal Systems

C. S. Hartley, J. E. Steedly, Jr., and L. D. Parsons

Studies of interdiffusion in bcc metal systems have lagged behind those in fcc systems for many years. The primary reasons seem to be the great commercial importance of a wide variety of fcc alloys and the relative ease with which diffusion experiments can be conducted with these materials because of the low temperatures generally involved. Recently the need for high-temperature structural material has focused attention on alloy systems involving Cb, Mo, W and Ta; hence, the commercial importance of studying diffusion behavior in such systems has increased. In addition, early studies of self-diffusion in bcc metals indicated that the mechanism for self-diffusion may be different from that in fcc metals (1). If these indications are correct, the mechanism of chemical diffusion also would be expected to be different. Although earlier experiments have demonstrated the existence of a Kirkendall effect in certain bcc systems, thus establishing the existence of vacancy-controlled diffusion (2, 3), the following results suggest that this is a general phenomenon in bcc metals and alloys.

All the diffusion studies to be discussed were conducted on infinite diffusion couples composed of pure metals or pure metals and alloys that satisfied the boundary conditions for either the Boltzmann-Matano solution or the Wagner solutions to Fick's second law (4). Where possible, intrinsic diffusion coefficients were computed by use of Darken's analysis (5). In the absence of detailed thermodynamic data, such experiments contribute little to the theoretical knowledge of diffusion behavior. In addition, it is only approximately correct under very restricted conditions to express the temperature dependence of the logarithm of the interdiffusion coefficient or the intrinsic diffusion coefficients as linear functions of reciprocal absolute temperature (6). There is also noted in the

The authors are with the Air Force Materials Laboratory, Research and Technology Division, Air Force Systems Command, Wright-Patterson Air Force Base, Ohio.

present work an apparent effect of the concentration gradient on the interdiffusion coefficient. This effect increased the difficulty of obtaining precise results over a broad composition range in a single experiment. Attempts to measure intrinsic diffusion coefficients were confounded in certain instances by the difficulty of determining marker displacement and composition at the marker interface with sufficient precision.

Nevertheless, it was decided to employ this method for preliminary studies because of the simplicity of the experiment and the useful qualitative information that could be obtained about the breadth of the diffusion zone, the nature of the concentration-penetration curve and the occurrence of the Kirkendall shift. Information on the first two is useful in joining applications and in estimates of the temperature dependence of diffusion-controlled processes; information on the third, in verifying the existence of vacancy diffusion in these materials. When suitable additional data are available, such as the activities of the components in solid solution, thermal expansivity and elastic properties of appropriate alloys at elevated temperatures, the data obtained will be more useful in evaluating proposed theoretical treatments of the diffusion process.

Experimental Procedure

Diffusion studies were conducted on the following systems by use of infinite diffusion couples: Cb-V, Cb-Mo, Cb-Ti, Mo-Ti, Mo-Zr, Cb-Zr and Ta-Pt. A summary of all the diffusion anneals in each system is listed in Table 1. The experimental procedures used for all systems except Mo-Zr were similar and are discussed in general below.

Suitable alloys of various compositions in each system were prepared by arc melting pure materials into buttons that were remelted several times to promote homogenization. The composition limits of each alloy button were established by weight loss after melting for all the systems and were also checked by chemical analysis in the Cb-Zr, Mo-Zr and Mo-Ti systems. The error in composition determined for the alloys was usually less than a few tenths of 1% and rarely exceeded 1% as a maximum. Semi-quantitative spectrographic analysis was used to analyze for trace impurities in the alloys. To break down the as-cast structure, buttons for the Cb-V, Cb-Mo, Cb-Ti, and Mo-Ti systems were canned in evacuated stainless steel cans and reduced 30 to 50% in thickness by rolling at temperatures of 1000 to 1100 C. This procedure caused some of the alloys in the Cb-Mo and Mo-Ti systems to break up during fabrication. The buttons were given homogenization anneals in a vacuum furnace at appropriate temperatures for each system. Samples of the pure metals that were to be used in diffusion couples were heat treated to induce grain

Table 1. Summary of Diffusion Anneals

System	Types of Couples(a)	Time, hr	Temp, °C
		Treatments	
Cb-V.......	Cb/V	48	1750
	Cb/50 at. % Cb–50 at. % V	190	1630
	V/50 at. % Cb–50 at. % V	168	1505
		401	1404
Cb-Mo......	Cb/Mo(b)	24	2163
	Cb/50 at. % Mo–50 at. % Cb	95	2000
	Mo/50 at. % Mo–50 at. % Cb	153	1800
Cb-Ti......	Cb/Ti	15	1588
	Cb/50 at. % Cb–50 at. % Ti(c)	90	1500
	Ti/50 at. % Cb–50 at. % Ti	222	1300
		874	1000
Mo-Ti......	Mo/Ti	9.75	1600
	Mo/50 at. % Mo–50 at. % Ti	40.6	1400
	Ti/50 at. % Mo–50 at. % Ti	164.6	1210
		317.6	1001
		519.2	820
Ta-Pt......	Ta/Pt	168	1600
		192	1400
		709	1300
Cb-Zr......	Cb/Zr	9.6	1690
		18.0	1690
		40.0	1550
		83.5	1550
		99.1	1445
		180.3	1445
		64.2	1225
		96.0	1225
		105.9	1050
		789.0	820
		1601.3	820
Mo-Zr......	Mo/90 wt % Mo–10 wt % Zr	168.3	1833
	Mo/80 wt % Mo–20 wt % Zr	168.3	1833
	Mo/80 wt % Mo–20 wt % Zr	401.6	1650
	90 wt % Mo–10 wt % Zr/50 wt % Mo–50 wt % Zr	247.1	1445
	90 wt % Mo–10 wt % Zr/50 wt % Mo–50 wt % Zr	140.0	1445
	90 wt % Mo–10 wt % Zr/50 wt % Mo–50 wt % Zr	67.0	1200

Table 1. Summary of Diffusion Anneals (Continued)

		Treatments	
System	Types of Couples(a)	Time, hr	Temp, °C
	90 wt % Mo–10 wt % Zr/50 wt % Mo–50 wt % Zr	895.3	1045
	90 wt % Mo–10 wt % Zr/50 wt % Mo–50 wt % Zr	384.3	1052
	90 wt % Mo–10 wt % Zr/50 wt % Mo–50 wt % Zr	2110.5	820
	80 wt % Mo–20 wt % Zr/60 wt % Mo–40 wt % Zr	585.8	1445
	80 wt % Mo–20 wt % Zr/60 wt % Mo–40 wt % Zr	317.6	1445

(a) All types of couples for Cb-V, Cb-Mo, Cb-Ti and Mo-Ti were subjected to all time-temperature treatments listed.
(b) Cb/Mo was also subjected to a treatment at 1300 C for 1728 hr.
(c) Cb/50 at. % Cb–50 at. % Ti was also subjected to a treatment at 1000 C for 868 hr.

growth. Specimens cut from the pure metals and alloy buttons were used for diffusion couples, as standards for the calibration of the microbeam probe, and for lattice parameter measurements to correct for molal volume changes in the diffusion couples.

Pure-metal and incremental diffusion couples were prepared for the diffusion anneals from samples that were approximately 0.125 to 0.250 in. on a side, except in the Ta-Pt system for which sheet was used for the couples. The surfaces of the samples to be bonded together for most of the diffusion couples were given a final metallographic polish. However, in the Cb-V system the samples were only ground down through 4/0 paper before bonding. In the Cb-V, Cb-Mo, Cb-Ti and Mo-Ti systems, three types of diffusion couples were prepared: pure metal to pure metal and both pure metals to a 50 at. % alloy. Only pure-metal diffusion couples were prepared in the Cb-Zr and Ta-Pt systems. Incremental diffusion couples of two phases and single phases were prepared in the Mo-Zr system, as shown in Table 1. These couples were either pure Mo to a two-phase alloy next to the Mo solid solution or a two-phase alloy to a two-phase alloy on either side of the Mo_2Zr intermediate phase.

The components of the diffusion couples were bonded together by one of two methods. The first method consisted of placing the components of the diffusion couple in a jig that maintained pressure on the couple while the assembly was heated to an elevated temperature for a short time in a vacuum furnace. In the second method, the diffusion couples were bonded in an electrical resistance bonding apparatus similar to that described by Bolk (7). The couple to be bonded was placed between two carbon-tipped copper electrodes and heated to a high temperature for a few seconds by passing a large current through the couple and thus weld-

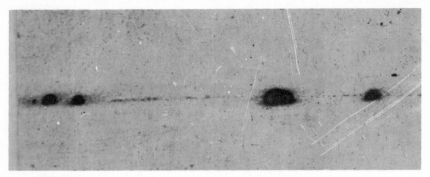

Fig. 1. Porosity interface in a Cb/Ti diffusion couple heat treated at 1500 C.
160×

ing it together. The diffusion couple was enclosed in an inert atmosphere and maintained under mechanical pressure during the bonding operation. This technique produced excellent bonds in the diffusion couples, giving a welded-type interface. During the electrical resistance bonding of some diffusion couples, a slight melting of the lower-melting component was observed at the edges of the samples. However, metallographic and electron microbeam probe examination showed that a sharp interface was maintained in all the bonded diffusion couples, even for those that showed a slight melting at the exterior surface.

Kirkendall marker measurements were made in the Cb-V, Cb-Mo, Cb-Ti, Cb-Zr and Mo-Ti systems. Tungsten wire markers were placed at the interface of the bonded diffusion couples in the Cb-V, Cb-Zr and Mo-Ti systems to measure marker movement. Because of observations in the Cb-V system and the suggestion of Guy (8) that the position of the marker interface could be established by the debris and porosity that existed in the original bonded interface, W wire markers were not used in the diffusion couples for the Cb-Mo and Cb-Ti systems. A photomicrograph of the marker interface in the Cb-Ti system is shown in Fig. 1 and supports this conclusion. Because doubt arose about the marker measurements in view of negative intrinsic diffusion coefficients that were later obtained, W wire markers were again used in the Cb-Zr and Mo-Ti systems. A flat was ground along the length of the couples perpendicular to the marker interface, and the marker position was measured directly before and after diffusion. Diamond-pyramid-hardness marks were placed in the ends of some couples to be used as reference points for measuring marker position, but this technique did not yield reliable results. Some of the diffusion couples were symmetrical, that is, of the type A/B/A, and the distances between the marker interfaces were measured directly before and after diffusion. None of the direct measurements of marker position gave satisfactory results because of wide scatter in the measurements of the marker movement. The marker shift was also obtained from the concentration-penetration curves by measuring the distance between the Matano interface and the marker interface position, which was established during analysis of the diffusion zones. These indirect measurements seemed to give more consistent results than the direct measurements.

The diffusion zones were analyzed by an electron microbeam probe to obtain the concentration-penetration curves. The interdiffusion coefficients were calculated from these concentration profiles by use of a computer program developed for the Matano solution (9). The concentration profiles for the couples in the Mo-Zr system were analyzed by use of appropriate solutions developed by Wagner (4). Interdiffusion coefficients were computed from measurements of the rate of growth of both the Mo solid solution and the Mo_2Zr intermediate phase.

Arrhenius-type plots were made from the diffusion data for various compositions and phases in each of the systems from which the apparent activation energies and frequency factors for interdiffusion were obtained. Attempts were also made to determine intrinsic diffusion coefficients by use of Darken's equations where suitable marker measurements were available.

Results

Cb-V System.   Diffusion in this system was studied at 1750, 1630, 1505 and 1404 C (10). Apparent activation energies and frequency factors for interdiffusion as a function of composition are shown in Fig. 2. At all temperatures the interdiffusion coefficient changes very slowly (about a factor of four) as the V content goes from 100 to 40 at. %. It then drops precipitously by two orders of magnitude as the V content goes to zero. Both incremental and pure-metal couples show this trend, as seen in Fig. 3 for the diffusion anneals at 1630 C. Diffusion coefficients in the Cb-rich region calculated from pure-metal couples are slightly higher than those computed from incremental couples, but the effect is not nearly as pronounced as that in some other systems studied. This may result because in this instance the concentration gradients for the two types of couples were more similar than those in other instances.

In this system a special effort was made to compare the computer calculated diffusivities with those obtained by manual calculation. A typical comparison is shown in Fig. 3. It is evident that although the apparent trend present in the computer results is absent in the manually calculated points, the values obtained agree quite well. The values

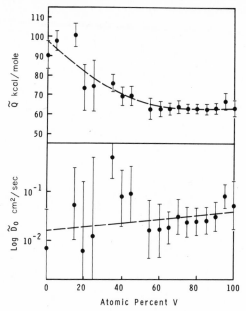

Fig. 2. Apparent activation energy and frequency factor versus composition for diffusion in the Cb-V system

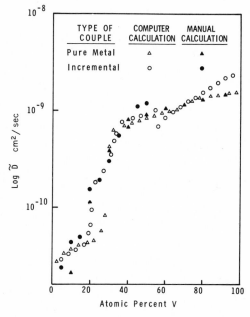

Fig. 3. Interdiffusion coefficient versus composition for diffusion at 1630 C in the Cb-V system

Table 2. Summary of Activation Energies and Frequency Factors for Intrinsic Diffusion Coefficients

System	Composition, at. %	Q, kcal/mole	D_0, cm²/sec	Q, kcal/mole	D_0, cm²/sec
		V	**V**	**V**	**Cb**	**Cb**
Cb-V.........	100	86.4(a)	17(a)	65.7	8.6×10^{-2}
	85	59.0	2.6×10^{-2}	66.4	4.9×10^{-2}
	80	60.5	4.2×10^{-2}	61.4	1.1×10^{-2}
	0	96.8	2.9	95.0(a)	1.3(a)
		Mo	**Cb**	**Cb**	**Mo**	**Mo**
Cb-Mo........	100	139.1	1.0×10^3	115.0	4.0
	19.9	139.9	1.3×10^4	136.5	1.4×10^3
	16.2	131.0	1.9×10^3	134.6	1.1×10^3
	0	95.0(a)	1.3(a)	131.2	9.2×10^2
		Ti	**Ti**	**Ti**	**Cb**	**Cb**
Cb-Ti.........	100	....	....	39.2	3.8×10^{-3}
	81.1	39.1	1.7×10^{-3}	42.3	2.2×10^{-3}
	0	61.9	5.0×10^{-4}	95.0(a)	1.3(a)
		Mo	**Ti**	**Ti**	**Mo**	**Mo**
Mo-Ti........	100	50.5	6.3×10^{-6}	115	4.0
	11.1	38.4	1.8×10^{-3}	48.7	1.0×10^{-2}
	0	....	....	47.0	2.5×10^{-2}
		Cb	**Zr**	**Zr**	**Cb**	**Cb**
Cb-Zr.........	100	99.2	2.2	95.0(a)	1.3(a)
	23.0	44.2	3.8×10^{-3}	65.0	0.69
	0	....	....	45.6	1.1×10^{-2}

(a) Self-diffusion data taken from literature.

obtained by both methods for the V/alloy couple were identical to two significant figures for five compositions in the range of 90 to 60 at. % V.

Intrinsic diffusion coefficients were calculated at the extremities and at 80 and 84 at. % V; the latter were the marker compositions in the Cb/V and V/alloy couples, respectively. The intrinsic diffusivity for V is three to five times that for Cb. The apparent activation energies for the intrinsic diffusion coefficients are given in Table 2.

The marker displacement in the Cb/alloy couples was greater than that which could be accounted for by the usual concept of vacancy diffusion. When appropriate values of the interdiffusion coefficient, marker velocity and concentration gradient were substituted into the Darken equation, a negative value was obtained for D_{Cb}. The difference between the inter-diffusion coefficients calculated from incremental couples at the marker composition and from pure-metal couples at the same composition was not large enough to account for the anomaly. Corrections for molal volume change, approximate error in the distance scale due to measurement on the microbeam probe, and approximate error in marker composition could not reconcile the results.

Similar results were obtained by Landergren, Birchenall and Mehl in a study of diffusion in β brass (11). These investigators found that if the marker velocity was computed from the distance between the Matano interface and the marker interface, as was done in this study, a negative intrinsic diffusivity for Cu, the slower diffusing component, was obtained from the Darken relations. However, if the marker shift was measured directly by optical means, this measurement gave positive values for D_{Cu} although the scatter in data was much greater in this instance. The discrepancy was attributed to a systematic error in the former measurement. In the present study, it is felt that no systematic error can account for the negative D_{Cb} obtained from the incremental Cb/alloy couples. However, no direct measurements of marker shift were made. If the possibility of systematic errors is eliminated, it is indeed strange that the two measurements should not yield the same values for marker velocities. DaSilva and Mehl studied the problem of marker movement in many fcc systems and reported that measurements of both types yield identical results within experimental error (12). It should also be noted that the difference in magnitude of the intrinsic diffusivities measured from the other couples was not so great that one would expect a very large error in the precision of this computation. Although this effect may possibly be explained by vacancy generation in the diffusion zone, as discussed later, no values of negative intrinsic diffusivities will be reported, but it will be noted where they were observed.

Cb-Mo System. Diffusion studies for this system were made at 2163, 2000, 1800 and 1300 C (13). The variation of the interdiffusion coefficient with composition for the three highest temperatures is shown in Fig. 4. It can be seen that the interdiffusion coefficient decreases by about half an order of magnitude as the composition goes from pure Cb to about 50 at. % Mo and then remains almost constant as the composition approaches pure Mo. The values of the diffusion coefficients for both the pure-metal couples and the incremental couples agree very well. The Mo/alloy incremental couples yielded ideal concentration-penetration curves (straight-line probability plots), thus giving a diffusion coefficient independent of concentration in this range.

Apparent activation energies and frequency factors were obtained as a function of composition by use of the interdiffusion coefficients for the temperatures 2163, 2000, and 1800 C. The activation energies increased from 132 kcal/mole at pure Cb up to 138 kcal/mole at pure Mo, as shown

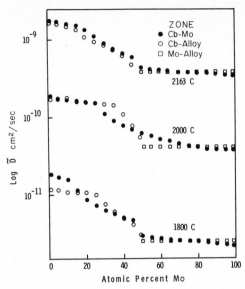

Fig. 4. Interdiffusion coefficient versus composition for diffusion in the Cb-Mo system

in Fig. 5. The frequency factors also are shown in Fig. 5 and are constant, with a value of 10^3 cm²/sec.

The interdiffusion coefficients calculated from the concentration-penetration curve for the pure-metal couple at 1300 C were two to three orders of magnitude greater than those obtained from extrapolating the Arrhenius plots from the three highest temperatures. It is possible that the width of the diffusion zone (less than one mil) might be too small for precise chemical analysis. Such a zone has a steep concentration gradient, and when the concentration profile is analyzed with a microbeam probe, there is a tendency to flatten out and elongate the steep region of the concentration curve. This results in a lower slope, which gives a higher calculated diffusion coefficient. This effect is caused by secondary fluorescence, which decreases the resolution of the probe trace (14). When a microbeam probe trace is made across an infinitely sharp interface, a concentration gradient with a measurable finite slope results. On the other hand, the higher diffusion rates could be due to gross deviation from a linear Arrhenius plot, caused by either an increasing difference in the intrinsic diffusivities at the lower temperature or short-circuiting paths for diffusion. As discussed later, the steep gradient could increase the vacancy concentration in the Cb-rich side, thereby enhancing diffusion. The possibility of grain-boundary diffusion has been ruled out

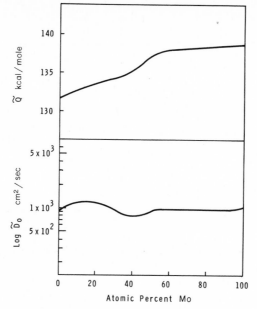

Fig. 5. Apparent activation energy and frequency factor versus composition for diffusion in the Cb-Mo system

because the grain size of the diffusion couples was very large, and the microbeam probe trace was made entirely within one or two grains.

Marker measurements were made in the diffusion couples for this system by the indirect method using the debris and porosity to mark the interface. The intrinsic diffusion coefficients were calculated from the concentration-penetration curves for the Cb/Mo and Cb/alloy diffusion couples, and the intrinsic diffusivity of Cb was about three to six times that for Mo. The apparent activation energies and frequency factors determined for the intrinsic diffusivities are listed in Table 2. Although negative intrinsic diffusion coefficients for Mo were obtained for the Mo/alloy incremental couples at the two highest temperatures, there is some question about the accuracy of the marker measurements in this system.

Cb-Ti System. Diffusion studies for this system were made at 1588, 1500, 1300, and 1000 C (13). The interdiffusion coefficient increased by about four orders of magnitude as the composition varied from pure Cb to pure Ti, as can be seen in Fig. 6 for the diffusion anneals at 1000 C. There was a tendency for the pure-metal couples to give higher interdiffusion coefficients on the Cb side of the system, especially at the lower temperatures. The concentration-penetration curves for the pure-metal

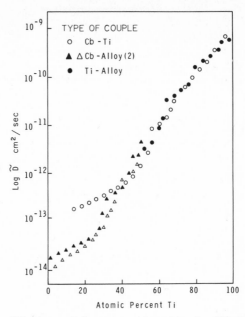

Fig. 6. Interdiffusion coefficient versus composition for diffusion at 1000 C in the Cb-Ti system

couples have very large gradients on the Cb-rich side and change to very small gradients on the Ti side. The effect of a steep gradient has been discussed previously for the Cb-Mo system. A similar enhancement has been observed in the Au-Ni system by Reynolds, Averbach and Cohen (6).

The apparent activation energies and frequency factors were determined by use of the interdiffusion coefficients from the incremental diffusion couples, because these were thought to be the better values. The apparent activation energy varies from about 40 kcal/mole in pure Ti to up to about 63 kcal/mole at 20 at. % Ti and remains constant as the composition approaches pure Cb, as shown in Fig. 7. It is felt that this graph should be extrapolated to about 70 kcal/mole for pure Cb, because there appeared to be a decrease in the concentration dependence of the interdiffusion coefficients determined from the incremental couples at 1000 C near pure Mo. This results in anomalously high interdiffusion coefficients in this region and a lower apparent activation energy.

Intrinsic diffusion coefficients were calculated from the marker movement measurements for the Cb/Ti couples. Activation energies for the couples are listed in Table 2. The intrinsic diffusivity for Ti is about two times that for Cb. Negative intrinsic diffusion coefficients for Cb were

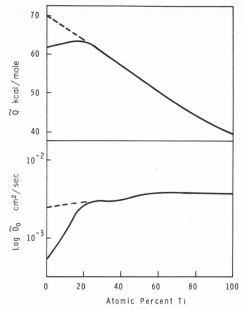

Fig. 7. Apparent activation energy and frequency factor versus composition for diffusion in the Cb-Ti system

obtained from the Cb/alloy couples at the three highest diffusion annealing temperatures.

Mo-Ti System. Diffusion in this system was studied at 1600, 1400, 1210, 1000, and 820 C (15). At all temperatures studied, the value of the interdiffusion coefficients decreases by about five orders of magnitude as the composition goes from pure Ti to pure Mo. The pure-metal couples and incremental couples give the same values of the interdiffusion coefficient, which decreases rapidly as the composition approaches 40 at. % Mo. As the composition increases to pure Mo, the dependence of the interdiffusion coefficient on concentration for the pure-metal couples changes more slowly, giving much higher values for the interdiffusion coefficient than the incremental couples. This effect is more pronounced at the lower temperature and appears to be similar to the results observed in the Cb-Ti system discussed earlier. A typical plot of the interdiffusion coefficient versus composition for the Mo-Ti is shown in Fig. 8 for the diffusion anneals at 1400 C.

The apparent activation energies were determined by use of the interdiffusion coefficients for the three highest temperatures and are shown in Fig. 9. The activation energy increased from about 47 kcal/mole at pure Ti to about 65 kcal/mole at 40 at. % Mo. Above this composition the

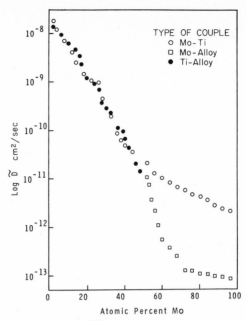

Fig. 8. Interdiffusion coefficient versus composition for diffusion at 1400 C in the Mo-Ti system

activation energies determined from the interdiffusion coefficients for the pure-metal couples decreased to about 45 kcal/mole. The interdiffusion coefficients for the incremental couples yielded much higher activation energies, which continued to increase to about 90 kcal/mole at 60 at. % Mo and then decreased to 55 kcal/mole at pure Mo. Consequently, it is believed that the plot of activation energy versus composition should be extrapolated to somewhere above 100 kcal/mole at pure Mo.

Intrinsic diffusion coefficients were calculated from the marker measurements for the pure-metal couples, and the ratio D_{Ti}/D_{Mo} varies from about 3 at 1600 C up to about 13 at 820 C. The activation energies for the intrinsic diffusivities are listed in Table 2. Negative intrinsic diffusion coefficients were obtained for Mo in the Mo/alloy diffusion couples.

Cb-Zr System.   Diffusion studies in this system were made at 1690, 1550, 1445, 1225, 1050 and 820 C for pure-metal diffusion couples with one to two different annealing times at each temperature (14). The interdiffusion coefficient decreases by about three orders of magnitude as the composition varies from pure Zr to pure Cb, as shown in Fig. 10 for the diffusion anneals at 1690 C. The values of the interdiffusion coefficient for the different diffusion annealing times at the same tem-

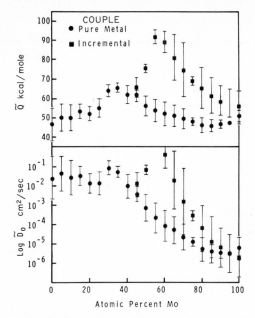

Fig. 9. *Apparent activation energy and frequency factor versus composition for diffusion in the Mo-Ti system*

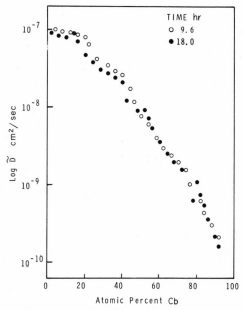

Fig. 10. *Interdiffusion coefficient versus composition for diffusion at 1690 C in the Cb-Zr system*

perature agree very well, as can be seen from Fig. 10. There was a tendency for the concentration dependence of the interdiffusion coefficient at the lower temperatures to decrease as the composition approached pure Cb. This may be the same effect that occurred in the Cb-Ti and Mo-Ti systems discussed previously. The pure Zr starting material contained about 2 at. % Hf, which could possibly affect the diffusion results obtained.

The apparent activation energies and frequency factors were determined from the interdiffusion coefficients obtained at the three highest temperatures. The apparent activation energy increases from about 50 kcal/mole for pure Zr to about 95 kcal/mole at pure Cb, as shown in Fig. 11. The frequency factor varies from about 10^{-2} cm²/sec at pure Zr to 10 cm²/sec at pure Cb, as seen in Fig. 11.

Kirkendall marker measurements were made with W wire markers by both direct and indirect methods. The direct measurements gave widely scattered data and were not considered reliable, but the indirect measurements were more consistent and were used to calculate the intrinsic diffusivities, for which the activation energies are listed in Table 2. The ratio of the intrinsic diffusion coefficients of Zr to Cb increase from 1.2 at

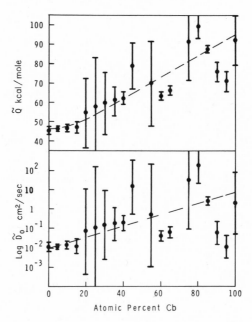

Fig. 11. Apparent activation energy and frequency factor versus composition for diffusion in the Cb-Zr system

1690 C to about 4 at 1225 C. The diffusion anneals at 1050 and 820 C did not yield good marker measurements.

Ta-Pt System. A preliminary study of diffusion in this binary system has been made, in conjunction with a phase-diagram study (17), to determine the applicability of pure-metal couples to the determination of diffusion coefficients in an alloy system exhibiting several intermediate phases. Pure-metal couples with components made of sheet material measuring 0.030 by 0.400 by 0.100 in. were diffusion bonded in a molybdenum-stainless steel jig for 4 hr at 800 C. These were then given diffusion treatments at 1300, 1400 and 1600 C. Concentration-distance profiles were determined by electron probe and analyzed by the Matano solution, with the same computer program used for the other systems. A graph of log $\tilde{D}$ versus composition is shown in Fig. 12, and Arrhenius-type plots of log $\tilde{D}$ versus $1/T$ are shown in Fig. 13.

The interdiffusion coefficient does not vary appreciably within the phases studied but is higher in the Pt-rich gamma and delta (Pt_2Ta and Pt_3Ta) intermediate phases than in the terminal solid solutions. The nonlinearity of the Arrhenius plots makes it impossible to obtain reasonable values for D_0 and Q.

The couples studied in this system showed a great deal of porosity near the intermediate phases, making the analysis rather questionable. In addition, the brittle sigma phase frequently cracked along the length of

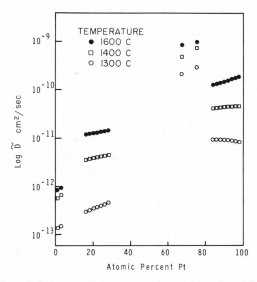

Fig. 12. Interdiffusion coefficient versus composition for diffusion in the Ta-Pt system

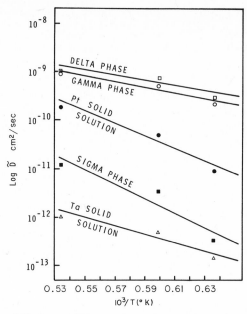

Fig. 13. Interdiffusion coefficient versus reciprocal absolute temperature for diffusion in the Ta-Pt system

the diffusion zone and thus added some uncertainty to the distance measurements in adjacent regions. It is felt that use of the pure-metal infinite couple is an unsatisfactory technique for measuring diffusion coefficients in this and similar systems. For such situations, the most feasible technique appears to be the Wagner (4) analysis.

Mo-Zr System. Interdiffusion coefficients were determined in the Mo-Zr system for the Mo solid-solution terminal phase and for the Mo_2Zr intermediate phase. Diffusion studies were conducted over the temperature range of 1200 to 1833 C for the Mo/90 wt % Mo–10 wt % Zr and Mo/80 wt % Mo–20 wt % Zr diffusion couples. Only three diffusion couples, which are listed in Table 1, had measurable diffusion zones for the temperatures and times investigated. The Mo/90 wt % Mo–10 wt % Zr diffusion couple heat treated at 1833 C was a solid-solution couple because the two-phase alloy is a single phase at this temperature. The Matano solution was used to analyze this diffusion couple and gave diffusion coefficients ranging from 1.3×10^{-11} cm²/sec at pure Mo up to 3.7×10^{-11} cm²/sec at 10 wt % Zr. The other two diffusion couples of Mo/80 wt % Mo–20 wt % Zr were analyzed with the solution developed by Wagner for a single-phase to a two-phase alloy (4). This solution assumes that the diffusion coefficient does not vary with composition. The

Table 3. Activation Energies and Frequency Factors
for Diffusion in the Mo-Zr System

Phase	$\tilde{Q}$, kcal/mole	$\tilde{D}_0$, cm²/sec
Mo solid solution.........	107.3	1.6
Mo₂Zr	55.6	1.0×10^{-3}
	56.4(a)	....

(a) Activation energy determined from Arrhenius plot of log of phase width squared divided by the time versus the reciprocal of temperature for the 90 wt % Mo–10 wt % Zr/50 wt % Mo–50 wt % Zr diffusion couples.

growth of the width of Mo solid solution is measured as a function of time. The diffusion coefficients obtained for these couples were 1.2×10^{-11} cm²/ sec at 1833 C and 1.0×10^{-12} cm²/sec at 1650 C. The diffusion coefficient for the couple at 1833 C compares favorably with the values obtained from the couple analyzed by the Matano solution. The two diffusion coefficients from the single-phase/two-phase couples were used to calculate an apparent activation energy of 107.3 kcal/mole, as shown in Table 3. Bronfin, Bokshteyn, and Kishkin (19) determined activation energies for the self-diffusion of Mo in various Mo-Zr alloys. The activation energy for the self-diffusion of Mo in a Mo–0.005% Zr alloy was 113 kcal/mole and increased to 131.5 kcal/mole in a Mo–0.26% Zr alloy.

Diffusion studies for the intermediate phase Mo₂Zr in the Mo-Zr system were made at 820, 1045, 1052, 1200 and 1445 C with couples of two-phase to two-phase alloys, that is, 90 wt % Mo–10 wt % Zr/50 wt % Mo–50 wt % Zr and 80 wt % Mo–20 wt % Zr/60 wt % Mo–40 wt % Zr, as given in Table 1. The growth of the intermediate phase Mo₂Zr between the two-phase alloys was measured as a function of time and temperature. These couples were analyzed with the solution developed by Wagner for this type of diffusion couple, which assumes the diffusion coefficient is constant (4). This appears to be a valid assumption because the concentration width of the Mo₂Zr phase is on the order of 1 at. %.

This method gives excellent results because all that is required is the composition limits of the phase and an accurate measurement of the width of the growing phase as a function of time and temperature. The 80 wt % Mo–20 wt % Zr/60 wt % Mo–40 wt % Zr couples gave a wider phase for the same time and temperature than the 90 wt % Mo–10 wt % Zr/50 wt % Mo–50 wt % Zr couples did, because less diffusion must take place in the first type of couple to change the composition of the two-phase alloys. The growth of the Mo₂Zr phase was parabolic with time as determined for couples with two diffusion times at the same

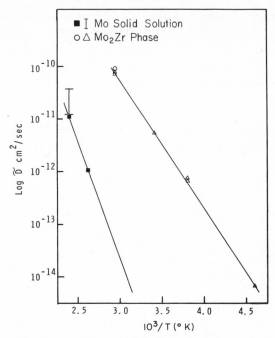

Fig. 14. Interdiffusion coefficient versus reciprocal absolute temperature for diffusion in the Mo-Zr system

temperature. The apparent activation energy obtained from an Arrhenius plot, which is shown in Fig. 14, for the diffusion coefficients for the Mo_2Zr phase was 55.6 kcal/mole. The activation energy was also determined from a plot of the log of the phase width squared divided by the time versus the reciprocal of absolute temperature. This plot yielded an activation energy of 56.4 kcal/mole, which agrees well with the activation energy obtained from the diffusion coefficients. A summary of the activation energies and frequency factors for the Mo-Zr system is given in Table 3.

The composition of the Mo_2Zr phase determined from the diffusion couples was shifted about 2 at. % from stoichiometry to the Zr side of the phase diagram. The pure-Zr starting material used in preparing the alloys contained about 2 at. % Hf, which may have affected the composition of the Mo_2Zr phase and also the diffusion results.

Discussion

Perhaps the most striking feature of the preceding results is the occurrence of negative intrinsic diffusion coefficients in certain instances. To our knowledge, such behavior was reported only once before and at that time there existed some question about the measurements of the marker shift (11). We believe that a more precise value can be obtained with indirect measurements on concentration-distance curves because direct measurements on diffusion couples always gave a great deal of scatter and were not self-consistent. Occasionally when indirect measurements showed an increasing marker shift with temperature, direct measurements would show an irregular behavior; that is, a marker shift at one temperature or time might be less than that at a lower temperature or shorter time. Consequently, we decided to use indirect measurements in all computations. The only error inherent in such measurements, aside from porosity occurring between the marker interface and Matano interface, should be the change in molal volume with composition. In all systems studied, the correction due to this effect was negligible. Other systematic errors, mentioned earlier, could not account for an anomalously high marker shift in certain instances. In addition, the markers never moved with a composition in a region where the concentration gradient was particularly high; hence, no appreciable errors due to the uncertainties in measuring the gradient should be present.

If such experimental errors are assumed negligible, we must conclude that the negative intrinsic diffusivities exist and have some physical explanation. One such explanation might arise from the fact that in the usual treatment of chemical diffusion by a vacancy mechanism, certain cross-effect terms are ignored. For instance it can be shown that (20)

$$D_1 = (D_{11} - D_{12})[1 + d \ln \gamma_1/d \ln N_1]$$
$$D_2 = (D_{22} - D_{21})[1 + d \ln \gamma_1/d \ln N_1] \tag{1}$$

where D_1 and D_2 are the usual intrinsic diffusion coefficients of species 1 and 2 respectively, D_{11} and D_{22} are the self-diffusion coefficients of species 1 and 2 in the alloy of composition N_1, γ_1 is the activity coefficient of species 1, and D_{12} and D_{21} are coupling terms, which arise from the deviation from ideality of the solid solution. The coupling terms may also be interpreted as arising from correlated jumps, that is, the tendency of an atom to return to its "original" position after a small number of subsequent jumps. Generally these terms are assumed negligible, relative to the "direct" diffusion coefficients D_{11} and D_{22}. The coupling diffusion coefficients are related by

$$D_{21} = (N_2/N_1)D_{12} = M_{12}kT/n_1 \tag{2}$$

where M_{12} is the mobility (flux per unit chemical potential gradient) of species 1 (or 2) in a chemical potential gradient of species 2 (or 1) and n_1 is the concentration of species 1 in atoms per unit volume. Le Claire

(21) has shown that if chemical diffusion is considered as a random walk upon which is superimposed the biasing effect of the concentration gradient, that is, an ideal solution, $M_{12} = 0$. Also the direct diffusion coefficients, D_{ii}, are

$$D_{ii} = M_{ii}kT/N_i \qquad i = 1, 2 \qquad (3)$$

Hence, if M_{12} were sufficiently large, relative to one of the M_{ii}, there could exist a composition range in which D_i would be negative. This would imply a very strong repulsive force between unlike atoms, a situation unlikely to exist in a continuous series of solid solutions such as those in the present study. Consequently, it seems unlikely that negative intrinsic diffusion coefficients arise from the cross terms.

In treatments of chemical diffusion by a vacancy mechanism, it is generally assumed that the chemical potential gradient due to vacancies is zero. If this is not true, an effect upon the diffusion flux of the atomic species would be expected. Hirth (22) has concluded that if the larger atoms are the slower diffusing atomic species, the vacancy supersaturation produced by the differing rates of diffusion of the atoms exerts a force on the dislocations originally at the weld interface. This force tends to drive them out of the crystal, and they migrate toward the region of higher concentration of the smaller, faster diffusing species. If the supersaturation is sufficiently high, an anomalously large marker shift toward the high concentrations of faster moving species would be observed. An anomalously large marker shift may lead to an apparent intrinsic diffusion coefficient for this species that is larger than the interdiffusion coefficient at the marker composition. Thus, for the relation

$$\tilde{D} = N_2 D_1 + N_1 D_2 \qquad (4)$$

to be satisfied, the other intrinsic diffusivity must be negative. Fara and Balluffi (23) have shown that if the vacancy lifetimes are sufficiently short, the effect of a nonequilibrium vacancy concentration is negligible at sufficiently long diffusion times and/or high equilibrium vacancy concentrations. This would be the case if sufficient sinks for vacancies existed in regions of high concentrations of the faster moving atomic species. However, because the equilibrium vacancy concentration varies across the diffusion zone, the nonequilibrium situation may exist only in a region of the zone near the component with lower equilibrium vacancy concentration.

A chemical potential gradient due to vacancies also could arise if one side of the couple were to act as a source and the other side as a sink for vacancies. Such a source-sink operation could conceivably be caused by stresses introduced by the concentration gradient. Stresses exist in the diffusion zone because of the variation in average atomic volume associated with the concentration gradient. As a first approximation, we assume that a diffusing atom experiences a hydrostatic stress as it travels through the diffusion zone. This stress may be estimated by considering that

$$\sigma = K\delta \tag{5}$$

where K is the bulk modulus (equal to Young's modulus for a Poisson's ratio of $1/3$) and δ is the dilation of the lattice. The dilation due to the concentration gradient may be estimated

$$d\delta = d\Omega_0/\Omega_0$$

hence

$$\delta = \ln[1 + \Delta\Omega_0/\Omega_0] \tag{6}$$

where Ω_0 is the average atomic volume. The dilation of a unit cell is thus

$$\delta \simeq (3/a_0)[da_0/dn_1][dn_1/dx]\,\Delta x = 3[da_0/dn_1][dn_1/dx] \tag{7}$$

where a_0 is the lattice parameter. Hence, the stress is

$$\sigma = 3K[da_0/dn_1][dn_1/dx] \tag{8}$$

and

$$d\sigma/dx = 3K[da_0/dn_1][d^2n_1/dx^2] \tag{9}$$

Thus, an increasing stress gradient exists on the Cb-rich side of the maximum concentration gradient, and a decreasing stress gradient exists on the V-rich side. Such a system would tend to squeeze vacancies out of the Cb-rich region by exchanging them with the smaller V atoms. This process would tend to increase the flux of V atoms and lead to a greater migration of V atoms past the original interface than that which would occur under only the influence of the chemical potential gradient due to the atomic species alone.

Because neglecting the chemical potential gradient due to vacancies leads to no physical explanation for negative intrinsic diffusivities, it is concluded that an appreciable gradient of this kind must exist.

Summary and Conclusions

Studies of interdiffusion in the Cb-V, Cb-Ti, and Mo-Ti systems indicate that under certain conditions, that is, an incremental couple of an equiatomic alloy with the pure slower moving component, negative intrinsic diffusion coefficients for the slower moving species are obtained from the observed marker shift by applying the Darken analysis. This behavior is attributed to a finite chemical potential gradient due to vacancies produced either by differing diffusion rates of the atomic species or by stresses due to the concentration gradient.

Enhanced diffusion was observed in regions of steep concentration gradients. This effect is believed to be related to the nonequilibrium vacancy concentration, which leads to negative intrinsic diffusion coefficients.

It is concluded that Matano analysis applied to diffusion couples made from pure metals whose alloys form intermediate phases does not yield accurate values of the diffusion coefficient in the intermediate phases. In such systems the Wagner analysis yields more self-consistent and precise results for the intermediate phases.

Acknowledgments. The authors wish to acknowledge the cooperation of the Air Force Institute of Technology in arranging the thesis programs upon which much of this work was based. The following individuals deserve particular credit for their efforts in carrying out the experimental programs: Capt. R. C. Geiss, Capt. A. H. Winkleman, Lt. F. J. Gurney, Capt. K. M. Skuza and Lt. C. J. Lemont. We also wish to thank Dr. S. H. Moll and Dr. D. M. Koffman, of Advanced Metals Research Corporation, for analyzing the diffusion couples with the microbeam probe, and Dr. A. Ray of the University of Dayton Research Institute for arranging for the arc melting of the alloys. The helpful comments of Prof. G. W. Powell of Ohio State University are greatly appreciated.

References

1 H. W. Paxton and T. Kunitake, Trans AIME, **218**, 1003 (1960)
2 H. W. Paxton and E. J. Pasierb, Trans AIME, **218**, 794 (1960)
3 P. G. Shewmon and J. H. Bechtold, Acta Met, **3**, 452 (1955)
4 W. Jost, Diffusion in Solids, Liquids, Gases, Academic Press Inc., New York, 1960
5 L. S. Darken, Trans AIME, **175**, 184 (1948)
6 J. E. Reynolds, B. L. Averbach and M. Cohen, Acta Met, **5**, 29 (1957)
7 A. Bolk, Acta Met, **9**, 632 (1961)
8 A. G. Guy, private communication
9 C. S. Hartley and K. Hubbard, A Computer Program for the Matano Analysis of Binary Diffusion Data, ASD TDR 62-858 (1962)
10 R. C. Geiss, An Investigation of Diffusion in the Cb-V System, Master's Thesis, Air Force Institute of Technology, 1962
11 U. S. Landergren, C. E. Birchenall and R. F. Mehl, Trans AIME, **206**, 73 (1956)
12 C. daSilva and R. F. Mehl, Trans AIME, **175**, 184 (1948)
13 A. H. Winklelman, A Study of Diffusion in the Molybdenum-Columbium and the

Columbium-Titanium Systems, Master's Thesis, Air Force Institute of Technology, 1963

14 D. M. Koffman, Norelco Rep, **XI**, 59 (1964)

15 F. J. Gurney, A Study of Substitutional Bulk Diffusion in the Molybdenum-Titanium System, Master's Thesis, Air Force Institute of Technology, 1964

16 K. M. Skuza, A Study of Diffusion in the Columbium-Zirconium System, Master's Thesis, Air Force Institute of Technology, 1964

17 C. S. Hartley, L. D. Parsons and J. E. Steedly, Jr., J Metals, **16** (1), 119

18 C. J. Lemont, A Study of Diffusion Rates for Molybdenum-Zirconium Alloys, Master's Thesis, Air Force Institute of Technology, 1964

19 M. B. Bronfin, S. Z. Bokshteyn and S. T. Kishkin, Self-Diffusion of Molybdenum-Zirconium Alloys, Issled Splavov Tsvetn Metal, Inst Met, Akad Nauf SSSR, No. 3, 12–18 (1962)

20 J. Bardeen and C. Herring, Atom Movements, American Society for Metals, Metals Park, 1951, p 87

21 A. D. Le Claire, Colloque sur La Diffusion a L'Etat Solide, North Holland Publishing Co., Amsterdam, 1959

22 J. P. Hirth, private communication

23 H. Fara and R. W. Balluffi, J Appl Phys, **30**, 325 (1959)

Chapter 5
The Diffusion of Carbon in Alpha Iron

C. G. HOMAN

The diffusivity of C in α-Fe has been quantitatively measured over 14 decades of its value. In the temperature range of -50 to 350 C, an Arrhenius expression involving a single relaxation process adequately represents the data. However, early measurements by Stanley (1) suggested that the low-temperature expression for the diffusivities obtained from the anelastic techniques of Wert (2), Maringer (3), Rathenau (4), Thomas and Leak (5), and others (6) could not be extrapolated to the high-temperature region. More recently, quantitative measurements in the high-temperature region from 500 to 860 C by Smith (7), who used permeability data from a moving-phase-boundary experiment in conjunction with available solubility data, and my diffusivity experiments (8) with a Grube diffusion couple and radioactive tracers clearly showed that a simple Arrhenius extrapolation of the low-temperature data to the high-temperature region is questionable.

In this paper, the results of the high-temperature diffusivity measurements will be presented, an empirical model will be proposed to explain the measurements, some ramifications of the model will be discussed and an attempt will be made at an unprejudiced critique of the model.

Experimental Procedures

The experimental procedures of all the measurements other than the tracer measurements are well known and are documented elsewhere (1–7). The radioactive techniques are described in the original paper (8); however, because this is in press, I will describe these techniques briefly.

High-purity Battelle Fe* was carefully machined into small cylindrical

---

* The Battelle iron used in this experiment was provided by J. W. Halley, Chairman of the Pure Iron Subcommittee of the American Iron and Steel Institute Research Committee. The analysis provided was Al, 15 ppm; Cu, 5 ppm; Co, 5 ppm; Cu, 7 ppm; Ni, 20 ppm; P, 9 ppm; Si, 10 ppm; C, 10 ppm (before carburization); O, 10 ppm; N, 2 ppm; S, 18 ppm. Other metallic impurities were not detected.

The author is with the Watervliet Arsenal, Watervliet, New York.

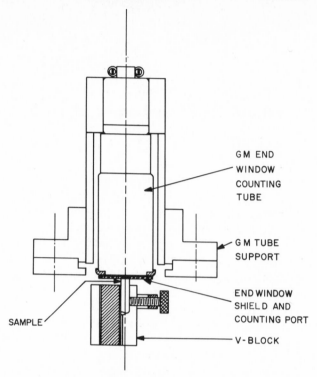

Fig. 1. Schematic of counting assembly

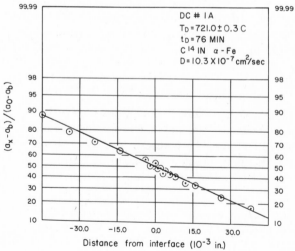

Fig. 2. Plot of $(a_x - a_b)/(a_0 - a_b)$ versus distance from weld on probability paper

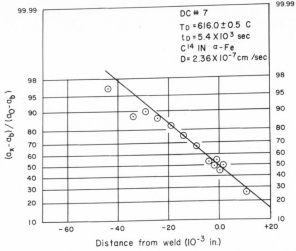

Fig. 3. Plot of $(a_x - a_b)/(a_0 - a_b)$ versus distance from weld on probability paper

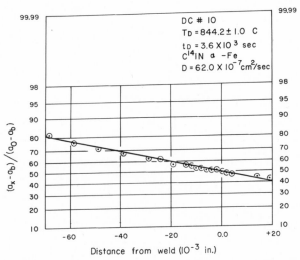

Fig. 4. Plot of $(a_x - a_b)/(a_0 - a_b)$ versus distance from weld on probability paper

specimens of 0.2-in. diameter and 1.5-in. length. Some of the cylinders were charged with various concentrations of C^{14} in the range of 0.006 to 0.022 wt % by use of radioactive methane. The carburized specimens were checked for uniformity and then welded to uncharged cylinders to form Grube diffusion couples. The couples were copper plated and then annealed at various temperatures in a diffusion furnace. The high density, nonporous copper coating prevented decarburization of the Fe in the annealing process.

After annealing, each couple was sectioned on a precision grinder, and the surface of the remaining specimen was counted in a fixture, as shown

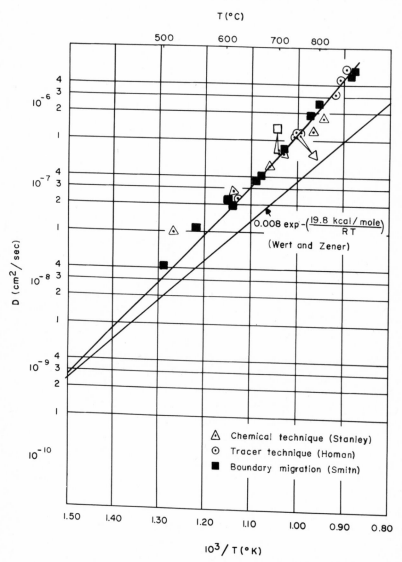

Fig. 5. Plot of diffusivity versus $10^3/T$ (°K) for C in α-Fe

in Fig. 1. This fixture insured reproducible geometry with respect to the GM end window counting tube.

Some of the penetration curves obtained in this experiment are plotted in Fig. 2, 3 and 4 in the usual manner. The straight-line behavior on a probability plot of all the penetration data indicates that, for the range of concentrations of the couple(s) used at each temperature, the diffusivity is independent of the C concentration. In all, nine couples were used at seven temperatures in the range of 616 to 844 C.

Experimental Results

Figure 5 is a plot of the diffusivity of C in α-Fe for the temperature range of 500 to 860 C from the measurements of Stanley (1), Smith (7) and Homan (8). Also included are lines representing the extrapolation of

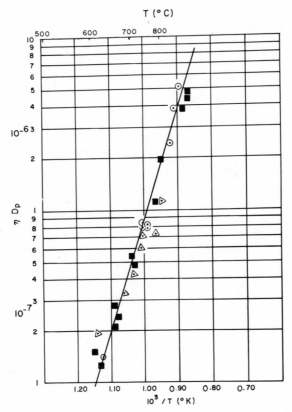

Fig. 6. ηD_p versus $10^3/T$ (°K) for C in α-Fe. $\eta D_p = D_{\text{exp}} - D_c$ where $D_c = 0.008 \exp\left[-(19.8 \text{ kcal/mole})/RT\right]$

the low-temperature data of Wert and Zener (9) and the empirical model proposed below. Even though the data are not plotted below 600 C, this model has the built-in feature of representing the diffusivity over its entire measured range.

Before developing the model, one may naturally surmise, from the character of the plot in Fig. 5, that a second activated process is operable in the high-temperature range and may be the cause of the deviation from simple Arrhenius behavior. Then one would plot the log of the differences of the diffusivities, that is, the measured value minus the low-temperature asymptotic value, versus $1/T$ and obtain Fig. 6. Although the ordinate in Fig. 6 is really $D_{\text{experimental}}$ minus $D_{\text{extrapolated}}$ (that is, D_c), I have used ηD_p, for reasons that will be explained later. From this plot, one obtains the activation energy and pre-exponential factor for the second process, and an expression for the effective diffusivity D_e of C in α-Fe over its entire measured range is

$$D_e = D_c + \eta D_p = 0.008 \exp\left(-\frac{19.8 \text{ kcal/mole}}{RT}\right)$$
$$+ 2.2 \exp\left(-\frac{29.3 \text{ kcal/mole}}{RT}\right) \quad (1)$$

where the expression for D_c is obtained from Wert (2).

Theory

Wert (2) was able to derive an expression for the diffusivity of C in α-Fe at low temperatures, using a single relaxation phenomenon. It is implicitly assumed in his paper (2) that at low temperatures almost all the diffusional jumps made by C occur when local surroundings are identical; that is, when every neighboring lattice site nearest the moving interstitial C is filled with an Fe atom.

As a generalization of this model, one may investigate the modification of the interstitial diffusion process if one had two (or more) different and distinct local surroundings for the moving C atom. The first choice, especially at elevated temperatures, would probably be the configuration in which one of the nearest-neighbor Fe sites is vacant. In lieu of the difficulties in deriving an analogous expression for a double relaxation phenomenon from first principles, the following empirical model is proposed.

An expression is needed for the number of C-vacancy pairs. The proposed reaction is

$$C + V \underset{\alpha_2}{\overset{\alpha_1}{\rightleftharpoons}} C \cdots V \quad (2)$$

The forward reaction requires the presence of a free C and a free vacancy and is of second order. Radiation damage measurements by Fujita and Damask (10) also suggest this assumption. The reverse reaction involves only the "pairs" and should be unimolecular. The differential equation describing this reaction is

$$\frac{dC_p}{dt} = \alpha_1 C_c C_v - \alpha_2 C_p \tag{3}$$

where C_p, C_c and C_v are the pair, total C and total vacancy concentrations and α_1 and α_2 are appropriate rate constants.

If one assumes that the free C atoms are more mobile than free vacancies, Eq 3 can be written

$$\frac{dC_p}{dt} = 6\nu_1 C_c C_v \exp\left(-\frac{E_{mc}}{RT}\right) - \nu_2 C_p \exp\left(-\frac{E_{mc} + B}{RT}\right) \tag{4}$$

where ν_1 and ν_2 are the vibrational frequencies of the C in the two configurations, E_{mc} the motional energy of the C in the "free" state and B the binding between C and vacancies.

At equilibrium, the ratio of paired carbons to total C concentrations η is

$$\eta = \frac{C_p}{C_c} = 6\frac{\nu_1}{\nu_2} C_v \exp\left(\frac{+B}{RT}\right)$$
$$= 6\frac{\nu_1}{\nu_2} \exp\left(\frac{B - E_{fv}}{RT}\right) \tag{5}$$

An effective diffusion coefficient D_e may be formulated as

$$D_e = (1 - \eta)D_c + \eta D_p \tag{6}$$

where the new term D_p is of the usual Arrhenius type

$$D_p = D_{0p} \exp\left(-\frac{E_{mp}}{RT}\right) \tag{7}$$

and D_{0p} contains the entropy changes and E_{mp} is the effective motional energy of the C in the paired configuration. The expression for the diffusivity, based on this model, for $\eta \ll 1$, is

$$D_e = 0.008 \exp\left(-\frac{19.8 \text{ kcal/mole}}{RT}\right) + 6\frac{\nu_1}{\nu_2} D_{0p} \exp\left(\frac{B - E_{fv} - E_{mp}}{RT}\right) \tag{8}$$

Hence, from Fig. 6 of ln $(D_e - D_c)$ or ln (ηD_p) versus $1/T$, one obtains values of the pre-exponential factor $[6(\nu_1/\nu_2)D_{0p}]$ and the energy sum $(B - E_{fv} - E_{mp})$.

Discussion

Comparison With the Results of Other Measurements. Comparison of the D_e values obtained in this experiment with previously reported D values (1, 7) indicates good agreement in the temperature range of 616 to 844 C. The quantitative agreement of this data with that obtained by Smith (7), who used nonradioactive C, indicates that an isotope effect, if any, was not detected. It would be expected that an isotope effect would yield values of diffusivities for C^{14} approximately 7% smaller than those for the nonradioactive carbon.

Most of the low-temperature diffusion measurements involve a quenching technique in the sample preparation stage. A certain fraction of the vacancies present at the quench temperature may be "frozen" into the lattice, depending on the individual quenching statistics, that is, the quench rate. The effect of these excess vacancies may cause the dispersion noticed by several investigators (2, 11) in the anelastic relaxation measurements. An annealing technique was developed by Kê (11) to eliminate this dispersion.

It has been shown by Damask *et al.* (10, 12, 13) in a series of measurements on α-Fe radiation damaged at low temperatures, that vacancies trap C atoms. Thus a binding energy for the pair is indicated. Furthermore, it was suggested in these studies of radiation damage annealing kinetics that the C atom may encounter many vacancies on its way to a precipitation site.

The smoothness of the curves in Fig. 5 and 6 over the temperature range of 600 to 850 C implies that the diffusivity of C in α-Fe is unaffected by the magnetic change at 770 C, the Curie temperature, as Smith (7) previously noted. This result is in striking contrast to the abrupt change observed in the self-diffusion coefficient in α-Fe (14) and the diffusivity of Ni in Fe (14).

Activation Energy $(E_{fv} + E_{mp} - B)$. A binding energy B of a C-vacancy pair of 9.5 kcal/mole may be assigned from radiation-damage calorimetric studies at Brookhaven (12); however, this value may be higher if all the C in solution does not participate in the reaction because of previous precipitation or an insufficiency of vacancy traps at the temperature of the reaction. The electron microscopy studies at Brookhaven (13) indicate that the latter effect may be occurring. Values of E_{fv} ranging from 29 to 40 kcal/mole have been suggested by various investigators (14–16). From the results of this experiment, an upper limit of the activation energy for motion in the pair state is about 10 kcal/mole. This energy is considerably less than the activation energies of motion of either the C or vacancy in α-Fe.

Consequences of the Model. * Pairing of interstitial impurities with vacancies in Fe need not be limited to C only. In fact, any impurity that has an appreciable binding energy to a vacancy may show marked deviations from a simple, single-relaxation model. For H, for which some evidence of strong binding exists from de-embrittlement studies of Wallin and Mack (18), the experimental data for the diffusivities (19) may be fit with a modified effective diffusion constant for which the ratio of paired H-vacancy complexes is no longer small compared with unity.

Furthermore, on the basis of this model and the results of Grievson and Turkdogan (20) for the Fe-N system, one may expect the binding energy of the N-vacancy complex to be smaller than the binding energy of the C-vacancy complex because the deviation from a low-temperature extrapolation of anelastic data appears to be small, if not negligible, in the high-temperature range.

Critique of the Model. One might ask if the deviation from a simple Arrhenius expression is really a vacancy effect. No experimental evidence that convincingly contradicts this assumption is known to this author. Hence, an experiment to test this assumption has been designed and is in progress. It is well known that there is no measurable high-pressure effect on the diffusion of C in α-Fe (21) at low temperatures. However, on the basis of the proposed model, it can be shown that a high-pressure, high-temperature effect (8) that is simply related to formation volume of vacancies in Fe may exist.

On the basis of this calculation, which predicts a measurable decrease in the experimental D_e at about 800 C and 4000 atm, one realizes that the high-pressure technique may be used to change the vacancy concentration, as it may be used, analogously, to vary other "normal" solute constituents. Hence, one may examine quite critically the influence of vacancies on physical phenomena in solids, especially in this instance of the diffusion of C in α-Fe.

Conclusion

The diffusion of C in α-Fe has been quantitatively measured over 14 decades of its value. Above 600 C, the measured diffusivities deviate from a simple Arrhenius expression. The entire range of measured

---

* The discussion in this section represents unpublished research in collaboration with L. V. Meisel and J. F. Cox.

diffusivities can be described with a two-mechanism process. An empirical model, which includes the possibility of carbon-vacancy interactions, is proposed to explain this deviation.

Acknowledgments. I would like to acknowledge the many helpful discussions and the encouragement given me by my thesis advisor Prof. H. B. Huntington of Rensselaer Polytechnic Institute. I would also like to acknowledge the help of my colleagues at Watervliet, especially Mr. J. F. Cox for his aid and ideas throughout the entire experiment, Dr. L. Meisel for active collaboration in clarifying the model and Mr. J. Frankel for helpful discussions.

References

1 J. K. Stanley, Trans AIME, **185**, 752 (1950)
2 C. A. Wert, Phys Rev, **79**, 601 (1950)
3 R. E. Maringer, J Appl Phys, **31**, 229S (1960); **35**, 2375 (1964)
4 G. W. Rathenau, J Appl Phys, **29**, 239 (1958)
5 W. R. Thomas and G. M. Leak, Phil Mag, **45**, 986 (1954)
6 A. E. Lord and D. N. Beshers, Ph.D. Thesis (AEL), Columbia University. (This thesis contains a comprehensive bibliography of all data in the Fe-C and Fe-N diffusion systems.)
7 R. P. Smith, Trans AIME, **224**, 105 (1962)
8 C. G. Homan, Acta Met, **12**, 1071 (1964); The Diffusion of Carbon in Alpha Iron, Watervliet Arsenal Tech Report WVT-RR-6402 (1964)
9 C. A. Wert and C. Zener, Phys Rev, **76**, 1169
10 F. Fujita and A. C. Damask, Acta Met, **12**, 331 (1964)
11 T. S. Kê, Metals Tech, TP 2370 (June 1948); Phys Rev, **74**, 9 (1948)
12 H. Wagenblast and A. C. Damask, J Phys Chem Solids, **23**, 221
13 R. Arndt and A. C. Damask, Acta Met, **12**, 341 (1964); H. Wagenblast, F. Fujita and A. Damask, Acta Met, **12**, 347 (1964)
14 R. Borg and C. Birchenall, Trans AIME, **218**, 980 (1960); G. Buffington, K. Hirano and M. Cohen, Acta Met, **9**, 434 (1961)
15 H. Brooks, in Impurities and Imperfections, American Society for Metals, Metals Park, 1957, p 1; R. Mehl, et al., Acta Met, **9**, 256; R. Doremus, Trans AIME, **218**, 591
16 E. Smith, Indirect Observation of Imperfections in Crystals, Interscience, New York, 1962, p 207
17 D. Lazarus, Solid State Physics, Vol 10, Academic Press, New York, 1960
18 H. Wallin and D. Mack, Acta Met, **7**, 687 (1959)
19 E. Johnson and M. Hill, Trans AIME, **218**, 1104 (1960)
20 P. Grievson and E. T. Turkdogan, Edgar Bain Laboratory, US Steel Progress Report PR-218; Trans AIME (in press)
21 A. J. Bosman et al., Physica, **23**, 1001 (1957); J. Bass and D. Lazarus, J Phys Chem Solids, **23**, 1820 (1962)

Chapter 6
The Electron-Concentration Concept and Diffusion

DR. NIELS ENGEL

The current theories for metallic bonding describe metal atoms as ionized cores with the electrons in new quantum states common to the entire lattice. All electrons are thrown into a common electron "gas." The transition metals are obviously bonded by d-electrons, which also are postulated to enter energy bands common to the lattice, but which still retain their characteristics as atomic quantum states, namely, as d-electrons (1). This concept has not been too successful in accounting for bonding energies, phase diagrams, and other phenomena such as diffusion, for example. The author has found it helpful to suggest another theory of bonding in which it is assumed that electrons remain in the pattern of quantum states determined by the nuclear charge and that covalent and metallic bonding result from interaction of electrons that remain unpaired in the atomic structure. This concept has been used with some success in accounting for phase diagrams (2), and certain thermodynamic properties of metals and alloys (3). In this paper these bonding ideas are used to discuss diffusion.

A postulate of the new theory is that the three metallic lattices are controlled by one, two or three outer bonding electrons. Thus the bcc lattice is controlled by one electron per atom; the hcp lattice, by two electrons per atom; the fcc, by three electrons per atom. Figure 1 indicates the distribution of the lattices over the periodic chart, and it is obvious that the center of the region for each lattice moves to the right as the electron concentration increases. The center of the region for the bcc lattice postulated to be formed when one outer bonding electron per atom is controlling the lattice is found on the left in the chart. This lattice is present either at all temperatures or at elevated temperatures. The hcp two-electron phase, which is either an all-temperature phase or a lower-temperature phase, is slightly further to the right. The fcc three-electron phase, mostly an all-temperature phase but often an intermediate-tem-

The author is with the School of Chemical Engineering, Georgia Institute of Technology, Atlanta, Ga., and the Oak Ridge National Laboratory, Oak Ridge, Tenn.

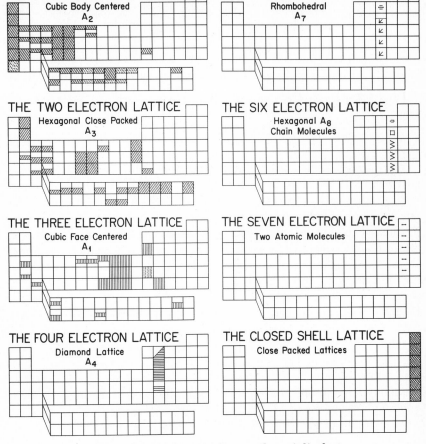

Fig. 1. Distribution of lattices over the periodic chart

perature phase, is most common in the center of the chart. The four-, five-, six- and seven-electron phases are Hume-Rothery $(18 - N)$ phases restricted to one column each.

Figure 2 shows another consequence of the basic assumption that bonding is caused by interaction of electrons that were unpaired in the neutral atoms.* The bonding energy over the two first periods exhibits a sharp maximum at C and Si, each having four unpaired bonding electrons. The bonding energy increases almost linearly over He, Li, Be, B

* This is only true for the first three periods. In the transition metals, for example, electrons may change quantum states to yield a more stable bonding pattern, and equilibria between atoms with different electron distributions may exist.

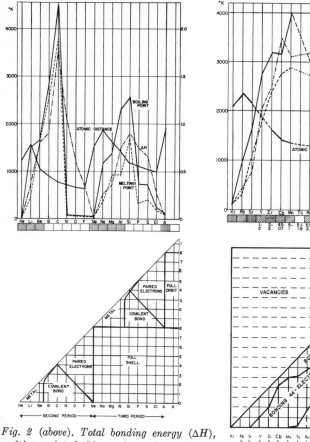

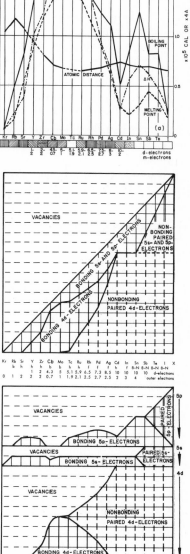

Fig. 2 (above). Total bonding energy (ΔH), melting point, boiling point and atomic distance for elements in the second and third periods of the periodic chart. The number of bonding electrons increases from 0 to 4 and then returns to zero in each period. The ΔH values follow this pattern with a sharp peak in the middle in spite of the decreasing atomic distance (3).

Fig. 3 (right). (a) Total bonding energy (ΔH), melting point, boiling point and atomic distance for elements in the fifth period of the periodic chart; (b) distribution of electrons between outer 5s- and 5p-electronic shells and inner 4d-shells. Ag is definitely a transition metal. The ΔH values follow the number of bonding electrons, considering the greater contribution to bonding by d-electrons, and are independent of atomic distance (3).

and C and over Ne, Na, Mg, Al and Si, and is proportional to the number of bonding electrons in each period. The bonding energy per electron pair formed is different for second- and third-period elements. When elements have more than four outer bonding electrons, some of them must pair internally, and the paired electrons cannot contribute to bonding. Therefore, the bonding energy decreases from C to Ne and from Si to A because the number of paired electrons increases and consequently the number of bonding electrons decreases.

For the transition elements, the bonding of the outer, lattice-controlling electrons and the bonding d-electrons may be different and contribute with different bonding energies. This can be calculated in the following manner. First, the distribution between outer bonding and d-electrons can be determined from the known lattices, as indicated in Fig. 3 for the fifth period. The fractional numbers of outer (s-p) and inner d-electrons mean that the pure element is composed of atoms with different electron distributions. For example, Cb has 4.3 d-electrons and 0.7 outer electrons, meaning that 30% of the Cb atoms are $4d^55s^0$ and 70% are $4d^45s^1$. This distribution may change with temperature. Some elements, for example Y and Zr, exhibit different lattices at low and high temperature, indicating that electrons transfer from outer-shell quantum states to d-positions with increasing temperature. This electron transfer is important for the understanding of diffusion behavior.

The contribution of the d-electrons to bonding can be found, as illustrated for the sixth period in Table 1. From the first and the last elements in the period, which elements have only outer bonding electrons and are called normal, the bonding energy per bonding electron can be determined. In the transition elements, the electron distribution can be determined from the lattice structures (Fig. 1). The number of outer electrons is used to calculate their contribution to total bonding energy (see Table 1). Subtracting this part from the experimental bonding energies gives the bonding due to d-electrons. Dividing this by the number of bonding d-electrons gives the bonding energy per bonding d-electron. In this calculation it must be considered that the d-electrons pair internally when their number exceeds five or that of a half-filled shell, as demonstrated in Fig. 3 for the fifth period. It turns out that the bonding energy per bonding d-electron is reasonably constant over the period and is slightly more than twice that of outer electrons.

Diffusion in solid metals and alloys will be influenced by lattice configuration and mass of atoms (4), but will be essentially determined by the strengths of bonding and the bonding pattern; that is, by how many outer bonding electrons and d-electrons participate in bonding and by how full the various electronic shells are. In Fig. 4 values of ΔH, the

Table 1. Sixth Period(a)

Element	Electron distribution	Effective d- and (s-p) electrons	ΔH Experiment in cal times 10^4	Calculated bonding energy of (s-p) electrons times 10^4	Difference between columns 4 and 5	Calculated bonding energy per d-electron times 10^4
X	$(0)^0$	$(0)^0$	0.36	0	0.36	....
Cs	$(0)^1$	$(0)^1$	1.9	1.5	0.4	....
Ba	$(0.5)^{1.5}$	$(0.5)^{1.5}$	4.05	2.25	1.8	3.6
La	$(2)^1$	$(2)^1$	8.6	1.5	7.1	3.55
Hf	$(3)^1$	$(3)^1$	16.6	1.5	15.1	5.03
Ta	$(4.3)^{0.7}$	$(4.3)^{0.7}$	20.0	1.05	18.95	4.4
W	$(5)^1$	$(5)^1$	20.0	1.5	18.5	3.8
Re	$(5.1)^{1.9}$	$(4.9)^{1.9}$	19.0	2.85	16.15	3.3
Os	$(5.9)^{2.1}$	$(4.1)^{2.1}$	17.6	3.15	14.45	3.5
Ir	$(6.5)^{2.5}$	$(3.5)^{2.5}$	16.4	3.75	12.65	3.6
Pt	$(7.3)^{2.7}$	$(2.7)^{2.7}$	13.5	4.05	9.45	3.5
Au	$(8.5)^{2.5}$	$(1.5)^{2.5}$	8.8	3.75	5.05	3.4
Hg	$(1f)^1$	$(1f)^1$	1.3	1.5	−0.2	....

(a) For the electron distribution given in the second column, the number of d-electrons is given in parentheses, and the number of outer electrons (s-p) is given as a superscript.

In the third column the number of active bonding d-electrons is given in parentheses, and the number of bonding outer (s-p) electrons is given as a superscript.

The ΔH values are those gathered by Prof. Leo Brewer of the University of California.

The fifth column gives the contribution to the bonding energy from the outer (s-p) electrons found from the first and last elements in the same period.

The sixth column gives the contribution to bonding from the active bonding d-electrons calculated as the difference between columns 4 and 5.

The last column gives the bonding energy per bonding d-electron calculated as the bonding energy given in column 6 divided by the number of active bonding d-electrons.

energy necessary to evaporate the solid crystal at room temperature to a monatomic gas, values of Q, activation energies for self-diffusion, and values of $(Q/\Delta H)$ for various elements are arranged on a periodic chart. Considering the inaccuracy in both numbers, it is surprising that the ratios do not vary more than from 3 to 9.4×10^{-1}. Among the normal metals, the two- and four-electron lattices exhibit the highest ratios, 7 to 9×10^{-1} (Mg, Zn, Cd, and C, Si, Ge); whereas, the odd numbers of electrons causing cubic structures exhibit low ratios 0.3 to 0.5 (Li, Na, Al, In, Tl and Pb).* The diamond lattices are characterized by a fully satu-

* Pb is in column 14 and is accordingly expected to be a four-electron element. The lattice, however, is fcc, which discloses it as a three-outer-electron phase according to proposed postulates. In the sixth period the elements Hg, Tl and Pb have dropped about one outer electron into the $5f$-shell, changing the lattices one column to the left. These elements therefore deviate from the normal pattern. Further details may be found elsewhere (3).

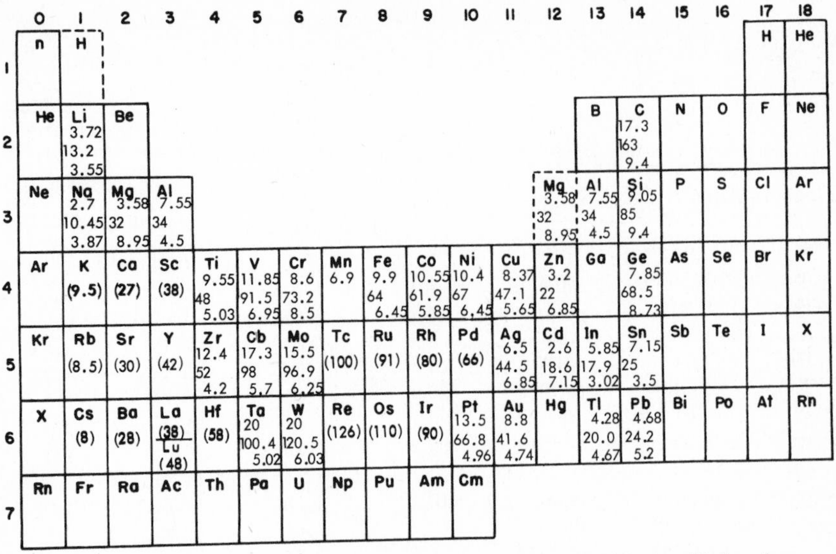

0	1	2	3	4	5	6	7	8	9	10	11	12	13	14	15	16	17	18
n	H																H	He
He	Li 3.72 13.2 3.55	Be											B	C 17.3 163 9.4	N	O	F	Ne
Ne	Na 2.7 10.45 3.87	Mg 3.58 32 8.95										Mg 3.58 32 8.95	Al 7.55 34 4.5	Si 9.05 85 9.4	P	S	Cl	Ar
Ar	K (9.5)	Ca (27)	Sc (38)	Ti 9.55 48 5.03	V 11.85 91.5 6.95	Cr 8.6 73.2 8.5	Mn 6.9	Fe 9.9 64 6.45	Co 10.55 61.9 5.85	Ni 10.4 67 6.45	Cu 8.37 47.1 5.65	Zn 3.2 22 6.85	Ga	Ge 7.85 68.5 8.73	As	Se	Br	Kr
Kr	Rb (8.5)	Sr (30)	Y (42)	Zr 12.4 52 4.2	Cb 17.3 98 5.7	Mo 15.5 96.9 6.25	Tc (100)	Ru (91)	Rh (80)	Pd (66)	Ag 6.5 44.5 6.85	Cd 2.6 18.6 7.15	In 5.85 17.9 3.02	Sn 7.15 25 3.5	Sb	Te	I	X
X	Cs (8)	Ba (28)	La (38) Lu (48)	Hf (58)	Ta 20 100.4 5.02	W 20 120.5 6.03	Re (126)	Os (110)	Ir (90)	Pt 13.5 66.8 4.96	Au 8.8 41.6 4.74	Hg	Tl 4.28 20.0 4.67	Pb 4.68 24.2 5.2	Bi	Po	At	Rn
Rn	Fr	Ra	Ac	Th	Pa	U	Np	Pu	Am	Cm								

Fig. 4. Known and predicted activation energies for self-diffusion. Values for ΔH (cal/mole $\times 10^4$) are given at top (3); values for Q (cal/mole $\times 10^3$), at center (5); values for Q:$\Delta H \times 10^{-1}$, at bottom. Values given parenthetically are predicted activation energies.

rated bonding pattern. To remove an atom in diffusion, all bonds must be broken. In determining the ΔH value by evaporating the metal all bonds are broken. Therefore Q is approximately equal to ΔH or the ratio is 0.94. The cubic metals have a rather incomplete bonding system with several vacant bond sites. Some atoms will build up complete bonding systems (complete eight shells) around themselves and other atoms will be depleted to about one-third (for the bcc lattices) or one-half (for the fcc lattices) of their expected average number of bonds. These latter atoms will be more loosely bonded and will diffuse first. (Also within an edge dislocation bonds are totally or practically absent.)

The transition metals exhibit ratios between 4 to 8.5×10^{-1} with a definite peak at column 6 according to available results. The real peak is probably at Te and Re. There are no results indicating that the hexagonal crystallizing transition metals exhibit higher ratios than the cubic ones. This may be because none have been investigated. Sc, Y, La, Ti, Zr, Hf and Co are hexagonal only at lower temperatures, and there are no investigations on the all-temperature hexagonal metals Tc, Re, Rh and Os. Comparison of the cubic transition metals with the cubic normal metals shows a higher $Q/\Delta H$ ratio for the transition metals and thus indicates that the d-electrons contribute more to Q than to ΔH.

It may be concluded that certain electron concentrations develop a special tie-down of atoms. These seem to be connected with shells filled by pairing (half-filled within the atoms). The diamond lattice and d^5-electron groups seem to be especially active in this respect and account for the much greater activation energy of Si (85,000 cal/mole) when compared with Al (34,000 cal/mole) and of V and Cb when compared with Ti and Zr (see Fig. 4). Both the ΔH values and the Q values indicate that V, Cb and Ta have almost half-filled d-shells, with a very low concentration of outer electrons in V and Cb.

Some of the transition metals exhibit phase changes that, according to the proposed theory, are caused by a change of the number of outer bonding electrons with temperature. The elements Sc, Y, La and Ti, Zr, Hf exhibit a hcp α phase at lower temperatures and a bcc β phase at elevated temperatures. In these elements the electron distribution changes appreciably with temperature. Because the number of outer electrons decreases with temperature, the β phase will have the maximum number of outer electrons, namely about 1.7 outer electrons (3) at the transition temperature, with 1.3 and 2.3 d-electrons per atom for the third- and fourth-column elements, respectively. As the temperature increases, the number of outer electrons will decrease further, approaching or possibly passing one, and the number of d-electrons will increase accordingly.

The Arrhenius-type formula for diffusion should apply when the bonding pattern or bonding energy determining the activation energy remains constant independent of temperature. In most normal metals, the electronic bonding pattern is temperature independent because there is no possibility of changing the electron distribution. In several transition metals, the actual electron distribution is much more stable than any other, and no, or practically no, change will occur when the temperature is varied. In other transition metals great changes can take place. Whether changes develop or not, depends on the stability differences between possibilities. Table 2 gives the energy levels of the ground state and the electron distributions corresponding to the bcc and hcp lattices for the first transition metals in the fourth and fifth periods. The bcc phase has one d-electron bond more and one outer bonding electron less than the hcp phase. With an energy release of about 30 kcal per formation of each d-bond and about 15 kcal per formation of outer electron bonds (Table 3) the transfer of one electron from outer bonding to d-bonding will release about 15 kcal per gram atom or about 0.65 ev. This is just enough energy to make the two electron distributions or lattices equally stable in the metal Sc (Table 2). Metals with energy differences in the magnitude of 0.5 to 1.5 ev between the two electron distributions will be sensitive to temperature and change from one state to another with increasing tem-

Table 2. Energy Levels (7) and Electron Distributions (3) Corresponding to the Ground State and the bcc and hcp Lattices for the Elements from Columns 2 to 7 for Fourth and Fifth Periods of the Periodic Chart

Element	Column of periodic table	Electron distribution and energy level, ev			Difference between energy levels for bcc and hcp lattices, ev
		Ground state	bcc lattice	hcp lattice	
Ca.........	2	$3p^6d^04s^2$ 0	$3p^6d^1s^1$ 2.52	$3p^64sp$ 1.88	−0.64
Sc.........	3	$3d4s^2$ 0	$3d^24s^1$ 1.3	$3d^14sp$ 1.94	0.64
Ti.........	4	$3d^24s^2$ 0	$3d^34s^1$ 0.81	$3d^24sp$ 1.97	1.16
V..........	5	$3d^34s^2$ 0	$3d^44s^1$ 0.27	$3d^34sp$ 2.03	1.76
Cr.........	6	$3d^44s^2$ 0.96	$3d^54s^1$ 0	$3d^44sp$ 3.1	3.1
Mn........	7	$3d^54s^2$ 0	$3d^64s$ 2.11	$3d^54sp$ 2.28	0.17
Sr.........	2	$4p^65s^2$ 0	$4p^6d^15s^1$ 2.25	$4p^65sp$ 1.65	−0.60
Y..........	3	$4d^15s^2$ 0	$4d^25s^1$ 1.36	$4d5sp$ 1.85	0.49
Zr.........	4	$4d^25s^2$ 0	$4d^35s^1$ 0.59	$4d^25sp$ 1.83	1.24
Cb.........	5	$4d^35s^2$ 0.14	$4d^45s^1$ 0	$4d^35sp$ 2.33	2.33
Mo........	6	$4d^45s^2$ 1.36	$4d^55s^1$ 0	$4d^45sp$ 3.82	3.82
Tc.........	7	$4d^55s^2$ 0	$4d^65s^1$ 3.19	$4d^55sp$ 2.04	−1.15

perature. Therefore Sc, Ti, Y and Zr exhibit lattice changes and are hcp at low temperatures and bcc at elevated temperatures. This change of electron distribution with temperature also changes the bonding energy and accordingly the activation energy for diffusion whereby the diffusion deviates from the Arrhenius-type curve. In the metals Cr, Cb and Mo the electron distribution corresponding to the bcc phase is so much more stable that temperature does not influence the equilibrium between states. No phase changes take place and diffusion occurs according to Arrhenius-type curves. For Mn, however, the difference is small enough to

Table 3. Bonding Energies Depending on Shell and Kind of Electrons in kcal/g-atom per Bonding Electron

Shell no.	$s + p$	d
1	80	....
2	40	....
3	20	....
4	16	26
5	15	30
6	15	36

allow both types of distributions to exist simultaneously. Therefore, Mn exhibits a compound structure and several phase changes.

In V the difference is not great enough to call for a phase change, but it is small enough to allow some redistribution due to temperature. In summary, β-Sc, β-Y, β-Ti, β-Zr (8) and V exhibit deviations from the Arrhenius-type equations (Fig. 5); whereas, the other transition metals agree or deviate so slightly that it is beyond experimental determination.

The new concept also accounts for alloy behavior and a few examples shall be mentioned.

The bonding mechanism and diffusion of the Cu-Zn system is very interesting (Fig. 6). Cu has the electron distribution $3d^{8.5}4s^1p^{1.5}$ (that is, 25% $3d^{10}4s^1$ atoms and 75% $3d^84s^1p^2$ atoms), which yields an average of 1.5 d-bonds and 2.5 outer bonds per atom (compare Fig. 3 for Ag and Table 1 for Au). Zn has the electron distribution $3d^{10}4s^1p^1$. The Zn atoms have a closed d-shell and do not contribute with d-bonding. When Zn atoms are added to Cu, many d-bonds are broken and a new equilibrium between the two kinds of Cu atoms is obtained. As a result, the concentration of outer electrons decreases. With additions of about 40% Zn, the d-bonding will decrease slowly and the number of outer electrons will decrease until the electron concentration reaches the lower limit of the three-electron range at 2.25 electrons per atom. This electron concentration corresponds to a loss of 0.62 d-bonds and 0.25 outer electron bonds and an electron distribution of about 19% Cu-$3d^{10}4s^1$ and 44% Cu-$3d^84s^1p^2$ plus 37% Zn-$3d^{10}4s^1p^1$. Because the d-electron bonding decreases, the activation energy for self-diffusion of Cu also decreases, from 47,100 cal/mole to about 38,000 cal/mole when extrapolated to 37% Zn (9). At 37% Zn, the fcc three-electron phase breaks down. When about 50% Zn has been added, neighbors are mostly of the other kind. Cu atoms surrounded by Zn atoms cannot form d-bonds with these and will therefore

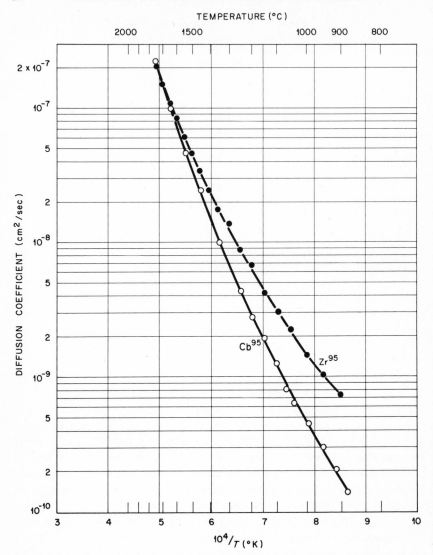

Fig. 5. *Deviation from the Arrhenius-type curve for self-diffusion of Zr and Cb (8)*

return to the electron distribution of the gaseous state, in which there are no nearest neighbors in bonding distance. Beta brass, the phase formed, is bcc and consists of 50% Cu-$3d^{10}4s^1$ atoms and 50% Zn-$3d^{10}4s^1p^1$ atoms, with very few Cu atoms in the $3d^84s^1p^2$ state. Electron concentration is slightly over 1.5. This phase is yellow and probably has few d-electron

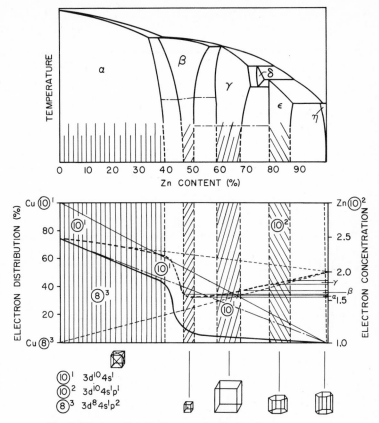

Fig. 6. Electron distribution over the Cu-Zn diagram

bonds and about 1.7 outer bonding electrons. According to the electron-concentration concept, the activation energy of this phase should be slightly above half that of Al or $\frac{3}{2}$ that of Na (see Fig. 4). It actually is found to be 19,800 cal/mole (10). Thus in the Cu-Zn diagram, pure Cu exhibits an activation energy of 47,100 cal/mole and Zn exhibits 22,000 cal/mole, with the β phase lower than both at 19,800 cal/mole. This agrees well with the bonding pattern of the Cu-Zn alloys according to the electron-concentration concept.

Diffusion of alloy atoms in infinite dilute solution is another interesting problem. The activation energies of self-diffusion of Cb^{95} in Zr and self-diffusion of Zr^{95} in Zr are given in Fig. 7 (8). The atomic-size factor is on the borderline, but solid solution is achieved across the diagram at elevated temperature. The difference in activation energy between Cb and Zr is 8000 cal/mole at 1600 K and increases with temperature. This

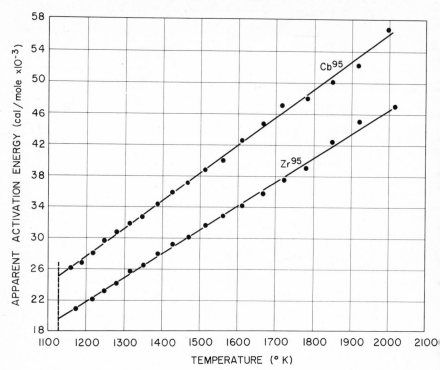

Fig. 7. Activation energies for diffusion of Zr and Cb in β-Zr (8)

increase in activation energy seems to be due to addition of one d-electron to the bonding pattern, as is also found when Ni is added to Cu in dilute solution (Fig. 8) (11). Cu and Ag are on the borderline of the transition metals where the d-electron bonding is about to suffer a catastrophic breakdown, as demonstrated in the preceding paragraphs between α and β brass.

Adding elements to Cu from the columns on the left of the periodic chart means adding d-bonds to the alloy atom, the number of d-bonds being proportional to the distance $(11 - X)$ where X is the column number in the periodic chart in Fig. 8 (11, 12). In adding $(11 - X)$ d-bonds per solute atom, these alloy elements will transfer the bonding pattern of the alloy atoms away from the catastrophic breakdown. When Ni is added to Cu, a full d-electron bond is added, and the self-diffusion activation energy of Ni is raised by 9400 cal/mole above that of Cu. This is about the same increase per d-electron bond as for Cb in Zr. This concept predicts that Pd and Pt in Cu will have approximately the same activation energies as Ni in Cu, that Rh and Ir will exhibit about twice

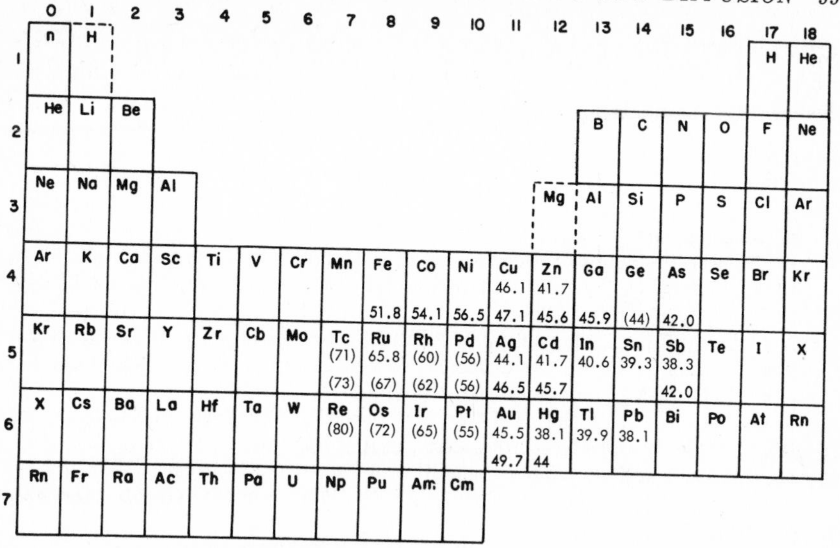

0	1	2	3	4	5	6	7	8	9	10	11	12	13	14	15	16	17	18
1 n	H																H	He
2 He	Li	Be											B	C	N	O	F	Ne
3 Ne	Na	Mg	Al									Mg	Al	Si	P	S	Cl	Ar
4 Ar	K	Ca	Sc	Ti	V	Cr	Mn	Fe 51.8	Co 54.1	Ni 56.5	Cu 46.1 47.1	Zn 41.7 45.6	Ga 45.9	Ge (44)	As 42.0	Se	Br	Kr
5 Kr	Rb	Sr	Y	Zr	Cb	Mo	Tc (71) (73)	Ru 65.8 (67)	Rh (60) (62)	Pd (56) (56)	Ag 44.1 46.5	Cd 41.7 45.7	In 40.6	Sn 39.3	Sb 38.3 42.0	Te	I	X
6 X	Cs	Ba	La	Hf	Ta	W	Re (80)	Os (72)	Ir (65)	Pt (55)	Au 45.5 49.7	Hg 38.1 44	Tl 39.9	Pb 38.1	Bi	Po	At	Rn
7 Rn	Fr	Ra	Ac	Th	Pa	U	Np	Pu	Am	Cm								

Fig. 8. Activation energies for alloy elements in dilute solutions in Cu and Ag. Values for Ag are given at top; values for Cu, at bottom. All values are experimental except parenthetical values, which are predicted.

this increase, and that Ru (13) and Os will exhibit slightly less than three times the increase.

Fe and Co, however, are ferromagnetic and have an entirely different electron distribution in the atoms, as suggested by the author. It appears that the Fe and Co atoms retain their electron distribution in the dilute solution, and because these atoms have few unpaired d-electrons (decreasing with the strength of ferromagnetism), the activation energies are raised only slightly and least at Fe.

The elements to the right of Cu in the periodic chart (columns 12 to 15) will promote the catastrophic breakdown of the α bonding in Cu. These atoms will have a closed d-shell and thereby cut all d-bonds between themselves and the neighboring Cu atoms, thus making themselves freer to move. Because such alloy atoms are essentially substituting for Cu $3d^{10}4s^1$ atoms, they will add $(X - 11)$ electrons, where X is the column number of the alloy element, to the outer bonding electrons. Only a small part of these added electrons will enter the d-level and influence d-electron bonding, that is, the d-bonds to the alloy atoms are totally broken, because of their closed d-shells, whereas the d-bonds in the base metal are only slightly changed.

If X is smaller than 11, the bonding is increased by a full d-bond per step to the left, which bonds tie down the alloy atom, except for the ferromagnetic Fe and Co. If X is greater than 11, the activation energy is only lowered a fraction of a d-bond, the amount being proportional to the number of electrons added. This is obvious from Fig. 8.

References

1 R. Kiesling, Met Rev, **2,** 77 (1957)
2 Leo Brewer, Prediction of High Temperature Metallic Phase Diagrams, U. C. R. L. 10701, Ernest O. Lawrence Radiation Laboratory, University of California, Berkeley, Calif. (July 1963)
3 Niels Engel, Kemisk Maanedsblad (in Danish), No. 5, 6, 8, 9 and 10 (1949) (translation is available from the author); brief summary in Powder Met Bull, No. 7/8 (1954); ASM Trans Quart, **57,** 610 (1964)
4 P. G. Shewmon, Diffusion in Solids, McGraw-Hill, New York, 1963
5 Oleg D. Sherby and Massond Simnad, ASM Trans Quart, **54,** 227 (1961)
6 C. S. Fuller and J. A. Ditzenberger, J Appl Phys, **27,** 544 (1956)
7 Charlotte E. More, Atomic Energy Levels, Natl Bur Std (U.S.), Circ, 467, **I** (1949), **II** (1952), **III** (1958)
8 J. I. Federer and T. S. Lundy, Trans AIME, **227,** 592 (1963)
9 J. Hino, C. Tomizuka and C. Wert, Acta Met, **5,** 41 (1957)
10 H. A. Froot and L. S. Castleman, Trans AIME, **227,** 838 (1963)
11 C. A. Makliet, Phys Rev, **109,** 1964 (1958)
12 M. Sakamoto, J. Phys Soc Japan, **13,** 845 (1958)
13 C. B. Pierce and D. Lazarus, Phys Rev, **114,** 686 (1959)
14 D. Lazarus, Solid State Physics, Vol 10, Academic Press, Inc., New York, 1960, p 117
15 A. Kuper, H. Letow, L. Slifkin, E. Sander and C. Tomizuka, Phys Rev, **96,** 1224 (1954) and **98,** 1870 (1955)
16 R. E. Hoffman, D. Turnbull and E. W. Hart, Acta Met, **3,** 417 (1955)
17 E. Sander, L. Slifkin and C. Tomizuka, Phys Rev, **93,** 970 (1954)
18 C. T. Tomizuka and L. O. Slifkin, Phys Rev, **96,** 610 (1954)
19 A. Sowatsky and F. Faumot, Trans AIME, **209,** 1207 (1957)
20 R. E. Hoffman, Acta Met, **6,** 95 (1958)
21 C. T. Tomizuka and D. Lazarus, J Appl Phys, **25,** 1443 (1954)

PART 2

Lattice Dynamics

Chapter 7
The Vibrational Frequency Spectrum of Some Body-Centered Cubic Metals

G. Leibfried

The interatomic force constants are the essential parameters in harmonic lattice theory. If they are known, one can calculate the vibrational frequencies and the corresponding spectrum. Methods for obtaining these force constants from elastic data and from x-ray and neutron scattering will be discussed. Typical spectra for various groups of bcc metals will be presented.

Born's Lattice Dynamics

The following review of the theoretical background of lattice dynamics is based on several sources (1–5). The rest positions of atoms in a simple Bravais lattice are given by

$$\mathbf{r^h} = \sum_{i=1,2,3} \mathbf{a}^{(i)} h_i = A\mathbf{h}; \; r_k{}^\mathbf{h} = \sum_i a_k{}^{(i)} h_i = \sum_i A_{ki} h_i \qquad (1)$$

where $\mathbf{a}^{(i)}$ are the three basic vectors of the lattice, $\mathbf{h}$ is a vector with integer components and A is a 3 by 3 matrix built from the three basic vectors. For a bcc lattice in particular, one has (Fig. 1)

$$A = \frac{a}{2} \begin{Bmatrix} 1 & 1 & -1 \\ -1 & 1 & 1 \\ 1 & -1 & 1 \end{Bmatrix} \qquad (2)$$

where a is the cubic lattice distance.* $\mathbf{h}$, then, labels the atoms of the lattice.

The author is with the Technical University, Aachen, Germany.
* Equation 2 is only one of several possibilities to describe the bcc lattice.

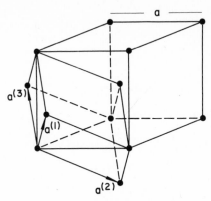

Fig. 1. Basic vectors of bcc lattice

The actual positions of the atoms are given by the displacements $\mathbf{g^h} = (g_i{}^h)$ from the rest positions. In the so-called harmonic approximation, the potential energy ϕ is expanded in powers of the displacements up to second order. The zero-order term is the energy of the lattice in equilibrium; it will be normalized to zero. The first-order term vanishes because one starts from equilibrium and obtains

$$\phi = \tfrac{1}{2} \sum \phi_{il}{}^{\mathbf{mn}} g_i{}^{\mathbf{m}} g_l{}^{\mathbf{n}} \tag{3}$$

where the sum extends over i, $l = 1, 2, 3$ and over all integer vectors $\mathbf{m}, \mathbf{n}$ for an infinite lattice. The potential energy determines the equation of motion

$$M\ddot{g}_i{}^{\mathbf{m}}(t) = -\sum_{l,\mathbf{n}} \phi_{il}{}^{\mathbf{m,n}} g_l{}^{\mathbf{n}} \tag{4}$$

By virtue of lattice symmetry, the 3 by 3 matrices $\phi_{il}{}^{\mathbf{mn}}$ depend only on the vector distance $\phi_{il}{}^{\mathbf{mn}} = \phi_{il}(\mathbf{r^m} - \mathbf{r^n}) = \phi_{il}{}^{(\mathbf{m-n})}$ and are further symmetrical in i, l. The eigenvibrations of the lattice have the form of plane waves

$$\mathbf{g^m}(t) = \mathbf{u} \exp i(\mathbf{kr^m} - \omega t) \tag{5}$$

with wave vector $\mathbf{k}$ and polarization (unit vector) $\mathbf{u}$. Introducing Eq 5 into Eq 4 one obtains

$$M\omega^2 \mathbf{u}_i = \sum_l t_{il}(\mathbf{k}) \mathbf{u}_l \tag{6}$$

where the matrix t is given by*

$$t_{il}(\mathbf{k}) = \sum_n \phi_{il}^{mn} \exp[i\mathbf{k}(\mathbf{r}^m - \mathbf{r}^n)] = \sum_h \phi_{il}^{(h)} \exp(i\mathbf{k}\mathbf{r}^h) \qquad (7)$$

$$= -2 \sum_h \phi_{il}^{(h)} \sin^2(\mathbf{k}\mathbf{r}^h/2)$$

Equation 6 gives three polarizations $\mathbf{u}^{(s)}(\mathbf{k})$ and eigenfrequencies $\omega_s(\mathbf{k})$ for each wave vector $\mathbf{k}$. The quantities t_{il}, $\mathbf{u}^{(s)}$ and ω_s are periodic functions in $\mathbf{k}$. A change of $\mathbf{k}$ by

$$\Delta\mathbf{k} = 2\pi \sum_i \mathbf{b}^{(i)} m_i = 2\pi B\mathbf{m}; \, \mathbf{b}^{(i)}\mathbf{a}^{(i')} = \delta_{ii'} = \sum_k B_{ki} A_{ki'} \qquad (8)$$

leaves t_{il} unchanged, $\Delta\mathbf{k} \cdot \mathbf{r}^h$ being an integral multiple of 2π. The vectors $\mathbf{b}^{(i)}$ establish the "reciprocal" lattice. For a bcc space lattice one obtains

$$B = \frac{1}{a} \begin{Bmatrix} 1 & 1 & 0 \\ 0 & 1 & 1 \\ 1 & 0 & 1 \end{Bmatrix} \qquad (9)$$

showing that the reciprocal lattice is a fcc lattice with cubic lattice distance $2/a$. The periodicity in $\mathbf{k}$ space, then, is represented by a fcc lattice with lattice distance $4\pi/a$. One obtains all vibrations already by considering only $\mathbf{k}$ values within one elementary volume V_{rec} of that fcc $\mathbf{k}$ lattice. If $V_{\text{at.}} = a^3/2$ is the atomic volume of the space lattice, one has $V_{\text{rec}} = (2\pi)^3/V_{\text{at.}} = 2^4 \cdot \pi^3/a^3$. Generally one chooses a more symmetrical volume in $\mathbf{k}$ space—the so-called first Brillouin zone, which is equivalent to one elementary volume but exhibits the cubic symmetry more fully. The first Brillouin zone is a regular dodecahedron. The faces are given by the planes bisecting the twelve distances from the origin to the nearest neighbors in the fcc lattice constructed from the vectors $2\pi b^{(i)}$. Figure 2 shows one boundary of this Brillouin zone perpendicular to (101). In the three directions given in Fig. 2, the zone extends up to absolute values of $\mathbf{k}$, that is, $2\pi/a$ in (100), $2^{1/2}\pi/a$ in (101) and $3^{1/2}\pi/a$ in (111). The length of a $\mathbf{k}$ vector within the first Brillouin zone is always shorter than that of an equivalent $\mathbf{k}$ vector $\mathbf{k} + \Delta\mathbf{k}$.

---

* One has $\phi_{il}^{(h)} = \phi_{il}^{(-h)}$ from lattice symmetry and $\sum_h \phi_{il}^{(h)} = 0$ from momentum conservation.

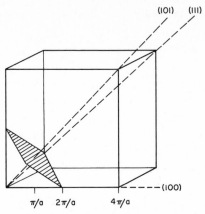

Fig. 2. One boundary of the first Brillouin zone of a bcc lattice

For a large crystal containing N atoms, one has $3N$ degrees of freedom and therefore $3N$ eigenvibrations ω. The frequencies and polarizations can be obtained from the corresponding quantities of an infinite crystal discussed before, by restricting oneself to a discrete set of $N\mathbf{k}$ values within the first zone. Moreover, these $\mathbf{k}$ vectors form a simple lattice with an average density N/V_{rec}. These statements are independent of the boundary conditions if the crystal is large.*

The spectrum $Z(\omega)$ is given by the number of frequencies $\omega_s(\mathbf{k})$ in the frequency interval $(\omega, \omega + d\omega)$

$$Z(\omega)\, d\omega = \sum_{s,\mathbf{k}} \text{ with } \omega \leq \omega_s(\mathbf{k}) \leq \omega + d\omega$$

By use of Dirac's δ function, this can be written as

$$Z(\omega) = \sum_{s,\mathbf{k}} \delta[\omega - \omega_s(\mathbf{k})] \tag{10}$$

The sum extends over the N discrete $\mathbf{k}$ values in the first Brillouin zone or an equivalent volume in reciprocal space. The total number of frequencies is $3N\left[\int_0^\infty Z(\omega)\, d\omega \doteq 3N = \sum_{s,\mathbf{k}}\right]$. The normalized frequency

---

* Generally one uses the most simple cyclic boundary conditions. When it is assumed that the volume is similar to the elementary cell built from the three vectors $n\mathbf{a}^{(i)}$ with $n^3 = N$ and with the cyclic boundary conditions $\mathbf{g}^{m+nl} = \mathbf{g}^m$, only the values $\mathbf{k} = 2\pi B\mathbf{h}/n$ satisfy the boundary conditions.

distribution is given by

$$z(\omega) = \frac{Z(\omega)}{3N}; \int_0^\infty z(\omega) \, d\omega = 1 \tag{11}$$

For a finite crystal, the distribution is really a sum of δ functions because the **k** values and the frequencies are discrete. However, it is more convenient to pass to an infinite crystal

$$z(\omega) = \frac{1}{3N} \sum_{s,\mathbf{k}} \delta[\omega - \omega_s(\mathbf{k})] \Rightarrow \frac{1}{3N} \sum_s \int_{V_{rec}} \frac{N}{V_{rec}} \, d\mathbf{k} \, \delta[\omega - \omega_s(\mathbf{k})]$$

where $\sum_{\mathbf{k}}$ can be replaced by $\int d\mathbf{k} \, N/V_{rec}$. This leads to

$$z(\omega) = \frac{1}{3V_{rec}} \sum_s \int_{V_{rec}} d\mathbf{k} \, \delta[\omega - \omega_s(\mathbf{k})] \tag{12}$$

The integration extends over the first Brillouin zone or an equivalent volume. Here $z(\omega)$ will be a smooth function of **k** except for a finite set of points where singularities (mostly in the derivatives) can occur.*

Simple averages can be directly obtained from the force constants $\phi_{il}^{(\mathbf{h})}$. We give only two examples:†

$$M\overline{\omega^2} = M\int \omega^2 z(\omega) \, d\omega = \frac{1}{3} \sum_i \phi_{ii}^{(o)} = -\frac{1}{3} \sum_{i,\mathbf{h} \neq l} \phi_{ii}^{(\mathbf{h})} \tag{13a}$$

$$M\overline{\omega^4} = \frac{1}{3} \sum_{\substack{i,l \\ \mathbf{h}}} \{\phi_{il}^{(\mathbf{h})}\}^2 \tag{13b}$$

---

* Sometimes the distribution of the squared frequencies $g(\omega^2) = \sum_s \int d\mathbf{k} \, \delta(\omega^2 - \omega_s^2(\mathbf{k}))/3V_{rec}$ is used rather than $z(\omega)$ because only ω^2 enters into Eq 6. For a stable lattice all the ω^2 are positive and $z(\omega) = 2\omega g(\omega^2)$

† One has $\sum_{\mathbf{h}} \phi_{il}^{(\mathbf{h})} = 0$ which follows from momentum conservation. One can see this relation from Eq 4. If the displacements are independent of **n** (displacement of the whole crystal), no force should act

$$\sum_{\mathbf{n}} \phi_{il}^{\mathbf{mn}} = \sum_{\mathbf{h}} \phi_{ii}^{(\mathbf{h})} = 0$$

In certain low-indexed directions, one knows the polarization vectors $\mathbf{u}^{(s)}$ from the symmetry of the crystal. The cubic Eq 6 need not be solved in this instance; instead one has $M\omega_s{}^2 = \sum_{i,l} u_i{}^{(s)} t_{il}(\mathbf{k}) u_l{}^{(s)}$. For the three directions indicated in Fig. 2 one has

$\mathbf{k} = \xi(1,0,0)$ and $\mathbf{k} = \xi(1,1,1)$: one longitudinal* polarization $\mathbf{u}^{(l)} = (1,0,0)$ and $\mathbf{u}^{(l)} = (1,1,1)/3^{1/2}$ with ω_l; two degenerate transversal polarizations $\mathbf{u}^{(t)}$ perpendicular to $\mathbf{u}^{(l)}$ with ω_t.

$\mathbf{k} = \xi(1,0,1)$: one longitudinal mode $\mathbf{u}^{(l)} = 2^{-1/2}(1,0,1)$ with ω_l; two transversal modes, $\mathbf{u}^{(t_1)} = (0,1,0)$ with ω_{t_1}, and $\mathbf{u}^{(t_2)} = 2^{-1/2}(1,0,-1)$ with ω_{t_2}.

Connection of Lattice and Elastic Theory

Lattice theory comprehends the elastic behavior. We only quote the results for simple cubic lattices (1, 2). First one calculates the tensor

$$\hat{C}_{il,mn} = -\frac{1}{2V_{\text{at.}}} \sum_{h} \phi_{il}{}^{(h)} r_m{}^h r_n{}^h \tag{14}$$

which has three independent components (in Voigt's notation)

$$\hat{c}_{11} = \hat{C}_{11,11}, \; \hat{c}_{12} = \hat{C}_{11,22}, \; \hat{c}_{44} = \hat{C}_{12,12} \tag{14a}$$

The tensor $C_{il,mn}$ of the elastic moduli also has three independent components c_{11}, c_{12} and c_{44}, the relation between c and $\hat{c}$ being

$$c_{11} = \hat{c}_{11}, \; c_{12} = 2\hat{c}_{44} - \hat{c}_{12}, \; c_{44} = \hat{c}_{12} \tag{15}$$

By combining these moduli one obtains the bulk modulus (reciprocal compressibility) $B = (c_{11} + 2c_{12})/3$ and the two shear moduli $C' = (c_{11} - c_{12})/2$ and $C = c_{44}$. Here C corresponds to a shear parallel to $(0,0,1)$ planes in $(1,0,0)$ directions and C' to $(1,1,0)$ planes in $(1,-1,0)$ directions. Elastic stability requires these three moduli to be positive.

---

* The notations longitudinal and transversal relating the polarization $\mathbf{u}$ to the wave vector $\mathbf{k}$ become meaningful only when $\mathbf{k}$ is confined to the first Brillouin zone. This is because modes belonging to $\mathbf{k}$ or to $\mathbf{k} + 2\pi B\mathbf{h}$ are identical. If the mode is longitudinal for $\mathbf{k}$, it will not in general be longitudinal for the choice $\mathbf{k} + 2\pi B\mathbf{h}$.

Coupling Parameters ($\phi_{il}^{(h)}$) for Near Neighbors

The matrix $\phi_{il}^{(h)} = \phi_{li}^{(h)} = \phi_{il}^{(-h)}$ is symmetrical and can be transformed to diagonal form by a simple rotation (1, 2). The six independent parameters contained in $\phi_{il}^{(h)}$ are the three (mutually perpendicular) eigenvectors of $\phi^{(h)}$, which determines three parameters, and the three eigenvalues. The physical meaning of $-\phi_{il}^{(h)}$ is the force on atom o in i direction if atom $\mathbf{h}$ is displaced by unit length in direction l. If the displacement is parallel to one of the eigenvectors, then force and displacement are parallel, and the eigenvalue of $-\phi^{(h)}$ corresponds to a spring constant. In many instances, particularly for near neighbors, the eigenvectors are already determined by symmetry alone, leaving less than six independent parameters, that is, $\phi_{il}^{(o)}$ is proportional to the unit tensor δ_{il} and contains only one single parameter.

Again we quote only results for the three nearest neighbors in a bcc lattice. For the first nearest neighbor in the center of the cube

$$\phi_{il}^{(1,1,1)} = \phi_{il}^{[1]} = - \begin{Bmatrix} \alpha & \beta & \beta \\ \beta & \alpha & \beta \\ \beta & \beta & \alpha \end{Bmatrix} \Rightarrow -\frac{f^{[1]}}{3} \begin{Bmatrix} 1 & 1 & 1 \\ 1 & 1 & 1 \\ 1 & 1 & 1 \end{Bmatrix} \qquad (16a)$$

For the second nearest neighbor in the (1,0,0) direction

$$\phi_{il}^{(1,1,0)} = \phi_{il}^{[2]} = - \begin{Bmatrix} \gamma & 0 & 0 \\ 0 & \delta & 0 \\ 0 & 0 & \delta \end{Bmatrix} \Rightarrow -f^{[2]} \begin{Bmatrix} 1 & 0 & 0 \\ 0 & 0 & 0 \\ 0 & 0 & 0 \end{Bmatrix} \qquad (16b)$$

For the third nearest neighbor in the (1,1,0) direction

$$\phi_{il}^{(1,2,1)} = \phi_{il}^{[3]} = - \begin{Bmatrix} \kappa & \mu & 0 \\ \mu & \kappa & 0 \\ 0 & 0 & \nu \end{Bmatrix} \Rightarrow -\frac{f^{[3]}}{2} \begin{Bmatrix} 1 & 1 & 0 \\ 1 & 1 & 0 \\ 0 & 0 & 0 \end{Bmatrix} \qquad (16c)$$

The eigenvectors and eigenvalues are illustrated in Fig. 3. For the next nearest neighbor, one eigenvector of $\phi^{[1]}$ lies in the cube diagonal with eigenvalue $-(\alpha + 2\beta)$; the two remaining eigenvalues $(\beta - \alpha)$ are degenerate, the eigenvectors being perpendicular to (1,1,1). The negative eigenvalues are plotted in Fig. 3. Obviously this corresponds to a spring with a spring constant $(\alpha + 2\beta)$ against longitudinal extension and with an isotropic bending constant $(\alpha - \beta)$. The bending forces correspond to many-body forces in the crystal, whereas the longitudinal force alone corresponds to central forces ($\alpha = \beta = f^{[1]}/3$, $\alpha + 2\beta = f^{[1]}$, where $f^{[1]}$ is the central-force spring constant). Analogous statements hold for the

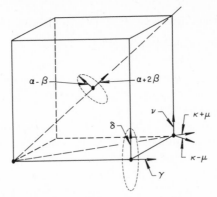

Fig. 3. Eigenvectors and eigenvalues of the coupling matrices to the three nearest neighbors of a bcc lattice

second and third next neighbors. The coupling matrices to all the first neighbors, that is, $\mathbf{h} = (1,0,0)$ or $(0,1,0)$, etc., can be obtained from $\phi^{[1]}$ by symmetry operations; the same holds true for the matrices belonging to all the second and third nearest neighbors.

Throughout this paper the term "central forces" is used somewhat incorrectly to mean simple springs under no initial tension. For a general two-body potential $\varphi(|\mathbf{r}^m + \mathbf{g}^m - \mathbf{r}^n - \mathbf{g}^n|)$ corresponding to central forces, each matrix $\phi^{(h)}$ contains only two independent terms, namely the first and the second derivatives of the potential function at the equilibrium distance $|\mathbf{r}^h|$. The condition for equilibrium (3) leads to a relation between all the first derivatives. Furthermore, one obtains relations between the coupling parameters for given $\mathbf{h}$, if $\phi^{(h)}$ contains more than two independent parameters due to lattice symmetry alone. An example is given below.

Coupling Parameters and Elastic Moduli

The range of interatomic forces in metals is presumably small, and one will obtain a rather good approximation by dropping the higher-order coupling parameters and keeping only first- and second-order neighbors (1, 3). The tensor (Eq 14) is easily calculated, leading to

$$a\hat{c}_{11} = 2(\alpha + \gamma); \quad a\hat{c}_{12} = 2(\alpha + \delta); \quad a\hat{c}_{44} = 2\beta \qquad (17)$$
$$ac_{11} = 2(\alpha + \gamma); \quad ac_{12} = 4\beta - 2(\alpha + \delta); \quad ac_{44} = 2(\alpha + \delta)$$

It is quite reasonable to assume central forces for the second next neighbors. This leaves only three independent coupling parameters, which can be expressed by the three elastic moduli

$$\alpha = ac_{44}/2; \beta = a(c_{11} + c_{44})/4; \gamma = a(c_{11} - c_{44})/2 \qquad (18)$$

Use of the first-order neighbors alone ($\gamma = 0$) would lead to $c_{11} = c_{44}$, a relation that is not well satisfied by the known elastic moduli of bcc metals, except approximately by Li and Na.

With the assumption of central forces only ($\beta = \alpha = f^{[1]}/3; \gamma = f^{[2]}$), the so-called "Cauchy relation" holds*

$$c_{12} = c_{44} \qquad (19)$$

and one obtains

$$C' = (c_{11} - c_{12})/2 = f^{[2]}/a; C = c_{44} = 2f^{[1]}/3a \qquad (20)$$

If, in addition, the crystal is isotropic, one has $C' = C$, $2f^{[1]}/3 = f^{[2]}$ or $\gamma = 2\alpha = 2\beta$. The elastic data can in this instance be described by central forces, although the Cauchy relations do not necessarily imply central forces. This behavior (Cauchy relations and isotropy) approximately is shown by the bcc metals Cr, Mo and W.

Dispersion Curves in Low-Indexed Directions

According to Eq 7, the near-neighbor coupling parameters determine the low-order terms of the Fourier expansion of the tensor $t_{il}(\mathbf{k})$ and therefore determine the rough shape of the dispersion curves $\omega_s(\mathbf{k})$ if long-range forces are not too important. Also, the spectrum is roughly determined from the near-neighbor coupling parameters and can be obtained in principle from the elastic data† by use of Eq 18.

To give a simple example, we discuss the $\omega_s(\mathbf{k})$ along the three directions indicated in Fig. 2 (where the polarizations are known) for nearest-neighbor interaction only ($\alpha, \beta \neq 0$). Again we quote only the results.

---

* The relation holds generally for central forces regardless of the number of neighbors taken into account. For general central forces (not just simple springs under no initial tension) one obtains $\alpha - \beta + \delta = 0$ from the equilibrium condition. This insures the Cauchy relation. Consequently a first and second neighbor model obeying the Cauchy relation can always be represented by a central-force model. Including third-order neighbors, one obtains $\alpha - \beta + \delta + 4\nu = 0$ from equilibrium, and further, $\kappa - \mu - \nu = 0$. The Cauchy relation, however, requires only $\alpha - \beta + \delta + 4\nu + 2(\gamma - \mu - \nu) = 0$. Consequently, the Cauchy relation does not imply central forces.

† In a fcc lattice, the relation between the elastic moduli and the coupling parameters is somewhat more unique because in the model with first neighbors alone, one has three coupling parameters uniquely determined by the elastic behavior.

For $\mathbf{k} = \xi(1,0,0)$

$$t_{il}(\mathbf{k}) = 16\alpha \sin^2 \frac{\xi a}{4} \delta_{il}$$

$$M\omega_l^2(\mathbf{k}) = M\omega_t^2(\mathbf{k}) = 16\alpha \sin^2 \frac{\xi a}{4} \tag{21}$$

$$\omega_l = \omega_t = 4 \left\{ \frac{\alpha}{M} \right\}^{1/2} \sin \frac{\xi a}{4}$$

The maximum value of ξ in the first Brillouin zone is

$$\xi_{\max} = 2\pi/a$$

For $\mathbf{k} = \xi(1,1,1)$

$$t_{il}(\mathbf{k}) = 4 \sin^2 \frac{\xi a}{4} \begin{Bmatrix} 3\alpha & -\beta & -\beta \\ -\beta & 3\alpha & -\beta \\ -\beta & -\beta & 3\alpha \end{Bmatrix} + 4 \sin^2 \frac{\xi a}{4} \sqrt{3} \begin{Bmatrix} \alpha & \beta & \beta \\ \beta & \alpha & \beta \\ \beta & \beta & \alpha \end{Bmatrix}$$

$$M\omega_l^2 = 4(3\alpha - 2\beta) \sin^2 \frac{\xi a}{4} + 4(\alpha + 2\beta) \sin^2 \frac{\xi a}{4} \sqrt{3} \tag{22}$$

$$M\omega_t^2 = 4(3\alpha + \beta) \sin^2 \frac{\xi a}{4} + 4(\alpha - \beta) \sin^2 \frac{\xi a}{4} \sqrt{3}$$

$$\xi_{\max} = \pi/a$$

For $\mathbf{k} = \xi(1,0,1)$

$$t_{il}(\mathbf{k}) = 4 \sin^2 \frac{\xi a}{2} \begin{Bmatrix} 2\alpha & 0 & 2\beta \\ 0 & 2\alpha & 0 \\ 2\beta & 0 & 2\alpha \end{Bmatrix}$$

$$M\omega_l^2 = 8(\alpha + \beta) \sin^2 \frac{\xi a}{2} \tag{23}$$

$$M\omega_{t_1}^2 = 8\alpha \sin^2 \frac{\xi a}{2}; \ \mathbf{u}^{(t_1)} = (0,1,0)$$

$$M\omega_{t_2}^2 = 8(\alpha - \beta) \sin^2 \frac{\xi a}{2}; \mathbf{u}^{(t_2)} = \frac{1}{\sqrt{2}} (1,0,-1)$$

$$\xi_{\max} = \pi/a$$

Figure 4 shows the dispersion curves for $\beta = \alpha/\alpha^*$ and two values of $\alpha^* (\alpha^* = 1, \beta = \alpha; \alpha^* = 4, \beta = \alpha/4)$. For $\alpha^* = 1$ one obtains $c_{11} = c_{12}$ or $C' = 0$, which means an elastically unstable lattice. In this instance, ω_{t_2} in the (1,0,1) direction vanishes for all $\mathbf{k}$ values. For $\alpha^* = 4$ one

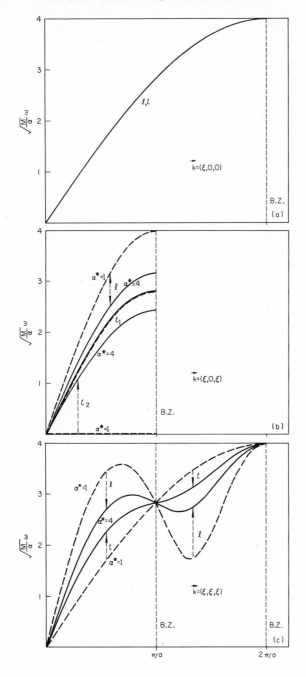

Fig. 4. Dispersion curves in some low-indexed directions of a bcc lattice (first-neighbor model: $\alpha^* = \alpha/\beta$). (a) (100). (b) (101). (c) (111).

obtains from Eq 17 a stable lattice with an anisotropy* ratio $C'/C = 0.75$. For the alkalies, one has $C'/C \cong 0.1$, corresponding to $\alpha^* \cong 0.9$ and thus values close to $\alpha^* = 1$. Actually, experimental dispersion curves for Na resemble quite closely the curves shown in Fig. 4, as will be discussed later. The boundary of the Brillouin zone is indicated. The values outside can be reduced to **k** vectors inside the first zone, that is, the point $2\pi/a$ in Fig. 4(b) corresponds to the cube center in Fig. 2 and is equivalent to the point $2\pi/a$ in Fig. 4(a). This shows that the frequency must be threefold degenerate at that point.

Elastic Moduli of Body-Centered Cubic Metals

In the foregoing it has been pointed out that the elastic moduli can be used to determine partly the near-neighbor coupling parameters. During the last years, elastic data for most of the bcc metals have been obtained. Table 1 contains a compilation of the measured elastic moduli and indicates the temperature dependence. All the data are adiabatic elastic moduli. These moduli are presumably not very accurate because (a) some of the elements, like Cr and Fe, are magnetic, which has not been taken into account in the foregoing discussion, (b) some metals, like Li, undergo phase transformations into the fcc structure, and (c) dislocations and impurities influence the elastic behavior and the dependence on temperature.† To obtain the elastic data of the harmonic theory‡ that correspond to the harmonic spectrum, one should extrapolate the "high"-temperature behavior $c_{\alpha\beta}(T) = c_{\alpha\beta}^{\text{har}} - c'_{\alpha\beta}T$ to $T = 0$ in order to obtain the harmonic values $c_{\alpha\beta}^{\text{har}}$. Because of all the uncertainties in obtaining the elastic moduli, this extrapolation has not yet been done properly. The elastic data given in Table 1 (for example, those for Ta, W and Mo) will only roughly correspond to the harmonic data within an accuracy of about 10%, depending sensitively on the numerical value of the Debye temperature.§ Consequently the elastic data of the table can give only approximate dispersion curves and spectra. Furthermore, the same procedure would have to be applied to the lattice distance $a(T)$ and its dependence on temperature to obtain the coupling parameters of har-

---

* Isotropy means $\beta = 0$ or $\alpha^* = \infty$. This leads to an unstable lattice with negative compressibility.

† This might be one reason why the moduli of some bcc metals show a rather peculiar temperature dependence at low temperatures (Ref g in Table 1).

‡ The theory is given by G. Leibfried and W. Ludwig in Solid State Phys, **12**, 275 (1961).

§ Li is an extreme example for which the deviations should be relatively large. The moduli are in the sequence $c_{\alpha\beta}(T = 195 \text{ K})$, $c_{\alpha\beta}(T = 78 \text{ K})$, $c_{\alpha\beta}^{\text{har}}$: $c_{11} = 1.34$, 1.48, 1.72; $c_{12} = 1.13$, 1.25, 1.46; $c_{44} = 0.96$, 1.08, 1.28.

Table 1. Elastic Moduli of bcc Metals

Metal	Temp, °K	Modulus, 10^{11} dynes/cm²				
		c_{11}	c_{12}	$C = c_{44}$	C'	B
Li (a).......	195	1.34	1.13	0.96	0.11	1.2
	78	1.48	1.25	1.08	0.12	1.3
Na.........	300(b)	0.74	0.62	0.42	0.059	0.66
	210(c)	0.56	0.43	0.49	0.065	0.47
	80(c)	0.61	0.46	0.59	0.07	0.51
K (d).......	80	0.46	0.37	0.26	0.05	0.45
V..........	300(e)	22.8	11.9	4.3	5.5	15.5
	~0(f)	23.2	11.9	4.6	5.6	15.7
Cb (e)......	300	24.6	13.4	2.9	5.6	17.2
Ta.........	300(e)	26.7	16.1	8.25	5.3	19.6
	300(g)	26.1	15.7	8.18	5.17	19.2
	~0(g)	26.6	15.8	8.73	5.41	19.4
Cr (h)......	300	35.0	6.8	10.0	14.1	16.2
	77	39.1	9.0	10.3	15.1	19.1
Mo (g).....	300	44.1	17.2	12.2	13.4	26.2
	~0	45.0	17.3	12.5	13.9	26.5
W (g).......	300	52.3	20.5	16.1	16	31.1
	~0	53.3	20.5	16.3	16.4	31.4
Fe (i).......	300	23.3	13.6	11.8	4.9	16.9
	~0	24.3	13.8	12.2	5.3	17.3

(a) H. C. Nash and C. S. Smith, J Phys Chem Solids, **9**, 113, (1959)
(b) W. B. Daniels, Phys Rev, **119**, 1246 (1960)
(c) S. Siegel and S. L. Quimby, Phys Rev, **54**, 76 and 293 (1938)
(d) O. Bender, Ann Physik, **34**, 359 (1939)
(e) D. I. Boleff, J Appl Phys, **32**, 100 (1961)
(f) G. A. Alers, Phys Rev, **119**, 1532 (1960)
(g) F. H. Featherstone and J. R. Neighbors, Phys Rev, **130**, 1324 (1963)
(h) D. I. Boleff and J. de Klerk, Phys Rev, **129**, 1063 (1963)
(i) J. A. Rayne and B. S. Chandrasekhar, Phys Rev, **122**, 1714 (1961)

monic theory. Fortunately both dependences tend to cancel each other because $a(T)$ increases and $C_{\alpha\beta}(T)$ generally decreases with increasing T.

Experimental Determination of Dispersion Curves

Dispersion curves along low-indexed directions can be measured by means of x-ray and neutron scattering. An analysis of the dispersion curves gives values for the coupling parameters, which in turn determine the spectrum. The theory is given elsewhere (5).

To give an illustrative example, Fig. 5 shows the results for Na obtained by neutron scattering at 90 K (6). Comparison with Fig. 4 shows a

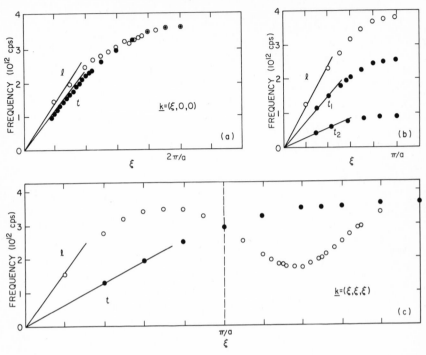

Fig. 5. Experimental dispersion curves for Na (6). (a) (100). (b) (101). (c) (111).

close similarity. An analysis of the dispersion curves gives the coupling parameters:*

$$\alpha \cong 1180; \ \beta \cong 1320; \ \gamma \cong 470; \ \delta \cong 100 \text{ dynes/cm}$$

The coupling parameters for higher-order neighbors are small, the absolute values being smaller than about 50 dynes/cm. This also shows that the assumption of central forces to second-order neighbors (neglecting δ) would be roughly justified in this instance. Figure 6 shows the longitudinal frequency for $\mathbf{k} \sim (1,1,1)$ in more detail. One sees that the first- and second-neighbor fit is already quite good.†

* The elastic data obtained from these coupling parameters do not agree well with the ones given in Table 1 (Ref b). The anisotropy ratio C/C' is consistent, but the ratio B/C' differs by about 30%. The elastic data corresponding to full lines in the elastic region of Fig. 5 are composite values (Ref b and c of Table 1).

† The agreement with purely theoretical curves obtained by T. Toya [J Res Inst Catalysis, Arkhardo Univ, **6,** 183 (1958)] is also remarkably good.

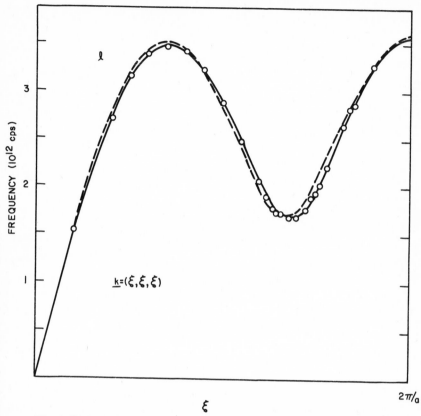

Fig. 6. *Longitudinal dispersion curve in (111) direction for Na (6). The dashed curve corresponds to a fit including first and second neighbors; the solid curve includes coupling parameters for neighbors up to fourth order.*

Methods Used in Spectrum Calculations

Once the coupling parameters are known, the frequencies and their spectral distribution can be calculated in principle. Approximation methods have to be used throughout. We will discuss these methods first and give examples for some bcc metals later.

Root Sampling. The most simple method is to calculate $\omega_s(\mathbf{k})$ as the three roots of $\mathrm{Det}[t_{il}(\mathbf{k}) - M\omega^2\delta_{il}] = 0$ for a finite set of $\mathbf{k}$ values corresponding to a finite crystal and cyclic boundary conditions. The spectrum is approximated by a normalized histogram.

Momentum Method. Because the even momenta $\overline{\omega^{2n}}$ are relatively easily calculated from the coupling parameters, one can represent $z(\omega)$

by a function containing parameters that are fitted to a certain number of low-order momenta. The oldest treatment can be attributed to Einstein who used only $\overline{\omega^2} = \omega_E{}^2$ and replaced the spectrum by a δ function at the Einstein frequency

$$Z_E(\omega) = \delta(\omega - \omega_E) \tag{24}$$

If the environment of an atom in a cubic lattice is fixed, the restoring forces are given by $\phi_{il}{}^{(0)} \sim \text{const } \delta_{il}$. The frequency of the corresponding isotropic oscillator is ω_E, according to Eq 13a.

Expanding $Z(\omega)$ in a series of Legendre polynomials and fitting to low-order momenta have been discussed first by Montroll (5). Usually this method gives poor results for small ω values in the elastic region.

In a model with three coupling parameters (α,β,γ), one can express* ω_E by the elastic data

$$M\overline{\omega^2} = M\omega_E{}^2 = 8\alpha + 2\gamma = a(c_{11} + 3c_{44}) \tag{25}$$

Debye Spectrum. In the elastic region for small ω, the distribution $Z(\omega)$ is proportional to ω^2. By extrapolating this behavior and cutting off at a frequency ω_D to have the right number of frequencies, one obtains

$$Z_D = 9N\omega^2/\omega_D{}^3, \quad z_D = 3\omega^2/\omega_D{}^3 \text{ for } 0 \leq \omega \leq \omega_D \tag{26}$$

The Debye frequency can be obtained from the elastic data alone. For an isotropic crystal, one has $\omega_D{}^{-3} = V_{at.}\{c_l{}^{-3} + 2c_t{}^{-3}\}/18\pi^2$ where $c_{l,t}$ are the longitudinal and transversal velocities of sound. In anisotropic crystals, ω_D has to be calculated numerically. Approximate values of $M\omega_D{}^2/a$ are given in Table 2. The elastic data of the lowest temperatures in Table 1 were used. The calculation was aided by diagrams in Ref 2.

The Debye spectrum can be improved by taking into account the polarization. In an isotropic medium, one can define a longitudinal and transversal contribution to density of frequencies

$$Z_{el} = Z_l + Z_t; \quad Z_l = 3N\omega^2/\omega_l{}^3; \quad Z_t = 6N\omega^2/\omega_t{}^3; \quad \omega \leq \omega_{l,t} \tag{27}$$

where $\omega_{l,t}$ are separate cutoff frequencies for the two branches. The simple Debye theory uses a common cutoff regardless of polarization and would lead to $1/\omega_D{}^3 = 1/3\omega_l{}^3 + 2/3\omega_t{}^3$. Only, if the crystal is completely "isotropic" $(c_l = c_t, \omega_l = \omega_t)$, ω_D coincides with $\omega_l = \omega_t$. Because of elastic

---

* In a fcc lattice with next-nearest-neighbor interaction (only three parameters), one has $M\overline{\omega^2} = a(c_{11} + 2c_{44})$.

Table 2. Debye and Einstein Frequencies for Some bcc Metals(a)

Frequency, 10^{11} dynes/cm^2	Li	Na	K	V	Cb	Ta	Cr	Mo	W	Fe
$M\omega_E^2/a$.............	4.7	2.4	1.2	37	33	53	70	83	102	61
$M\omega_D^2/a$.............	4.8	...	1.9	69	58	110	170	190	230	127
$3M\omega_D^2/5a$..........	2.9	...	1.1	41	35	66	102	114	138	76

(a) Mostly the spectrum is used to calculate the specific heat of the lattice. The specific heat is expressed by use of the Debye spectrum with an effective Debye temperature θ depending on T. Then, one obtains for very low temperatures

$$\theta \ (T \text{ small}) = h\omega_D/k = \theta_D$$

and
$$\theta \ (T \text{ large}) = \theta_D(5\overline{\omega^2}/3\omega_D{}^2)^{1/2}$$
$$= \theta_D(5\omega_E{}^2/3\omega_D{}^2)^{1/2} = \theta_\infty$$

Therefore, if the values in the first row are larger than the ones in the third ($\theta_\infty > \theta_D$), then $\theta(T)$ should rise with temperature and vice versa.

stability, however, one always has $c_i^2/c_t^2 = c_{11}/c_{44} > \frac{4}{3}$ and there always is a spread of the two cutoff frequencies. In the Debye procedure the high-frequency longitudinal part is dropped and shifted to lower frequencies. This is similar to the lattice effect, which also shifts the maximum frequencies (at the boundaries of the Brillouin zone in simple instances) toward lower values. That is the reason for the Debye theory working quite well in general. For anisotropic crystals one can use essentially the same improvement. One considers small elements of solid angle containing $3N \, d\Omega/4\pi$ frequencies. There are three branches for each given direction (not necessarily longitudinal and transversal), and each branch has $N \, d\Omega/4\pi$ frequencies and its own cutoff $\omega_l(\Omega)$. The total spectrum is obtained by integrating over the solid angle

$$Z_{el} = \int d\Omega \, \frac{3N}{4\pi} \sum_{l=1}^{3} \frac{\omega^2}{\omega_l{}^3(\Omega)} \, F(\omega,\omega_l); \, z_{el} = Z_{el}/3N; \, F(\omega,\omega_l) = \begin{matrix} 1 & 0 \leq \omega \leq \omega_l \\ 0 & \text{else} \end{matrix}$$

$$(28)$$

This method was first applied to Li (7). Actually this improvement of the Debye procedure is not an improvement at all. Naturally this elastic spectrum extends to much higher frequencies than the lattice spectrum, which in the Debye spectrum is taken care of by shifting the high frequencies to lower values. For large anisotropy, the spread of cutoff frequencies ω_l is large and the difference between Debye spectrum and elastic spectrum becomes more pronounced.

Momentum-Debye Method. Because the momentum method alone gives poor agreement for the low ω part of the spectrum, one can improve this method by using a trial function with the right elastic ω^2

behavior for small ω. The Debye spectrum is already correct for low frequencies. The most simple trial function is therefore

$$Z(\omega) = \frac{3\omega^2}{\omega_D{}^3} F(\omega,\omega_G) + \eta\delta(\omega - \omega_E) \qquad (29)$$

which combines a Debye spectrum (cutoff ω_G) with an Einstein spectrum. Because of normalization one has $\omega_G{}^3/\omega_D{}^3 + \eta = 1$. The remaining two parameters (that is, ω_G, ω_E) can be obtained by fitting $\overline{\omega^2}$ and $\overline{\omega^4}$. This spectrum, for instance, gives the correct behavior of the harmonic specific heat at low and high temperatures.*

Houston's method (5) is essentially as follows: The integral over **k** in Eq 12 is transformed into an integration over the solid angle. The integrand, which is the contribution to the spectrum per solid angle, is expanded into cubic harmonics; only the cubic harmonics of low order are kept. The coefficients of the expansion can then be obtained from the dispersion curves in low-indexed directions. This spectrum contains spurious singularities.

Singularities (5). To obtain finer details of the spectrum, one has to study critical points. In general one has in three-dimensional crystals only discontinuous derivatives at a few points. The environment of the spectrum near critical points can be studied. This can be combined with other information about the spectrum (moments, elastic behavior) to construct an approximate spectrum including the correct behavior near critical points.

Spectra of Some Body-Centered Cubic Metals

Isotropic Central-Force Model With First and Second Neighbors. Here one has $\alpha = \beta = \gamma/2 = ac_{44}$; $c_{44} = c_{12} = c_{11}/3$; $f^{[2]}/f^{[1]} = \frac{2}{3}$. This model has been investigated first by P. C. Fine (8) and was meant for W. The spectrum is essentially obtained by a root sampling method. W is practically isotropic, and the Cauchy relations are almost satisfied. Therefore, one can represent the lattice dynamics by central forces.† With

---

* The low-temperature part is given by the small frequencies; the high-temperature part depends on the low-order even moments only.

† It must be pointed out again that $c_{12} = c_{44}$ does not necessarily imply central forces alone. In a metal like W one certainly should have many body forces due to the electrons. If one uses, for example, a first- and second-neighbor model with coupling parameters α, β, γ, δ, one obtains from Eq 17 $\delta = \beta - \alpha$ due to the Cauchy relations and $\gamma = 3\beta - \alpha$ due to isotropy. The ratio β/α is free. The spectrum, of course, depends on that ratio, and it is not obvious at all that the ratio 1 corresponding to central forces gives a good spectrum for W.

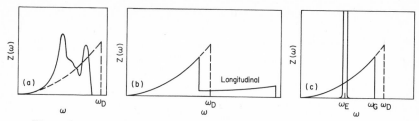

Fig. 7. Spectra for W. (a) Lattice and Debye spectra. (b) Debye and elastic
spectra. (c) Debye-Einstein spectrum.

the value $c_{44} \cong 15.3 \cdot 10^{11}$ dynes/cm², as chosen by Fine, one has $\omega_D \cong$
$5 \cdot 10^{13}$/sec. For the other metals of the group, Cr, Mo and W, the
behavior should be similar. The spectrum has the same shape except for
a scaling* factor $(ac_{44}/M)^{1/2}$. The spectrum is represented in Fig. 7. Figure
7(a) shows a comparison between lattice and Debye spectra; Fig. 7(b)
shows the Debye spectrum and the "improvement" by taking into
account polarization; Fig. 7(c) gives the result of the momentum-Debye
method. One almost can see how the lattice spectrum originates from
the elastic spectrum by shortening the high frequencies due to the lattice
effect.

Central-Force Model With First and Second Neighbors. Here
one has $\alpha = \beta = f^{[1]}/3$, $\gamma = f^{[2]}$, $c_{44} = c_{12} = 2f^{[1]}/3a$ and $c_{11} = 2f^{[1]}/3 +$
$2f^{[2]}$. The Cauchy relation holds. If this relation holds only approxi-
mately, one should determine the central-force data from the shear
moduli C' and C because the electrons presumably do not contribute to
the shear moduli: $f^{[1]} = 3aC/2$, $f^{[2]} = aC'$, $f^{[2]}/f^{[1]} = 2C'/3C$. Extensive
calculations have been carried out by Clark (9) for various ratios $f^{[2]}/f^{[1]}$
by use of a root-sampling method.† Figure 8 shows a spectrum for a ratio
0.82 thought to represent the spectrum of V. The spectrum is quite
similar to that of W (with a ratio of ⅔) because V is nearly isotropic.
The deviation from the measured‡ spectrum (10) is considerable. This
might be due to the fact that in the framework of this model not even the
elastic data are correctly given because instead of the Cauchy relations
one has $c_{12} \cong 3c_{44}$, according to Table 1. According to Table 1, the same

* For instance, $\omega_D{}^W/\omega_D{}^{Mo} = (a^W c_{44}{}^W M^{Mo}/a^{Mo} c_{44}{}^{Mo} M^W)^{1/2}$

† H. B. Rosenstock (11) has treated the same model, including the singularities of
the spectrum.

‡ V is a singular substance with respect to n-scattering because the scattering is
incoherent. In this instance, the spectrum can be obtained directly from n-scattering
experiments. The spectrum has been measured by various authors (10, 12–14). In
Ref 14 a comparison also is made with calculated spectra by use of different models.
But from the data given in this paper one cannot see how the coupling parameters
were actually fitted to the elastic data.

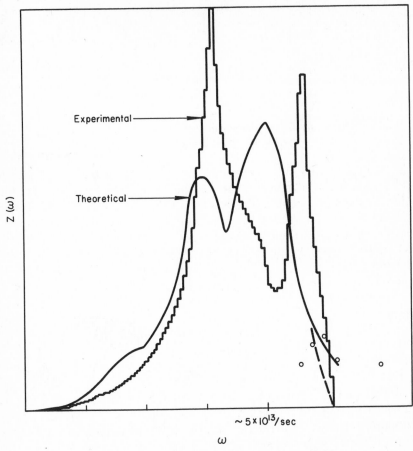

Fig. 8. Experimental and theoretical spectra for V (5)

model could be used for Li and for Fe because the Cauchy relations are approximately satisfied

$$f^{[2]}/f^{[1]} = \gamma/3\alpha = 2C'/3C \cong 0.77 \text{ for Li, } \cong 0.3 \text{ for Fe}$$

Several calculations have been made for Li by use of the theoretical elastic moduli* calculated by Fuchs (7). Figure 9(a) shows the Debye spectrum and the elastic spectrum (7). Because of the large anisotropy, the elastic spectrum is very much spread out and does not give a good

* $c_{11} = 1.53$, $c_{12} = 1.19$, $c_{44} = 1.33 \cdot 10^{13}$ dynes/cm²; $f^{[2]}/f^{[1]} \cong 0.85$.

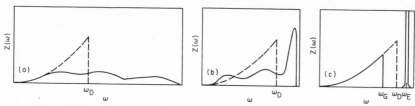

Fig. 9. Spectra for Li. (a) Debye and elastic spectra. (b) Lattice and Debye spectra. (c) Debye-Einstein spectrum.

description of the lattice spectrum* (15) shown in Fig. 9(b). Figure 9(c) shows the Debye-Einstein representation. Figure 10 shows a more detailed spectrum calculated by Dayal and Sharan (16). For both figures, one has $\omega_D \cong 5 \cdot 10^{13}$/sec. In Ref 16 the method of de Launay (4) is used. Here the force parameters are assumed to be different for the longitudinal and transversal components of a lattice wave to take account of the electronic contribution. Because, as has been pointed out before, the terms longitudinal or transversal do not have a strict physical meaning due to periodicity in **k** space, the tensor $t_{il}(\mathbf{k})$ in this model does not correspond to Born's lattice dynamics.† The tensor t_{il} in the de Launay model does not possess the required periodicity.‡ However, if the Cauchy relations are satisfied, the de Launay model is identical with the central-force model of this section. For Li, the Cauchy relations are very nearly satisfied ($c_{12}/c_{44} \cong 1.1$) and the calculations of Dayal and Sharan correspond approximately to a central-force model. The spectrum for Li has again been calculated by Clark (9). The result is shown in Fig. 11.

General Forces for First Neighbors and Central Forces for Second Neighbors. This model contains three coupling parameters (α, β, γ; $\delta = 0$), and the spectrum depends only on the ratios γ/α and β/α apart from a scaling factor. The three coupling parameters can be obtained from the elastic data. Spectra for this model have been worked

---

* The deviation from the Cauchy relation was taken approximately into account by introducing force parameters corresponding to volume forces due to the electrons. In Li this influence is small and the model is practically a central-force model. Only a few frequencies were calculated and the spectrum is not very accurate.

† The elastic behavior (small **k**) is correct.

‡ Dayal and Sharan (17) have also calculated spectra for Na and K, using the de Launay model. Here the deviations from Born's lattice theory are more serious ($c_{12}/c_{44} \cong 1.5$ for the elastic moduli used in their work). Bauer (18) has calculated the spectrum of Na with the central-force model using Houston's method. Bhatia (19) used a "lattice" model similar to that of de Launay and constructed a spectrum according to Houston.

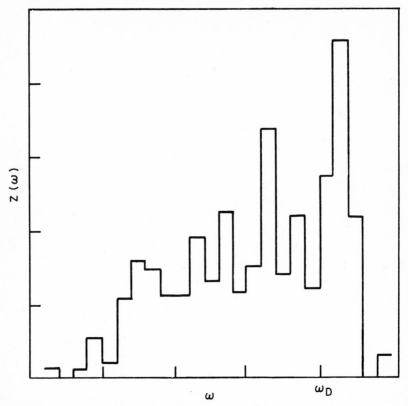

Fig. 10. Spectrum of Li (16) (approximately central-force model)

out in Ref 18 for two examples thought to represent* V and Li. The elastic data of Table 1 were used [V: Ref f of Table 1; Li: Ref a of Table 1 (78 K)]. Figure 12 shows the results for V.† If one compares the result with the experimental spectrum of V in Fig. 8, one only realizes a slight improvement in comparison with the central-force model. This seems to show that the model employed here is still not adequate to give the right spectrum.

Models Considering Higher-Order Neighbors.   Only a few calculations including higher-order neighbors or more than three force constants have been carried out. Champier (21) has determined the coupling parameters up to third-order neighbors by fitting to dispersion curves of

---

* The authors also have calculated spectra for the de Launay model. Histograms are given in Document No. 7476, American Documentation Institute.

† Singh and Bowers (20) have employed the same model, using different elastic data for V, and obtained a quite different spectrum. A comparison is given in Ref 18.

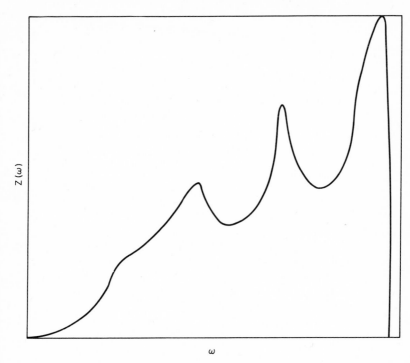

Fig. 11. Spectrum of Li (18) (central-force model)

Li obtained at room temperature with x-rays.* The elastic data (300 K) obtained from the measurements were $c_{11} = 1.0$, $c_{12} = 0.76$, $c_{44} = 0.7 \cdot 10^{11}$ dynes/cm^2. The coupling parameters in the notation of Fig. 3 were obtained from the dispersion curves to be as follows: $\alpha = 1060$, $\beta = 1330$, $\gamma = 800$, $\delta = 210$, $\kappa = \mu = -25$ dynes/cm. The spectrum was calculated by root sampling and is shown in Fig. 13. Curien (22) has computed the spectrum of Fe by use of Houston's method and experimentally (x-rays) determined dispersion curves along (100), (110) and (111) directions.* The spectrum is shown in Fig. 14.

Conclusion

In conclusion one might say that the actual spectra of bcc metals are not very accurately known. If one is only interested in the harmonic

* Force constants including third neighbors have been obtained from the dispersion curves. More recently (23) the dispersion curve in (100) direction of Fe has been measured by n-scattering. The results do not agree well, the neutron experiments giving much higher frequencies particularly near the boundary of the Brillouin zone.

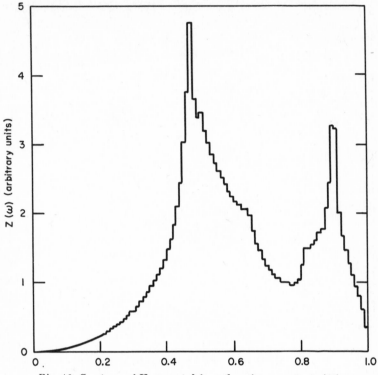

Fig. 12. Spectrum of V computed from three force constants (18)

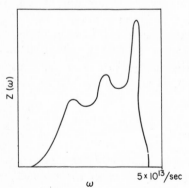

Fig. 13. Spectrum of Li computed
from five force constants (21)

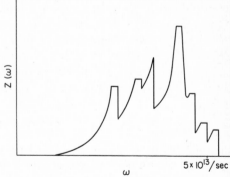

Fig. 14. Spectrum of Fe computed by use of
Houston's method

spectrum,* there are two reasons for it. One is experimental. The measured dispersion curves and elastic data contain a certain amount of anharmonic contribution. By measurements at various temperatures, one could reduce the data to the harmonic values and obtain harmonic force constants, which in turn determine the spectrum. Secondly the models investigated so far theoretically usually employ only first- and second-neighbor interaction. Actually, contributions by higher-order neighbors could change the spectrum substantially.

References

1 M. Born and K. Huang, Dynamical Theory of Crystal Lattices, Oxford University Press, London and New York, 1954
2 M. Blackman, Encyclopedia of Physics, Vol VII, Part 1
3 G. Leibfried, Encyclopedia of Physics, Vol VII, Part 1
4 J. de Launay, Solid State Phys, 2, 219 (1956)
5 A. A. Maradudin, E. W. Montroll and G. H. Weiss, Solid State Phys Suppl, 3 (1963)
6 A. D. B. Woods, B. N. Brockhouse, R. A. March and A. T. Stewart, Phys Rev, 128, 1112 (1962)
7 K. Fuchs, Proc Roy Soc London, Ser A, 157, 144 (1936)
8 P. C. Fine, Phys Rev, 56, 355 (1939)
9 C. B. Clark, J Grad Res Center, 29, 1 (1961)
10 C. M. Eisenhauer, I. Pelah, D. J. Hughes and H. Palevsky, Phys Rev, 109, 1046 (1958)
11 H. B. Rosenstock, Phys Rev, 97, 290 (1955)
12 A. T. Stewart and B. N. Brockhouse, Rev Mod Phys, 30, 250 (1958)
13 K. C. Thurberfield and P. A. Egelstaff, in Inelastic Scattering of Neutrons, Vol I, IAEA, Vienna, 1961, p 581
14 R. Haas, W. Kley, K. H. Krebs and R. Rubin, in Inelastic Scattering of Neutrons, Vol II, IAEA, Vienna, 1961, p 145
15 G. Leibfried and W. Brenig, Z Physik, 134, 451 (1953)
16 B. Dayal and B. Sharan, Proc Roy Soc London Ser A, 259, 361 (1960)
17 B. Dayal and B. Sharan, Proc Roy Soc London Ser A, 262, 136 (1961)
18 J. B. Hendricks, H. N. Riser and C. B. Clark, Phys Rev, 130, 1377 (1963)
19 A. B. Bhatia, Phys Rev, 97, 363 (1955)
20 D. N. Singh and W. A. Bowers, Phys Rev, 116, 279 (1959)
21 G. Champier, Bull Soc Franc Mineral Crist, 82, 61, 137 (1959)
22 H. Curien, Acta Cryst, 5, 393 (1952)
23 P. K. Iyengar, N. S. Satya Murthy and B. A. Dasannacharya, in Inelastic Scattering of Neutrons, Vol I, IAEA, Vienna, 1961, p 555

* If anharmonic effects are present, one can define various spectra for different purposes. These questions have been dealt with at the Lattice Dynamics Conference held in Copenhagen in 1964 (to be published in J Phys Chem Solids). Physical models like the shell model including forces of longer ranges also have been discussed at this conference.

PART 3
Diffusion by Stress Relaxation Methods

Chapter 8

The Measurement of Diffusion Coefficients
by Internal Friction

R. GIBALA AND C. A. WERT

The diffusion coefficient in solids is determined, for the most part, by measuring macroscopic mass flow. The differential equation for diffusion is solved for the particular configuration at hand, and the material constants that characterize the mass flow are determined by fitting the experimental data to this solution. The simplest way to do this is to measure the mean-square penetration $\overline{X^2}$ in one dimension. To the accuracy that the diffusion coefficient D is independent of concentration, D may be determined for cubic crystals from the equation

$$\overline{X^2} = 2\,Dt \tag{1}$$

where t is the time during which diffusion has been permitted to occur. Here the atoms are permitted to jump in all three coordinate directions, although the penetration is measured only along one coordinate.

The corresponding equation for the mean-square radial penetration $\overline{R^2}$ may readily be calculated. In terms of the D in Eq 1,

$$\overline{R^2}/3 = 2\,Dt$$

Now let the time t be shortened to some time τ during which the particle moves such that $\overline{R^2}$ should be d^2, where d is the nearest-neighbor distance. Then

$$d^2/3 = 2\,D\tau$$

so that (for cubic systems)

$$D = d^2/6\tau \tag{2}$$

The time τ is referred to as the mean-jump-time. If it can be measured and if d is known, then D can be determined without the necessity of a

The authors are with the University of Illinois, Urbana, Ill.

large penetration of the diffusing atoms. Mechanical, dielectric and magnetic relaxation methods are techniques of measuring τ (and hence D) directly.

The Acoustical Spectrum

Relaxation of atoms in crystals will occur under an external force, be it a mechanical stress, electric field or magnetic field, if the force alters the population of the atoms among the several permissible configurations. In the simplest example, we consider a distribution of N atoms on two types of sites. These sites are energetically equivalent under no stress and the atoms can move between them. Let an external stress alter the energy of the sites, making one type favored over the other, so that a difference in population of the two sites would exist at equilibrium. Because the motion of atoms from one site to another is controlled by diffusional processes, the excess of atoms (over the average) that accumulates in the favored sites, ΔN, is given as a function of time by the expression

$$\Delta N = \Delta N_\infty \exp\left(-t/\tau_r\right) \tag{3}$$

where ΔN_∞ is the final population excess at infinite time and τ_r is a time constant called the relaxation time. If the configuration of site distribution is such that simple diffusion jumps occur only between sites of opposite kind, then

$$\tau = 2\tau_r$$

For this simple case then, the diffusion coefficient that can be associated with these jumps is given by

$$D = d^2/12\tau_r \tag{4}$$

The more general case can readily be calculated. Let the atoms occupy N types of positions with equal probability under no stress. Furthermore, let an external force divide these N sites into two groups, N' being preferred over the remaining $(N - N')$ sites. Suppose further that, under no stress, an atom can jump with equal probability from any of the N sites into n other N sites; under stress, let n' be the number of the N' preferred sites reached in a single jump from any of the preferred sites. Then the constant, α, relating τ and τ_r

$$\tau = \alpha\tau_r \tag{5}$$

can be written

$$\alpha = [N(n - n')]/[(N - N')n] \tag{6}$$

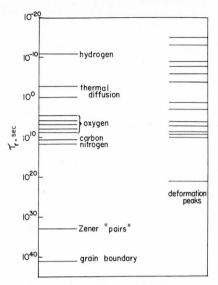

Fig. 1. The acoustical spectrum for Cb at 25 C. The temperature dependence of the relaxation time τ_r is assumed to obey the expression $\tau_r = \tau_{r0}\ exp\ (\Delta H/RT)$. When τ_{r0} was not known, it was assumed to have the value 10^{-15} sec.

This relation holds for any of the relaxation phenomena, mechanical, dielectric or magnetic, whenever the external stress divides the population into two groups.

A particular solid may have many simultaneous atomic processes by means of which it can relax; the relaxation times for these phenomena may cover a broad spectrum. For Cb, all of the spectral lines reported in the literature are tabulated in Fig. 1. Here τ_r for the several lines found in undeformed Cb are on the left. To make this a constant-temperature plot, all lines for which τ_r is temperature dependent are assumed to obey the equation

$$\tau_r = \tau_{r0} \exp\ (\Delta H/RT) \qquad (7)$$

For many of the relaxations, τ_{r0} has been found to be equal to about 10^{-15} sec; when unknown, it has been assumed to have this value. The energy ΔH has been selected as the best experimental value when known; when unknown it has been estimated from the known position of the peak in the usual way. Both of these procedures may cause an error in position of some of the lines in Fig. 1 of several powers of ten; the purpose of Fig. 1 is not to give highly accurate data, but to show the large number of lines in the known acoustical spectrum.

The Snoek Relaxation

Several of the relaxations cited in Fig. 1 are useful in measuring diffusion of atoms in Cb (or several other bcc metals). Of these, perhaps the most interesting and well understood are the Snoek relaxations, which involve the diffusion of small atoms H, N, C and O. These atoms are usually assumed to fit into the interstitial holes that have octahedral symmetry in the bcc crystal (Fig. 2). Diffusion of these atoms is assumed to go from site to site without the necessity of vacancy motion. For their configuration the quantity $\alpha = \frac{3}{2}$, and D is therefore given by

$$D = d^2/9\tau_r = a^2/36\tau_r$$

where a is the cube edge. Measurement of D by this technique for O

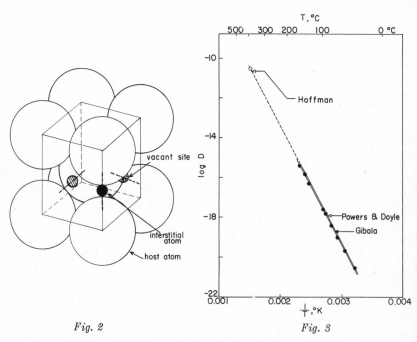

Fig. 2   Fig. 3

Fig. 2. The three types of octahedral sites available for interstitial occupancy in a bcc crystal

Fig. 3. The variation of the diffusion coefficient D of O in Cb with temperature. The data of Hoffman (1) and of Powers and Doyle (2) were obtained from low-concentration O alloys (<0.1 at. % O); the data of Gibala (3) were obtained from measurements on high-O alloys that were corrected for O clustering.

Table 1. Interstitial Diffusion in bcc Metals

Host metal	Diffusion coefficient(a)	Diffusant			
		H	C	N	O
V.........	D_0	....	0.0045	0.0092	0.0130
	ΔH	....	27,290	34,060	29,010
Cr........	D_0	....	....	0.0003	....
	ΔH	....	....	24,300	....
Fe........	D_0	....	0.026(0.0041)(b)	0.003	....
	ΔH	2000	20,400(19,200)(b)	18,200	....
Cb........	D_0	....	0.0040	0.0086	0.021
	ΔH	....	33,020	34,920	26,910
Mo........	D_0	....	....	....	....
	ΔH	....	{31,000}(c)	....	....
Ta........	D_0	....	0.0061	0.0056	0.0044
	ΔH	6000	38,510	37,840	25,450
W.........	D_0	....	....	....	....
	ΔH	....	....	....	....

(a) Values for D_0 are given in cm²/sec; values for ΔH, the activation energy, in cal/mole.
(b) The values given parenthetically have recently been proposed by Lord and Beshers (4).
(c) Value is enclosed in braces because the assignment of relaxation effects is not as certain as that for the other metals.

diffusing in Cb is shown in Fig. 3. Data for D_0 and the activation energy of interstitials diffusing in numerous metals are given in Table 1.

Interstitials could occupy tetrahedrally coordinated sites in the bcc metals (Fig. 4). If this is so and if diffusion between these sites is a direct jump, then α equals $\frac{3}{2}$. Consequently for this model,

$$D = d^2/9\tau_r = a^2/72\tau_r \qquad (8)$$

In Chapter 9 in this volume, Beshers works out in detail the arguments in favor of occupancy of tetrahedral sites over the more generally assumed occupancy of octahedral sites. His findings imply that C and N occupy octahedral sites in Fe but C, N and O may favor tetrahedral sites in the refractory metals. All of his studies are based on the surmise that elastic strain energy is the sole factor determining the choice of occupancy. Whether he or earlier investigators are correct is not determined at this time.

Two parameters define the relaxation process. One of these, the relaxation time τ_r, which gives the rate of the jumping atoms, is the main topic of this paper. It determines the position in time of the spectral line. The other, the relaxation strength, gives the magnitude of the absorption line.

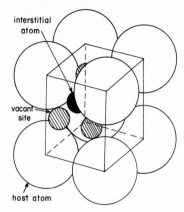

Fig. 4. The various types of tetrahedral sites available for interstitial occupancy in a bcc crystal

In terms of the earlier example for which Eq 3 expresses the atom redistribution, the relaxation strength may be defined as

$$\Delta = AN$$

where A is a constant that depends on details of the atomic configuration responsible for the relaxation and N is the number of atoms that can relax. Whereas τ_r has never been found to be a function of the direction in which the stress is applied in a single crystal, Δ is usually an anisotropic property of single crystals.

A recent measurement has been made by Hoffman (1) of the anisotropy of Δ for interstitial O and N in Cb. Δ is found to be maximum for a stress in a [100] direction and zero for a stress in a [111] direction. For any angle, Δ for a longitudinal mode of vibration obeys the following relation (5):

$$\Delta = \frac{2\epsilon^2(VC_0/gRT)C_{44}(C_{11} + 2C_{12})[1 - 3(\alpha^2\beta^2 + \beta^2\gamma^2 + \gamma^2\alpha^2)]}{(C_{11}^2 - C_{12}^2)C_{44} + (C_{11} - C_{12})(C_{11} + 2C_{12})(C_{11} - C_{12} - 2C_{44}) \times (\alpha^2\beta^2 + \beta^2\gamma^2 + \gamma^2\alpha^2)}$$

where V = molar volume of the solvent metal, R = universal gas constant, T = absolute temperature of the peak, C_0 = molar concentration of the interstitial atom causing the damping peak, α, β, γ = direction cosines between the applied stress and the basic crystallographic directions, C_{11}, C_{12}, C_{44} = elastic stiffness of the solvent metal, and ϵ = a parameter related to the strain produced by the interstitial atom in its appropriate site.

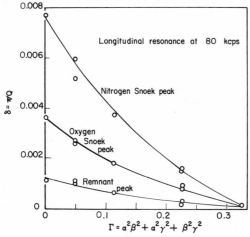

Fig. 5. *The variation of the Snoek relaxation strength with orientation of the crystal for O and N in Cb. The remnant peak (from Hoffman, Ref 1) may be due to interstitial C.*

For Hoffman's data, see the curves in Fig. 5. Polder first applied his theory to the Snoek relaxation of C in Fe using a value for ϵ derived from known martensite strain (5). The values of Δ for a crystal [100] orientation, that is, for $\Gamma = 0$, agreed well with the value of Δ observed by Dijkstra (6) for a [100] crystal of Fe containing a known amount of C. From Hoffman's data, the value calculated for the quantity $\epsilon/(C_{11} - C_{12})$ is 0.54 for O in Cb and 0.66 for N in Cb; these numbers imply a local strain about the same as that for C in Fe, for which $\epsilon/(C_{11} - C_{12})$ is 1.04.

One should note that a zero effect for a [111] crystal does not differentiate between octahedral and tetrahedral occupancy of sites. A [111] stress is a symmetrical stress for both. Consequently these measurements by themselves do not rule out tetrahedral occupancy of interstitial sites. The constancy of the specific effect per interstitial for a [100] orientation in both Fe and Cb is a factor to be explained by any theory of site occupancy, however.

Relaxation of Clusters

The diffusion models quoted here are based on the premise that the interstitial atoms are singly dispersed. If they are not, if they exist in clusters of various sizes as well as singly, then a variety of diffusion rates can exist, because the clusters may tumble through the crystal in a variety of ways, each at its own rate. The diffusion coefficient, D_n, for each cluster is given by a quantity

$$D_n = d^2/B_n \tau_{r,n} \tag{10}$$

where B_n is a constant for a cluster of size n and $\tau_{r,n}$ is the appropriate relaxation time for the cluster.

The net transport of interstitial atoms in a concentration gradient is a rather complicated function of the gradient and the temperature. Formally the net flux dN/dt is given by

$$dN/dt = - \sum_n D_n(\partial C_n/\partial x) \tag{11}$$

where C_n is the concentration of clusters of size n. The quantity C_n, however, can be a complicated function of x as well as T because the clusters are not independent of each other. For solutions for which most of the atoms are present singly

$$C_n = Z_n C_1{}^n \exp (E_n/RT) \tag{12}$$

where E_n is the energy necessary to decompose a cluster of size n into n single atoms and Z_n is a geometrical constant.

The coefficients D_n have not been determined for any material (except for D_1). For several materials, however, the time constants $\tau_{r,n}$ have been determined for clusters of small size, say 1 to 4 atoms per cluster. The following paragraphs will illustrate the way in which this is done for diffusion of clusters of O in Cb.

Details of the terminal solid solution of O in Cb are fairly well known. At high temperatures several atomic per cent of O can be dissolved; this solid solution is retained on rapid cooling to temperatures in the vicinity of room temperature. Here reasonable numbers of clusters of small size form fairly rapidly, and their presence can be detected by appropriate anelastic measurements. The requirement that a cluster produce an anelastic effect is not a severe one; it is only that the strain field about the cluster have lower symmetry than that of the crystal itself. Under this condition, clusters of the various sizes relax with time into minimum energy configurations, producing an anelastic strain with a relaxation time characteristic of the size of the cluster. The group of four lines in Fig. 1 for O are the τ_r's found for what are believed to be singles, pairs, triplets and quadruplets of O atoms in Cb. The positions of these lines in this time scale are known with moderate precision, say $\pm 3\%$.

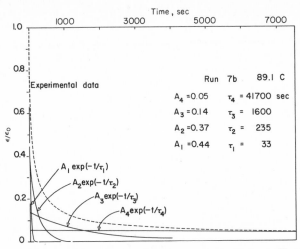

Fig. 6. A strain-relaxation measurement at constant stress for a Cb−1.5 at. % O alloy. In addition to the Snoek effect ($A_1 = 0.44$, $\tau_1 = 33$ sec), there exist relaxations believed to be caused by O pairs ($A_2 = 0.37$, $\tau_2 = 235$ sec), O triplets ($A_3 = 0.14$, $\tau_3 = 1600$ sec) and O quadruplets ($A_4 = 0.05$, $\tau_4 = 41,700$ sec).

The actual method of finding the τ_r's from these absorption lines is complicated by the fact that in Cb all lines can be present at once and the τ_r's are sufficiently near to each other so that the lines overlap. This causes some difficulty in analysis of the experimental data, but the problems of separation are not insuperable if the initial data are sufficiently accurate. The original curve for relaxation of strain at constant stress in an alloy of about 1.5 at. % O in Cb held at 89 C is plotted in Fig. 6; the four component exponential curves into which this experimental curve can be decomposed are also plotted. The τ_r's determined from this analysis along with those determined for a wide variety of other compositions and temperatures are plotted in Fig. 7.

Several things about this plot are noteworthy. First, the τ_r's fall into four distinct groups; the activation energies ΔH are tabulated in Table 2. The identification of the several relaxations as being due to singles, pairs, etc., was made by varying the over-all composition of the alloy and seeing how the relative strength of the several relaxations varied. One sees that ΔH increases with cluster size, indicating that the rate of diffusion decreases as the cluster size increases.

The binding energies of the clusters are important quantities. By observing how the strengths of the relaxations vary with temperature, one can deduce this quantity from Eq 12. These binding energies (Table 2)

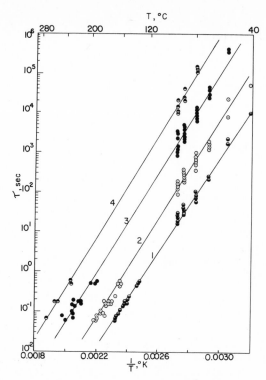

Fig. 7. The temperature dependence of the relaxation times for Cb − 0.1 to 2.0 at. % O alloys for the four processes shown in Fig. 6. The activation energies for these processes are given in Table 2.

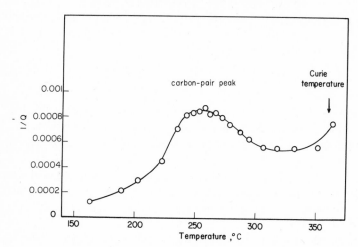

Fig. 8. The C-pair peak in Ni at a frequency of 1.08 cps.

Table 2. Activation Energy, Binding Energy and Per Cent Bound Atoms for Clusters of Various Sizes in an Alloy Containing Cb and 0.1 to 2.0 at. % O

Cluster size	ΔH, kcal/mole	E_n, kcal/mole	N at 100 C for a 2% alloy, %
Singles............	26.8	....	48
Pairs..............	28.6	2.0 ± 0.4	39
Triplets............	29.3	5.0 ± 0.7	12
Quadruplets.........	29.8	6.5 ± 1.0	1

are of appreciable magnitude, so that relatively large fractions of the atoms are found in clusters of two, three and four near room temperature in alloys where the over-all composition is several per cent. Table 2 also shows the fraction of atoms expected to be bound up in the clusters of various sizes at 100 C for a 2% alloy if these values of E_n are correct.

Clusters should exist in interstitial alloys of fcc and hcp metals too. Furthermore, the clusters of two or more may well produce measurable anelastic effects in these metals even if the cluster of one, the singly dispersed atom, produces no effect. Such a phenomenon has been observed in two metals containing C; a Ni-C solid solution (7) and a Co-C solid solution (8). A damping peak for pairs of C in Ni at a frequency of 1 cps is plotted in Fig. 8. This peak has an activation energy of about 33,000 cal/mole, which is close to that measured for diffusion of C in Ni. This peak is too broad for a single relaxation process, so it is likely that it is a superposition of effects of diffusion under stress of several sizes or configurations of clusters. Although little metallurgical use has been made of this peak or any other like it, it seems to offer the possibility of permitting study of clustering in close-packed metals.

Relaxation of Oxygen in Elemental Semiconductors

Alloys of O with the semiconductors Ge and Si also display anelasticity arising from the motion of interstitial atoms in an otherwise pure host crystal. The interstitial hole into which the O fits has geometrically the same radius as that of the host atom. A dissolved O atom, however, does not sit comfortably in this rather large hole, which has the four nearest neighboring host atoms symmetrically disposed about it. Instead it assumes a configuration (Fig. 9) in which it has two host atoms in nearest-neighbor positions and others, of course, at greater distances.

Two diffusional motions of the dissolved O atom are possible. One is a sort of rotating motion of the O atom about the line between the nearest

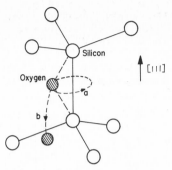

Fig. 9. The motion of O atoms in the diamond cubic crystal. Motion "b"
results in long-range diffusion, whereas motion "a" does not.

host atoms. This motion is not perfectly free; six sites in which the energy
of the atom is a minimum exist about this line. Rather small potential
barriers over which the atom must pass in its motion from site to site
exist. This motion does not produce long-range diffusion and is not
involved with any anelastic energy loss. The other motion, a transfer of
the O from one pair of the host atoms to another—line b in Fig. 9—produces an anelastic effect and results in normal diffusional mass transfer.
A damping peak at high frequency (≈ 60 kc) caused by this motion of
dissolved O has been observed by Southgate (9) in both Si and Ge. The
diffusion coefficient for this motion, as it has been interpreted by Haas
(10), is

$$D = a^2/64\tau_r \tag{13}$$

From the data of Southgate, Haas finds the following constants for O
diffusion:

Constant	Si	Ge
D_0	0.21 cm²/sec	0.17 cm²/sec
ΔH	58.5 kcal/mole	46.5 kcal/mole

Relaxation of Bound Pairs

All previous discussion has been concerned with relaxation in binary
alloys. Numerous relaxations are also observed in ternary or higher alloys;
these relaxations often have special features that make their study
highly profitable. The particular relaxation described here is that which
arises from reorientation under stress of a pair consisting of a substitutional impurity atom and a dissolved interstitial such as C, N or O, both
in dilute solution. Two aspects of pairs need to be considered, first, the

equilibrium number that exists at given concentrations of the substitutional and the interstitial impurity, and second, the diffusional motion of the pairs.

The equilibrium number of pairs at any temperature depends both on the stoichiometry of the ternary alloy and on the energy of attraction or repulsion between the interstitial and the substitutional impurities. For a dilute solution and a number of pairs that is small compared with the number of dissociated impurities

$$n_p/n_i = Zn_s \exp (E_b/kT) \tag{14}$$

where n_p = atom fraction of paired interstitials, n_i = atom fraction of unpaired interstitials, n_s = atom fraction of substitutional impurities, E_b = binding energy of an interstitial to a substitutional atom, and Z = ratio of the number of equivalent paired positions of an interstitial about a substitutional impurity to the number of equivalent sites per host atom. Here the term atom fraction refers to the ratio of the alloying element to the number of lattice points in the crystal. For interstitial-substitutional pairs in bcc metals, E_b is apparently never negative. Hence one has, for these alloys, an atom fraction of paired interstitials either equal to or greater than the random number Zn_sn_i.

Three types of movement of the interstitials can be distinguished. One is movement of the interstitial about the substitutional impurity from one equivalent site to another. This motion, which we will call local diffusion, and to which we will ascribe a diffusion coefficient D_l, obviously results in no long-range diffusion of the impurity atom if the substitutional impurity remains fixed on one site in the crystal. A second motion of the pair, a tumbling motion of this pseudo-molecule through the crystal, will be assigned a diffusion coefficient D_p. Finally, there is the long-range motion of the interstitials and the long-range motion of the substitutional atoms in which they diffuse mainly as single atoms and not as a tightly bound complex; the corresponding diffusion coefficients will be designated D_i and D_s, respectively.

In principle, all of these motions may produce internal friction effects in specific crystals and several have been seen. The first, the rotation of the interstitial about a stationary substitutional atom, has been observed in numerous metals; several examples are cited in succeeding paragraphs. The second, simultaneous motion of the interstitial and substitutional atoms, should be seen, in principle, but it probably has not been observed. Presumably most pairs would dissociate at temperatures corresponding to reasonable mean-jump-times, say minutes or seconds. The third, motion of the interstitial in the free crystal, is characterized by the

Snoek-type relaxation, provided that the interstitial spends most of its time in the free crystal and little of its time in associated complexes. The last, motion of the substitutional alone, would not be observed in extraordinarily dilute alloys, but would be seen as the Zener relaxation in alloys of sufficiently high concentration.

The first extensive study of damping caused by a rotating motion of interstitials around stationary substitutional atoms was made by Dijkstra and Sladek (11) for N in Fe alloyed with Mn, Cr, Mo or V. This work was followed by studies on N in other alloys of Fe and on C in Fe-Si alloys. Although damping peaks caused by motion of these interstitials in the vicinity of substitutional impurities were observed in numerous investigations, little use has been made of them. Primarily this lack of use is caused by an imperfect understanding of the detailed configuration of the motion of the interstitial; at least two jumps are required for an N atom to go from one interstitial site adjacent to the impurity to another. However, this is not all; no one has apparently deemed the study of the detailed configuration and thermodynamics of the associated pair to be interesting enough or important enough to warrant the expenditure of time and effort necessary to study any one system in sufficient detail to understand it completely.

A damping peak of this type observed in a bcc metal is that in the Cb-Zr-O alloy. In this alloy, Zr atoms, which seem to be fairly randomly dispersed in the crystal, bind O atoms to them, apparently with a very high binding energy. Motion of these bound O atoms produces a damping peak (Fig. 10a) with a motional energy slightly higher than that of the normal Snoek peak in Cb. That the binding energy is high is attested to by the fact that the rotational peak, called the Zr-O peak by Bunn, Cummings and Leavenworth (12), reaches its maximum at an over-all O level of nearly the composition ZrO_2 before the normal O Snoek-peak can be seen.

Similar interaction peaks have been observed in fcc metals and alloys. The first reported were for fcc alloys of C in a Mn steel (Fig. 10b). Ke and his co-workers (13) both observed the effects and interpreted them successfully. They showed that diffusion coefficients obtained from their internal friction data with Eq 2 agree nicely with data for bulk diffusion of C in the same alloys if α is chosen to be 1. Apparently the long extrapolation of data necessary for comparison (Fig. 11) does not permit closer evaluation of the constant α, which they did not attempt to determine from calculation of possible geometrical models.

The hexagonal metals Ti and Hf both exhibit pair relaxations of this type. Long studies were made on Ti-O alloys containing a number of metallic third additions by Gupta and Weinig (14) and by Miller (15).

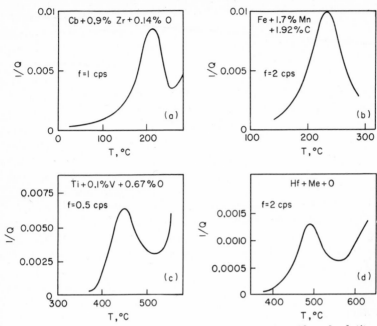

*Fig. 10. Examples of relaxation peaks due to the motion of bound substitu-
tional-interstitial impurity pairs in the (a) bcc lattice, (b) fcc lattice, and
(c) and (d) hcp lattice*

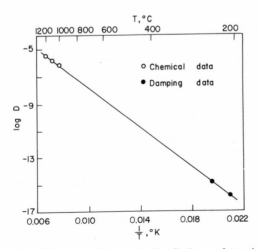

*Fig. 11. The diffusion of C in an Fe-Mn-C alloy as determined by damping
methods and by bulk-diffusion measurements. α in Eq 5 is assumed to be
unity.*

Altogether, these studies show the relaxation to be absent in the pure Ti-O binaries, but present in a wide variety of ternaries. An example from the work of Gupta and Weinig for a Ti-O alloy is presented in Fig. 10 (c). Importantly, they find the position in temperature of the peak to be not a function of the specific metallic impurity. The height of the peak for a specific Ti-Me composition was observed to be a linear function of the O content; at all O contents, the peak is too broad to be a single relaxation phenomenon.

Investigations in the hcp phase of Hf show the same general phenomena. Bisogni, Mah and Wert (16) have reported peaks to be present in alloys of Hf, Me and O (Fig. 10d) and Hf, Me and N, where Me is some unknown impurity. Again the height of the peak increases with increasing interstitial content, but exact linearity has not been established. In this instance the peak position and activation energy were about the same for both O and N interstitials. The activation energy for O in this motion is close to that observed for bulk diffusion, leading one to believe that the activation energy associated with the coefficient D_l is not much different from that associated with D_i, the same conclusion reached by Ke and co-workers for C in their γ-Fe.

Several conclusions can be reached from consideration of all of these investigations. These include:

1. Pair peaks of Me-interstitial pairs are a general feature of ternary alloys of all crystal types.

2. Measurement of the activation energy associated with the peaks apparently gives one a reasonably accurate measure of that for interstitial diffusion in the host metal.

3. Binding energies of the interstitials to the metallic impurities can be determined, in principle, but few actual measurements of binding energies have been made.

4. The configuration of the pairs might be deduced from a study of peak height as a function of orientation angle of single crystals, but this has not yet been done.

The Zener Relaxation

The examples cited in the previous sections exhaust the mechanical relaxations in metals for which generally accepted models have been established. Nevertheless, several other potentially useful relaxations exist; one of them is the Zener relaxation. This phenomenon, not dependent on the presence of any interstitial, occurs by rearrangement of substitutionally alloyed atoms under stress. It has, in our opinion, three potentially useful applications:

1. The activation energy for the relaxation ΔH_r, in any instance, gives a close approximation to the activation energy for diffusion in the alloy. Numerous investigations have shown that ΔH_r is close to, but somewhat less than, the activation energy for tracer diffusion of the fastest moving constituent in the alloy. This topic is discussed by Wert with detailed references in a forthcoming publication.

2. The equilibrium thermodynamics of vacancies, the kinetics of vacancy motion and details of the kinetics of vacancy production and decay can be investigated.

3. The details of decomposition of substitutional solid solutions into mixed phases can be followed, in principle. The Zener relaxation of a solid solution should be altered both in magnitude and in relaxation time as the change in phase occurs. Several attempts to follow phase changes in substitutional alloys by use of the Zener relaxation have not met with notable success, however.

Relaxations Associated With Deformation

Nearly half the spectral lines in Fig. 1 exist only in deformed specimens, but those associated with the presence of dislocations or other deformation-produced defects have been of little use in describing the nature of deformed Cb. Perhaps this lack is caused by lack of study because most of them have been only recently observed. It seems to us, however, that the difficulty of application of the deformation-associated relaxations to problems in metals is inherently the same as that of detailed application of dislocation principles to general problems of deformation in metals; the detailed configuration of dislocation-dislocation and dislocation-impurity interactions is extremely difficult to work out.

Perhaps one can see the direction one must go to make useful the deformation-associated relaxations by considering what has caused progress to be possible in application of some of the simpler relaxation phenomena. Without exception, the most successful applications have been for those relaxations for which the detailed configuration of the relaxing entity can be deduced; compare the great usefulness of the Snoek relaxations to the present limited usefulness of the Zener relaxations. The great difficulty in analyzing data obtained from deformed specimens lies in the richness of the spectrum, the departure from ideal narrowness of most of the individual lines in the spectrum and the difficulty of describing the origin of any line with a geometrical model.

Acknowledgments. Permission to use unpublished data of two of our colleagues, R. Hoffman and S. Diamond, is gratefully acknowledged. Financial support for part of the new experimental work on interstitial clusters in Cb was received from contracts with ARL at Wright-Patterson Air Force Base and the Air Force Office of Scientific Research. The support of the Center for Materials Research and the hospitality of the Materials Science Department, both of Stanford University, for Charles Wert during the writing of the paper is acknowledged.

References

1   R. A. Hoffman, Thesis, University of Illinois, 1963
2   R. W. Powers and M. V. Doyle, J Appl Phys, **30,** 514 (1959)
3   R. Gibala, Thesis, University of Illinois, 1964
4   A. E. Lord, ONR Contract No. 266 (61), Technical Report No. 5 (1964)
5   D. Polder, Philips Res Rept, **1,** 5 (1945)
6   L. Dijkstra, Philips Res Rept, **2,** 357 (1947)
7   T. S. Ke, C. T. Tsien and K. Misek, Sci Sinica Peking, **4,** 519 (1955); C. T. Tsien, Sci Sinica Peking, **10,** 930 (1961)
8   G. Mah, private communication
9   P. D. Southgate, Proc Phys Soc London, **B70,** 800 (1957); Phys Rev, **110,** 855 (1958)
10 C. Haas, J Phys Chem Solids, **15,** 108 (1960)
11 L. Dijkstra and R. Sladek, Trans AIME, **197,** 69 (1953)
12 P. W. Bunn, D. G. Cummings and H. W. Leavenworth, J Appl Phys, **30,** 3009 (1962)
13 T. S. Ke and C. M. Wang, Sci Sinica Peking, **4,** 501 (1955)
14 D. Gupta and S. Weinig, Acta Met, **10,** 292 (1962)
15 D. Miller, Trans AIME, **224,** 275 (1962)
16 E. Bisogni, G. Mah and C. A. Wert, J Less-Common Metals, in press

Chapter 9
Diffusion of Interstitial Impurities in
Body-Centered Cubic Metals

Daniel N. Beshers

After a decade of work that seemed to support Snoek's (1) model of the diffusion of interstitial impurities in bcc metals, a burst of new work, some of it not yet published, has shown that there is certainly one anomaly that is not understood, and that some other deviations from the previous picture may well be expected.

The basis for much of the work has been the possibility of determining diffusion coefficients by anelastic means, a possibility that depends on having a model from which a relation between the anelastic relaxation time and the diffusion coefficient can be deduced. The model that has actually been used is Snoek's. Wert's (2) anelastic relaxation times for C in Fe, when treated according to Snoek's model, gave values of the diffusion coefficient D over a range of temperatures such that D varied from 10^{-20} to 10^{-13}. When plotted as log D versus $1/T$ (Arrhenius plot), these data gave a straight line that passed close to the points, ranging from $D = 10^{-7}$ to 10^{-5}, obtained by Stanley (3) with a direct conventional technique. Wert actually took the straight line that the two sets of data best fitted as the best representation of the variation of D with T. Similar anelastic work was carried out for N in Fe, but there were then no direct data for comparison.

Recently, data on the diffusion of C in α-Fe at high temperatures have been obtained by Smith (4), who used permeability measurements, and Homan (5), who used a direct tracer technique. These data show that the variation of D with T for C in α-Fe cannot be represented by a single straight line on an Arrhenius plot. Lord (6) has obtained an anelastic point for $D \approx 10^{-9}$, which lies so close to the best line through the other anelastic data that we may say that the anomaly lies at higher temperatures (higher D).

The author is with the Henry Krumb School of Mines, Columbia University, New York, N.Y.

By contrast, new data on N in Fe (6–10) show that a single straight line on an Arrhenius plot represents all the data on bcc Fe from −50 C to the melting point. They show further, by direct comparison at (nearly) the same temperature, that the expression deduced from Snoek's model relating the diffusion coefficients to the anelastic relaxation time yields the same coefficient as that determined by direct experiment.

The situation is then that the diffusion of N in Fe is completely in accord with the standard model, but the analogous diffusion of C shows a clear anomaly. Borg (11) has attempted to explain the C anomaly as a magnetic effect. It undoubtedly occurs in the general vicinity of the Curie temperature, but there are objections to this explanation. The first is that the anomaly does not show up for N, as would be expected, and the second is that the evidence is incomplete because the very-high-temperature data necessary to establish a complete analogy with the magnetic effect observed for diffusion of substitutional species have not been taken.

Another hypothesis, by Homan (5), is that a C-vacancy interaction is responsible for the anomaly, which leads him to the conclusion that a C-vacancy pair diffuses faster than either alone. That this actually is true seems unlikely to me because he pictures the C as occupying the vacancy to form the pair, which means that dissociation must occur before any motion occurs, and that the motion which does occur is individual motion of the C and the vacancy. A more mobile complex might be a C in a divacancy. Although one vacancy would be pinned by the C, the other would be free to move, and the C, being small, might move easily from one to the other. However, these complexes might not be numerous. To restate the matter in other words, the diffusion of C is observed to be anomalously fast at high temperatures, although any interaction with a vacancy would appear to trap the C and slow it down.

Opinions on which sites are occupied by the interstitial impurities and which diffusion path they take have varied from one extreme to the other. The first guess was that the interstitials would prefer the tetrahedral site because it is larger than the octahedral in the perfect lattice. When it was shown that the octahedral site was preferred in two instances (C and N in Fe), it came to be believed that it was preferred in all instances. After the octahedral site was established for C in Fe, the diffusion path was guessed to be an octahedral-octahedral jump. This guess led to apparently good agreement in that system, so it was adopted for all. In a recent paper (12) these matters have been examined systematically by use of elementary strain-energy methods, with the finding that the preferred site and path vary from system to system. It appears that the final decisions on these matters will have to be made separately for each instance.

The question about how to make such decisions then arises. The site can be identified if the sign of the departure from sphericity of the strains about the ellipsoid can be determined. It cannot be determined from internal friction because the asphericity enters as the square. In the instance of Fe, it has been taken as positive because the c/a ratio of martensite is greater than one. Lacking similar phases associated with other bcc metals, we must look for other measurements. Berry and Orehotsky (13) have recently shown how to make anelastic piezoresistance measurements, which may, with the accumulation of sufficient data, lead to a distinction about the occupied sites.

Nowick and Berry (14) have recently attempted a phenomenological analysis of the situation and have obtained conclusions somewhat different from those of Ref 12. Both papers emphasize that a study of the relaxation strength per unit concentration may be helpful, but Nowick and Berry point out that most of the present data are taken on polycrystalline wires of unknown texture. Single-crystal data are necessary to complete the picture.

A distinction between diffusion paths may be more difficult. Condit (15) has derived the following expression for the diffusion coefficient for interstitials that may jump from octahedral to tetrahedral sites and then either to octahedral or other tetrahedral sites:

$$D = \frac{a^2}{48} \frac{\phi_{ot}(\phi_{tt} + \phi_{to})}{(\phi_{to} + \phi_{ot})}$$

where a is the lattice parameter, ϕ_{ij} is the average frequency of jump from sites of type i to sites of type j, and i and j may stand for either o or t. Using this expression Lord (16) has deduced that when the tetrahedral-tetrahedral jumps are negligible, the relation between the anelastic relaxation time and the diffusion coefficient is the same as that for octahedral-octahedral jumps.

For other situations, the matter is more complicated, but, pending the mathematical solution, we can say that it is not impossible that the relation between relaxation time and diffusion coefficient will be altered. The present data for C in Fe do not exclude such a possibility. For systems based on the other bcc metals, there is practically no classical diffusion data for comparison.

To cast one more doubt on the situation, we may note that the best line through the anelastic C data gives a value of D_0 essentially the same as that obtained for N, but distinctly below the value predicted by Wert and Zener (17) from strain-energy considerations. The previous agreement of experiment with this theoretical value has been one of the mainstays of the Snoek model. It appears that other considerations are important, as suggested by Johnson's (18) calculations.

In summary, because of the demonstrated anomaly in the diffusivity of C in Fe, and the lack of sufficient evidence in most other systems, we must say that most questions concerning interstitial impurities in bcc metals remain open.

Acknowledgment.   This work was supported in part by the Office of Naval Research.

References

1   J. L. Snoek, Physica, **8**, 711 (1941)
2   C. A. Wert, Phys Rev, **79**, 601 (1950)
3   J. K. Stanley, Trans AIME, **185**, 752 (1949)
4   R. P. Smith, Trans AIME, **224**, 105 (1962)
5   C. G. Homan, Acta Met, **12**, 1071 (1964), and Chapter 5 in this volume
6   A. E. Lord, Jr., Ph.D. Thesis, Columbia University, 1964
7   H. H. Podgurski and D. Gonzales, unpublished data of United States Steel Corporation Research Laboratory
8   P. Grieveson and E. T. Turkdogan, Trans AIME, **230**, 1604 (1964)
9   P. E. Busby, D. P. Hart and C. Wells, Trans AIME, **206**, 686 (1956)
10   J. D. Fast and M. B. Verrijp, J Iron Steel Inst, **176**, 24 (1954)
11   R. J. Borg, J Appl Phys, **35**, 567 (1964), and Chapter 15 in this volume
12   D. N. Beshers, J Appl Phys, **36**, 291 (1965)
13   B. S. Berry and J. L. Orehotsky, Phil Mag, **9**, 467 (1964)
14   B. S. Berry and A. S. Nowick, Physical Acoustics, Vol 3, edited by W. P. Mason, Academic Press, New York, Chapter 1, to be published
15   R. H. Condit, private communication
16   A. E. Lord, Jr., private communication
17   C. Wert and C. Zener, Phys Rev, **76**, 1169 (1949)
18   R. A. Johnson, G. J. Dienes and A. C. Damask, Acta Met, **12**, 1215 (1964), and Chapter 27 in this volume

PART 4
Chemical and Tracer Diffusion

Chapter 10

Diffusion in Body-Centered Cubic Transition Metals—a Theoretical Critique

David Lazarus

Until recent years, the field of diffusion appeared to have achieved, if not a firm and rigorous scientific basis, at least a satisfactory steady state between experiment and theory. By use of radio-isotopes of high purity, combined with careful sectioning techniques, it had become possible to make reproducible measurements of diffusion coefficients for a large number of interesting systems. With improved techniques, many of the "spectacular" results reported two and three decades ago disappeared, and a new set of precise data became gradually accepted as the norm. The original theoretical speculations relating to various diffusion mechanisms were somewhat expanded and correlated with the new data in a satisfactorily consistent manner, so that the lattice vacancy emerged as the sole defect responsible for bulk diffusion in almost all pure monatomic materials. Interstitials appeared to be important only for a few obvious instances of impurity diffusion in bcc and diamond cubic substances, and for diffusion in Ag halides. Complex mechanisms that had been suggested for diffusion, such as crowdions, rings and relaxions, were no longer invoked with much seriousness. Simple semi-empirical rules correlating values of diffusion coefficients and activation energies with melting temperatures, latent heats of fusion and vaporization, and elastic properties gave such extraordinary agreement with experimental values that they achieved the status of physical "laws."

This pleasant situation has been disturbed, if not positively destroyed, by the recent results obtained on some of the bcc refractory metals, for which the diffusion coefficients apparently do not conform to the established "laws." We now have "normal" bcc metals, such as Fe, Cb and Mo, and "anomalous" bcc metals, such as Ti, Zr and U. Investigators are again speculating, sometimes a bit wildly, on new diffusion mechanisms for the anomalous metals. In the present paper, an attempt will be made

The author is with the Department of Physics and Materials Research Laboratory, University of Illinois, Urbana, Ill.

to establish some ground rules for this speculation, by delineation of those aspects of diffusion theory that are, or at least ought to be, generally acceptable, and those that are not, in fact, fully supportable.

Temperature Dependence of Self-Diffusion

In "normal" solids, the diffusion coefficient is invariably found experimentally to vary with temperature in accordance with the simple Arrhenius relation

$$D = D_0 \exp (-Q/RT) \tag{1}$$

where D_0 is a frequency factor, Q is the activation energy, R is the gas constant, and T is the absolute temperature. D_0 and Q are temperature independent. In addition, as may be seen from the compilation of self-diffusion coefficients in Tables 1 and 2, "normal" values of D_0 and Q lie generally in a fairly restricted range:

$$D_0 \approx 1 \text{ cm}^2/\text{sec (within a factor of 10)}$$
$$Q \approx 33 \times T_m \text{ (within 10\%)} \tag{2}$$

where T_m is the absolute temperature of the melting point. The "anomalous" solids, on the other hand, show strikingly different values for D_0 and Q, as given in Table 2. Values for the frequency factor and activation energy are invariably much smaller than those indicated by Eq 2, and, worse yet, as indicated in Fig. 1 and 2, the data usually do not even conform to Eq 1 with constant D_0 and Q. Before a judgment is made about whether or not these instances are truly anomalous, it is useful to review the theoretical basis for Eq 1.

Table 1. Coefficients of Self-Diffusion in Close-Packed Metals

Metal	D_0, cm²/sec	Q, kcal/mole	T_m, °K	Q/T_m
Ag...	0.40	44.1	1233	35.6
Au...	0.09	41.7	1336	31.2
Cu...	0.20	47.1	1356	34.7
Zn...	0.13	21.8	692	31.5
Cd...	0.10	19.7	594	33.2
Al...	1.3	35.5	933	35.9
Mg...	1.0	32.2	924	34.9

Table 2. Coefficients of Self-Diffusion in bcc Transition Metals

Metal	D_0, cm²/sec	Q, kcal/mole	T_m, °K	Q/T_m
Fe.........	0.5	60.4	1805	33.4
Cr..........	0.3	73.2	2160	33.9
Cb.........	1.3	95	2738	34.5
Mo.........	0.1	92.2	2895	31.8
Ti..........	10^{-6} to 0.1	31 to 49	1941	16.0 to 25.3
Zr..........	10^{-5} to 0.2	22 to 47	2130	10.3 to 22.0
U..........	$\sim 2 \times 10^{-3}$	~ 28.5	1420	20.1
V..........	0.35, 130	72.5, 92.5	2170	33.4, 42.5
Ta.........	2.0	110	3270	33.6
W..........	10^7	136	3640	37.4

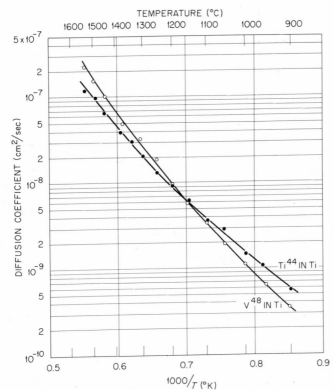

Fig. 1. Diffusion in Ti (data from Lundy)

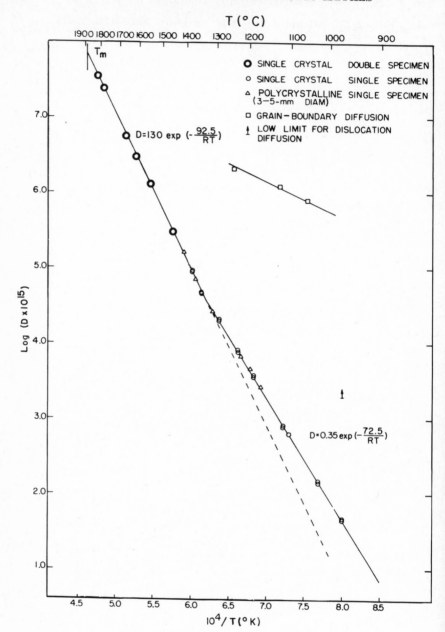

Fig. 2. Diffusion in V (data from Peart)

Justification for Eq 1 is derived from models based on the familiar Wigner-Eyering theory of absolute reaction rates. The model most frequently used in diffusion studies is that first introduced by Zener and Wert (1). In this formulation, the diffusion coefficient is expressed as a product

$$D = \gamma a^2 p_d \nu_j \tag{3}$$

where γ is a numerical constant of about unity, a is the lattice parameter, p_d is the probability that a defect exists adjacent to a diffusing atom if required for jump to occur, and ν_j is the jump frequency. If the necessary defects are randomly distributed throughout the lattice in thermal equilibrium, then p_d is just equal to the relative concentration of defects and is given rigorously by

$$p_d = \exp\left(-\Delta G_f / RT\right) \tag{4}$$

where ΔG_f is the increment in Gibbs free energy required to form a mole of defects.

In the Zener-Wert treatment, the jump frequency ν_j is derived from a considerably simplified model for the jump process itself. The diffusional jump is considered to be equivalent to the *reversible* motion of an atom across a potential barrier of height W, in thermal equilibrium, while the atom, vibrating with a constant frequency ν_0, is *constrained to a plane perpendicular to the direction of motion*. In this special instance, the barrier height W is simply the isothermal, isobaric work required for traversal and is equatable to an increment in Gibbs free energy ΔG_m. Thus

$$\nu_j = \nu_0 \exp\left[-(\Delta G_m)/RT\right] \tag{5}$$

Combining Eq 3, 4 and 5, we obtain

$$D = \gamma a^2 \nu_0 \exp\left[-(\Delta G_f + \Delta G_m)/RT\right] \tag{6}$$

and, using the thermodynamic identity $\Delta G = \Delta H - T\,\Delta S$ relating the Gibbs free energy to the enthalpy H and entropy S, we obtain

$$D = \gamma a^2 \nu_0 \exp\left[(\Delta S_f + \Delta S_m)/R\right] \exp\left[-(\Delta H_f + \Delta H_m)/RT\right] \tag{7}$$

From comparison of Eq 1 and 7, we may make the obvious identifications

$$\begin{aligned} D_0 &= \gamma a^2 \nu_0 \exp\left[(\Delta S_f + \Delta S_m)/R\right] \\ Q &= (\Delta H_f + \Delta H_m) \end{aligned} \tag{8}$$

The frequency term ν_0 is usually taken as equal to the Debye frequency, without much justification. The two entropic terms, by their nature, would be positive for a vacancy or interstitial mechanism, because the presence of the defect, as well as the jump, clearly disorders the lattice. With the further assumption that *all* the free-energy change is associated simply with an elastic strain of the lattice, the entropy terms can be derived explicitly and shown to be proportional to the product of the enthalpy and the temperature derivative of the elastic shear modulus, so that

$$D_0 = \gamma a^2 \nu_0 \exp (\lambda \beta Q / T_m) \tag{9}$$

where λ is an empirical constant equal to $+0.55$ for fcc lattices and unity for bcc lattices, and $\beta = d \log \mu / d(T/T_m)$ is the experimentally determined temperature derivative of the shear modulus. Equation 9 gives remarkable agreement with observed values of D_0 for all "normal" solids.

It should be noted, however, that this model does *not* show that D_0 and Q should, of necessity, be temperature independent. Instead, because we may only write as thermodynamic identity

$$(\partial \Delta H / \partial T) = T(\partial \Delta S / \partial T) \tag{10}$$

if Q is, in fact, temperature dependent, ΔS must also be temperature dependent, according to Eq 10. The slope of the Arrhenius plot, however, always gives ΔH at that particular temperature.

The Zener-Wert model, although it can be successfully applied to diffusion, deals with a particular simplified system and hence cannot be considered as rigorous. A far more rigorous approach, still by use of reaction-rate theory, has been given by Vineyard (2). In Vineyard's treatment, the entire crystal, with $N/3$ atoms, is considered as a many-body system with N degrees of freedom, $x_1 \ldots x_N$, with a mass m_j associated with each x_j. The diffusional jump is considered as a transition in thermal equilibrium between two adjacent stable states separated by a saddle point in the N-dimensional configuration space of coordinates $y_j = x_j m_j^{1/2}$. The average diffusional jump frequency is then simply the ratio of the number of points in the configurational space corresponding to states at the saddle point to the number corresponding to ground states, and is rigorously derivable in terms of the ratio of the partition functions for the saddle point and ground state. The partition functions may be evaluated explicitly if it is further assumed that the N-dimensional potential energies can be properly represented, by use of the theory of small vibrations, by expansion only to second order in the normal coordinates and normal frequencies. The jump frequency in Eq 3 is then given by

$$\nu_j = \nu^* \exp\left[-(\varphi_S - \varphi_G)/RT\right] \tag{11}$$

in which φ_S and φ_G are the molar potential energies of the entire crystal and are characteristic of the saddle and ground configurations, respectively. The frequency term ν^*, rather than being simply equatable with the Debye frequency, here has the form

$$\nu^* = \left(\prod_{j=1}^{N} \nu_j\right) \Big/ \left(\prod_{j=1}^{N-1} \nu_j'\right) \tag{12}$$

where the ν_j are the N normal frequencies of the system in the ground-state configuration, and the ν_j' are the $N-1$ normal frequencies of the system in the saddle-point configuration, omitting the one mode corresponding to the direction of motion across the saddle point. If the normal mode spectrum is not disturbed by the large configurational change associated with the jump, then $\nu_j = \nu_j'$, and $\nu^* = \nu_N$, the highest normal frequency of the system of the ground state.

This model can be recast in the Zener-Wert form of Eq 7, where the motional entropy and enthalpy enter explicitly, by taking a constrained ground state of $N-1$ degrees of freedom. The free-energy term is then derived from the ratio of the partition functions of the constrained ground and saddle-point configurations, in a manner quite analogous to the previous simple treatment. A new frequency factor, $\nu_0 = \nu^* \exp(+\Delta S_m/R)$, now enters, in which the motional entropy is given explicitly by

$$\Delta S_m = R \log\left(\prod_{j=1}^{N-1} \nu_j^0\right) \Big/ \left(\prod_{j=1}^{N-1} \nu_j'\right) \tag{13}$$

where the ν_j^0 are the $N-1$ normal frequencies of the constrained ground state. This many-body treatment thus can give essentially the same thermodynamic functions as the simpler treatment, and is somewhat more appealing, because to define free energies we need now omit only one out of perhaps 10^{22} degrees of freedom rather than one out of three.

Despite the considerable success and empirical justification of the reaction-rate model for diffusion, valid questions about the basic assumptions employed still remain, in particular:

1. The jump is assumed to result entirely from thermal activation; quantum effects are ignored. Such effects are not expected to be large for

diffusion of atoms larger than H or He, but the problem has not been considered explicitly, except in perturbation theory (3).

2. The process is considered basically reversible, by fiat in the Zener-Wert treatment and by use of the harmonic approximation in Vineyard's model, despite the fact that diffusion is clearly an irreversible process. Attempts to date to derive the equations from an *a priori* irreversible model have been largely unsuccessful (4).

3. The assumption of thermal equilibrium at all stages of the jump implies that the lifetime of the excited state and all intermediate states must be long in comparison with the thermal relaxation time of an appreciable portion of the lattice, so that it is meaningful to ascribe thermodynamic properties to such states. This assumption has never been tested by direct experiment. There is some indirect evidence from pre-Mössbauer nuclear resonant absorption studies that, at least for atoms with 10 ev of energy, the relaxation time is much shorter than 10^{-13} sec (5).

4. There is no consideration in the models of the possibility of changes in electronic configuration during jump; by implication, the atom at the saddle point is assumed to be electronically indistinguishable from that in the ground state. Such nonthermal effects might conceivably be of some importance, particularly for such instances as bcc transition elements that have unfilled d-shells, but have never been considered. Moreover, evidence for such effects is very real because all of these substances transform to close-packed phases at room temperature when compressed hydrostatically and at volume changes corresponding to changes in nearest-neighbor distance that are no larger than those associated with a diffusional jump.

In summary, we may make the following general statements regarding the theoretical basis for interpretation of D_0 and Q for self-diffusion:

1. No completely rigorous treatment of the diffusional jump has been thus far proposed, but the simple reaction-rate model has been largely substantiated by the many-body treatment.

2. The reaction-rate model may ignore some important electronic effects, particularly for bcc transition metals, so that these may not, in fact, be treatable on the same basis as the fcc solids.

3. The reaction-rate model does not prove that D_0 and Q must be temperature independent, but merely states that the temperature dependence of the entropy and enthalpy must be related. However, to the extent that the jump is reversible and the harmonic approximation is valid, there are no terms that would, in fact, give rise to any appreciable variation in D_0 and Q for self-diffusion with temperature, in the absence of phase changes.

4. The reaction-rate model gives some justification for values of D_0 near unity, but this is by no means rigorous. However, values of D_0 of about 10^{-5} cm²/sec seem clearly incompatible with the model, because this would require excessively small values for the frequency ν^* and could arise only from a major perturbation of the frequency spectrum of the whole solid during the jump, which appears unlikely.

5. The reaction-rate model provides no justification for the validity of Eq 2, which relates the activation energy and the melting temperature, and the great success of this empirical expression remains obscure. In fact, the model makes no prediction about the magnitude of Q, but merely identifies the measured Q with the sum of the enthalpy changes for formation and motion of defects. If the enthalpy is temperature independent, the measured Q should then be equatable with the change in free energy for diffusion at the absolute zero, as calculated by atomistic models.

Pressure Dependence of Diffusion

Acceptance of the reaction-rate model to describe the temperature dependence provides a simple interpretation of the pressure dependence of the diffusion rate. Because the differential of the Gibbs free energy can be written as

$$dG = V\,dP - S\,dT \tag{14}$$

it follows from Eq 6 that

$$(\partial \ln D/\partial P)_T = -\Delta V/RT + (\partial \ln \gamma a^2 \nu_0/\partial P)_T \tag{15}$$

The activation volume ΔV can be identified as the sum of the molar volumes of formation and motion of defects, $\Delta V = \Delta V_f + \Delta V_m$, in exactly the same manner that Q can be identified with the sum of the enthalpies. The second term on the right in Eq 15 is expected to be small.

There is a paucity of data for pressure effects on self-diffusion for "normal" and "anomalous" metals. However, for all "normal" metals, the measured value of ΔV is positive, and about one half to one molar volume, consistent with a relaxed vacancy mechanism. Preliminary results for the only "anomalous" metals studied are shown in Fig. 3. Here the diffusion coefficient appears to *increase* with pressure, but not exponentially, and then perhaps to decrease. These data are completely inconsistent with Eq 15 in terms of any well-understood mechanism for diffusion, and it is not possible to calculate an activation volume. Indeed, the behavior is so inconsistent that it may be possible to conclude that

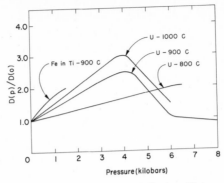

*Fig. 3. Anomalous pressure dependence of diffusion. Values for U are pre-
liminary data of Adda; values for Fe in Ti are preliminary data of Peart.*

under the conditions of the experiment (in a high-pressure A atmosphere),
clearly something *besides* pure thermally activated bulk diffusion must
have been taking place. High-pressure diffusion measurements furnish
valuable information, and this field should be pursued more vigorously.

Impurity Diffusion

Studies of diffusion of impurities, particularly in very small tracer
amounts in an otherwise pure matrix, have provided considerable insight
into the details of the diffusion process. Analysis of such results is more
complicated than that for self-diffusion, because the impurity may have
a different affinity for defects, as well as a different potential barrier for
jump. The impurity atom will not move with the essentially random
motion of the solvent atom, because of possible correlations between
successive jumps. Such correlations dictate addition of a factor f in Eq 3
to take account of the nonrandomness of the jumps of the impurity.
Moreover, values of Q for impurity diffusion cannot be equated simply
with $\Delta H_f + \Delta H_m$, as in Eq 8, because f will normally be temperature
dependent and because

$$Q = R(\partial \ln D/\partial T^{-1})_P = -(\Delta H_f + \Delta H_m) + R(\partial \ln \gamma a^2 \nu_0 f/\partial T^{-1})_P \quad (16)$$

and the second term on the right may be appreciable.

Approximate treatments of the correlation factor f have been given
by Lidiard and Le Claire (6) and by Manning (7), among others. In all
these, a highly approximate model is employed in which the interaction
between the defect and impurity is expressed in terms of a simple binding
energy. The interaction affects only the motion of the solute atom and its

immediate solvent neighbors, by modification of a few local frequency terms. Atoms that tend to attract defects are shown to diffuse faster than solvent atoms, but the actual diffusion coefficient depends strongly on the rate of interchange of the *solvent* atoms with the defects, so that solvent and solute diffusion rates must be closely correlated. For impurities in "normal" metals, the binding energies between solutes and defects appear to be small, and solute diffusion rates are never more than an order of magnitude larger than the rate of self-diffusion of the solvent. However, if the solute repels the defect, the impurity diffusion rate can be much smaller than the self-diffusion coefficient of the solvent, consistent with experiment.

Here again, measurements of impurity diffusion in "anomalous" metals give unusual results. As shown in Fig. 4, apparently Ni and Co diffuse in Ti at rates two full orders of magnitude faster than the rate of self-

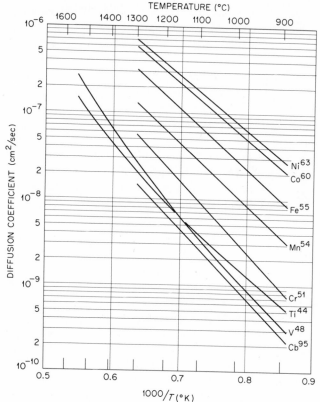

Fig. 4. Impurity diffusion in Ti (data from Peart, Graham and Tomlin)

diffusion. Because of correlation effects, such behavior could only result for volume diffusion if there were an exceedingly large binding energy between the defects and solutes, about 0.5 ev or greater. Such large inter-action energies do not seem probable in metals, at least in "normal" metals, because the conduction electrons should effectively screen the potential perturbation created by the presence of the impurity. However, because these elements have unfilled d-shells, there is a possibility that impurities are screened by bound d-states, rather than by the conduction electrons, and the model that gives satisfactory results for "normal" metals (8) may be completely inappropriate to the transition metals. Further theoretical work is required before these instances can be considered as truly anomalous.

Mass Dependence of Diffusion

According to the detailed reaction-rate model of Vineyard (2), the diffusion coefficient should depend inversely on the square root of the *effective mass* of the tracer, rather than on its actual mass. Moreover, the mass dependence will be reduced by correlation effects (9), for instances of impurity diffusion.

The only data available for mass dependence of diffusion in "normal" metals are for slow-diffusing impurities, Fe in Cu and Ag (9), and for self-diffusion (10) in Pd. In both these instances, the data are in excellent agreement with the reaction-rate model and provide exceedingly strong support for the validity of the vacancy mechanism for diffusion. The one instance reported (11) for "anomalous" metals, Fe in Ti, involved an exceptionally fast-diffusing impurity. The reported total lack of a mass dependence is thus in no way inconsistent with a simple vacancy model because the effect would be expected to be negated by the large correlation effects.

Other Considerations

Another effect that has received surprisingly little theoretical consideration may be noted by comparing self-diffusion coefficients for "normal" and "anomalous" metals on a relative temperature scale, as shown in Fig. 5 and 6. Here the "anomalous" metals show a new and striking phenomenon. Not only are the activation energies far too low relative to the empirical rule $Q \approx 33T_m$, but the self-diffusion coefficients for U, Zr and Ti are one to two orders of magnitude higher than those for normal metals! This effect is particularly noticeable for values of self-diffusion coefficients near the melting point, where possible short-circuiting effects

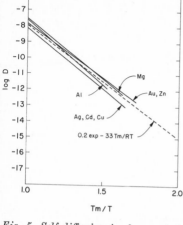

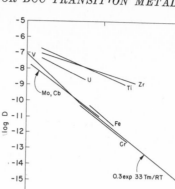

Fig. 5. Self-diffusion in close-packed metals as a function of relative temperature. The solid lines cover the range of the reported data.

Fig. 6. Self-diffusion in bcc transition metals as a function of relative temperature. The solid lines cover the range of the reported data.

might presumably be negligible. Indeed, the values of the diffusion coefficients for the "anomalous" bcc metals are nearly the same as those for liquids.

Unfortunately there are no firm theoretical models relating to the value of the diffusion coefficient itself. However, because the mechanical properties of these exceptional materials show no spectacular high-temperature effects, this behavior seems quite inexplicable on any simple model. Theoretical consideration of the values of diffusivity, rather than of the derived D_0's and Q's, may prove a fertile ground for future study.

The only other instances known where such enormous diffusion coefficients are commonplace is for diffusion of interstitial impurities in bcc metals, as shown in Fig. 7. It is therefore tempting to associate the anomalous diffusional behavior in the "anomalous" bcc transition metals with the presence of interstitial impurities. In this connection, it is interesting to note, as shown in Table 3, that there is a striking correlation between the high-temperature solubility and stability of O and N in the bcc transition metals and the observed anomalous diffusional behavior. Indeed, the solubilities of atmospheric gases are so large and the vapor pressures so small in Ti and Zr, that it is clear that these well-known "getters" could *never* really have been previously studied in the absence of considerable amounts of interstitial impurities! Although such data are lacking for γ-U, the noted high-temperature stability of the

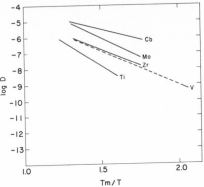

Fig. 7. Diffusion of interstitials in bcc metals

oxide is suggestive of the fact that it, too, may be classed with Ti and Zr. Tentative models based on the presence of interstitial impurities have been advanced (12), but these require considerable further theoretical development before they can provide an unambiguous explanation for all the observed phenomena.

It should be pointed out that the basic validity of the vacancy mechanism for diffusion has not, in fact, yet been established for any of the bcc transition metals. For fcc metals the validity of the mechanism rests not on the basic atomistic theory, which is subject to considerable quantitative uncertainties, but mostly on the following specific observations:

1. The fact that a specimen can be completely homogenized by diffusion shows that there must be some bulk diffusion mechanism.

Table 3. O and N in bcc Metals

Metal	Solubility, at. %	Temp, °K	Remarks
Ti.......	0.1	1200	VP $< 10^{-5}$ mm at 1800 K
	5	1800	MP oxide $\gg$ MP metal
Zr.......	0.1	900	VP $< 10^{-5}$ mm at 1800 K
	10	1900	MP oxide $\gg$ MP metal
U........	0.05	1100–1400	MP oxide $\gg$ MP metal
V........	2	0–1600	MP oxide $\approx$ MP metal
Cb	....	1000	MP oxide $\ll$ MP metal
	10	1400	
Mo......	0.1	2000	VP $\gg 10^{-3}$ mm at 1800 K
			MP oxide $\ll$ MP metal
Cr.......	$\sim$0	1200	MP oxide $\ll$ MP metal
	$<0.1\%$?	1900	

2. Observation of a Kirkendall effect shows that the basic bulk-diffusion mechanism must involve defects that can be created or annihilated locally in the lattice, such as vacancies or interstitialcies.

3. Observation of the mass dependence of diffusion shows that nearly all of the kinetic energy in a single elementary diffusion jump is carried by a single atom.

Only the vacancy mechanism is consistent with all three observations. To date, only the validity of 1 and 2 have been established for either the "normal" or the "anomalous" bcc transition metals. Measurement of the mass dependence for self-diffusion or for a slow-diffusing impurity is essential before the vacancy mechanism can be completely established or negated.

Conclusions

The diffusional behavior of the bcc transition metals has been compared with basic theoretical models to determine which of the observed effects can be considered truly anomalous. The following facts appear to be inconsistent with theory, at least for a simple vacancy mechanism:

1. Excessively small or excessively large values of the frequency factor D_0, as found in Ti, Zr, U, and W.

2. Large variations of D_0 and Q with temperature, as found for Ti, Zr, and U.

3. Observed increases in diffusion coefficients with hydrostatic pressure.

4. Large differences between rates of diffusion of fast-diffusing solute atoms and solvent atoms.

However, the basic validity of the theoretical models has not yet been established for the bcc transition metals. In particular, the presence of unfilled d-shells gives at least the possibility that the reaction-rate theory may have to be considerably modified to account for possible changes in electronic configuration of atoms during diffusion, and theories of impurity diffusion may have to take account of possible screening by bound states. In addition, the mass dependence of diffusion must be measured for the bcc metals before the vacancy mechanism can be clearly established.

Finally, it is noted that the strikingly large values observed for self-diffusion at high temperatures correlate strongly with the observed large solubility and low vapor pressures for dissolved atmospheric gases in Ti, Zr, and possibly U, so that the reported "anomalous" diffusional behavior in these elements may not be truly characteristic of the pure materials.

Acknowledgment. This work was supported in part by the U. S. Atomic Energy Commission under Contract AT (11-1)-1198.

References

1   C. Wert and C. Zener, Phys Rev, **76,** 1169 (1949)
2   G. Vineyard, J Phys Chem Solids, **3,** 121 (1957)
3   E. Wigner, Phys Rev, **40,** 749 (1932)
4   I. Prigogine and T. Bak, J Chem Phys, **31,** 1360 (1959)
5   H. Lipkin, private communication
6   A. Lidiard and A. Le Claire, Phil Mag, **1,** 518 (1956)
7   J. Manning, Phys Rev, **116,** 819 (1959)
8   D. Lazarus, Phys Rev, **93,** 973 (1954); A. Le Claire, Phil Mag, **7,** 141 (1962)
9   J. Mullen, Phys Rev, **121,** 1649 (1961)
10   N. Peterson, Phys Rev, in press
11   G. Gibbs, Thesis, University of Reading, 1961
12   G. Kidson, Can J Phys, **41,** 1563 (1963)

Chapter 11
The Isotope Effect in Sodium Self-Diffusion

L. W. BARR AND J. N. MUNDY

The diffusion coefficient of atoms moving in a solid by a series of random jumps on an isotropic lattice is

$$D = \Gamma r^2 f / 6 \tag{1}$$

where Γ is the number of jumps per second, r is the jump distance, and f is the correlation factor introduced by Bardeen and Herring (1) to take into account the fact that atoms jumping by many defect mechanisms do not move at random although the defect does. An obvious example is diffusion by a vacancy mechanism. Discussions of methods for calculating f for different mechanisms and lattices and numerical values are given in several places (2, 3).

If f can be determined, a comparison with the calculated values allows the mechanism to be identified. Unfortunately Γ cannot be calculated with sufficient accuracy to enable f to be obtained from measurements of D alone; less direct methods must be sought.

The first method suggested uses the property that although atomic jumps are correlated, the defect movements are not. Thus, if a comparison is made between the defect mobility and the diffusion coefficient, f can be determined. In the instance of an ionic conductor, the defect mobility can be determined from the electrical conductivity; the diffusion coefficient, from radio-tracer measurements. Several instances of such measurements can be found in the literature (3, 4, 5). One of particular interest to us is the demonstration that, in the instance of NaCl, the cation diffusion is by vacancies, a conclusion substantiating earlier experiments on doped material (6).

This technique has the limitation of being applicable only to ionic conductors, and the sole method so far suggested for determining f in the general instance is that of Schoen (7). Schoen pointed out that for two

The authors are with the Solid State Physics Division, Atomic Energy Research Establishment, Harwell, England.

isotopes of the same element, α and β, the ratio of the vibrational frequencies is

$$\nu^\alpha/\nu^\beta = \omega^\alpha/\omega^\beta = (m^\beta/m^\alpha)^{1/2} \qquad (2)$$

where the w's are the jump frequencies and the m's are the atomic masses. Using this equation and the following expression for f

$$f = U/(\omega_2{}^\alpha + U) \qquad (3)$$

where w_2 is the jump frequency with which the tracer, whose diffusion is being studied, exchanges with the defect and U contains the jump frequencies for the exchange of the defect with the other atoms of the crystal, leads directly to Schoen's equation (8)

$$[(D^\alpha/D^\beta) - 1] = f[(m^\beta/m^\alpha)^{1/2} - 1] \qquad (4)$$

It should be noted that f can be written in the form of Eq 3 not only for vacancy diffusion (9) but also interstitialcy diffusion (10). Equation 4 thus applies to self-diffusion and impurity diffusion by vacancies and interstitialcies in all systems having at least twofold rotational symmetry about the jump direction of the diffusing atom (11). For instances where this symmetry condition does not apply, for example when solvent diffusion occurs by means of impurity-vacancy pairs, a more general equation than Eq 4 must be used (8).

Equation 2 applies to mechanisms involving only one atom jumping. When diffusion involves the simultaneous motion of a number of atoms (two in the instance of interstitialcies, four in the instance of four-atom ring diffusion), a proposed extension (12) of Eq 2 is

$$\omega_2{}^\alpha/\omega_2{}^\beta = \{[m^\beta + (n - 1)m]/[m^\alpha + (n - 1)m]\}^{1/2} \qquad (5)$$

where m is the average mass of the nontracer atoms and n is the total number of atoms involved.

The instance in which only one atom moves its position during the diffusion step but several atoms are involved during the motion has been discussed by Mullen (13). He shows that in this instance the general form of Eq 4 can be retained by introducing another factor on the right side. This equation is then

$$[(D^\alpha/D^\beta) - 1] = \Delta K f[(m^\beta/m^\alpha)^{1/2} - 1] \qquad (6)$$

where ΔK has the physical significance of being the fraction of the total translational kinetic energy, associated with the crossing of the saddle point of the potential energy barrier, which is possessed by the diffusing atom. Obviously a knowledge of ΔK would give information on intimate details of the diffusion process.

In principle, when ΔK is one, Eq 4 allows the mechanism of self-diffusion to be determined. The right side of Eq 4 can take a set of values, one for each mechanism; thus comparison with the experimentally measured left side decides the mechanism.

Use of Eq 4 in this way depends on the correctness of Eq 2 and 5 and on ΔK being one. These assumptions can only be checked by studying the isotope effect for systems for which the mechanism of self-diffusion is established. Such systems are few. Unfortunately verification of these equations in any particular instance does not establish their truth in general; the most that can be inferred is the likelihood of their holding in similar materials.

In this paper we are concerned with the application of Eq 2 and 6 to measurements of Na self-diffusion and a discussion of the results obtained. Because of these results, similar self-diffusion measurements in NaCl will be mentioned briefly.

Experimental Method

Two isotopes of Na are particularly convenient for isotope-effect measurements. The isotopes, Na^{22} and Na^{24}, have the largest mass difference of any radio-isotopes readily available. In addition, although they both emit γ rays of fairly similar energy, they have markedly dissimilar half-lives (Na^{24}, 15 hr; Na^{22} 2.6 yr) and thus the half-life method of discrimination (8) can be used in determinations of their relative concentration. This is of paramount importance.

In Table 1 are listed f's and calculated values of the right side of Eq 4 for various mechanisms in the NaCl and the Na (bcc) lattices. The theoretical values of $[(D^{\alpha}/D^{\beta}) - 1]$ show the smallness of the isotope effect even in this favorable instance.

For this reason isotope effects are best measured by diffusing both isotopes simultaneously. This procedure eliminates errors arising from specimen preparation and time and temperature of anneal. Additionally, if a thin surface layer of tracer is used, with the well-established sectioning technique for measuring D, the isotope effect can be determined without any measurement of the penetration distance (8). This latter feature is easily seen from the appropriate solution of the diffusion equation

$$C_x{}^{\alpha} = C_0{}^{\alpha} \exp \left(-x^2/4D_{\alpha}t \right) \tag{7}$$

where the C's are the specific activities at penetration x and t is the anneal time. Thus for both isotopes

$$\ln C_x{}^\alpha/C_x{}^\beta = \text{constant} - \ln C_x{}^\alpha[(D^\alpha/D^\beta) - 1] \qquad (8)$$

and a plot of $\ln C_x{}^\alpha/C_x{}^\beta$ against $\ln C_x{}^\alpha$ gives the left side of Eq 4 directly. From this equation it is clear that only counting and weighing of the collected material from each section are necessary. This considerable simplification of the experimental problem requires only the determination of the specific activity of each isotope in the presence of the other. Thus, the greatly differing half-lives of the isotopes are of such importance.

The method used in this work to obtain the ratio of the specific activities of the isotopes involves counting the γ rays emitted by both isotopes together several times, then allowing sufficient time (about 10 Na^{24} half-lives) for the Na^{24} to decay to negligible proportions, and then recounting to obtain the Na^{22} specific activity. Subtraction of the Na^{22} count from each count of Na^{24} plus Na^{22} gives a value of the Na^{24} activity. Each set of Na^{24} and Na^{22} counts is used to give a measure of the isotope effect. Thus each experiment yields several determinations of $[(D^\alpha/D^\beta) - 1]$.

The experimental arrangements for NaCl have been indicated elsewhere (8).

Realization of the thin-surface-layer boundary condition for Na metal is complicated by handling problems, particularly the rapid oxidation of Na. Because of the advantage in using this boundary condition, methods were devised to make it possible. Briefly, the technique developed involves preparing a clean oxide-free surface on a cast cylinder of Na contained in a hand microtome. This is done by sectioning the Na under a high vacuum by a remote-controlled razor. The mixture of Na isotopes is then deposited on the clean surface by vacuum evaporation. Na isotopes are more readily obtained and conveniently handled as their chlorides, and the metal isotopes are prepared by isotopic exchange. This is done, *in situ*, by melting the Na halides and Na metal together on the evaporating electrode under an inert atmosphere. This step is completed before the surface-preparation cut.

After the tracer deposition, the microtome is sealed with an O-ring and tightly fitting screw cap and transferred for the diffusion anneal to an oil bath controlled to ± 0.05 C. Subsequent sectioning is done in a dry box. The moderate oxidation that occurs after each cut allows the grain size, usually ~ 4 mm, to be observed. The sections are dissolved in dilute HCl and counted in a well-type scintillation counter. Drying the solution subsequently allows the section weight to be measured.

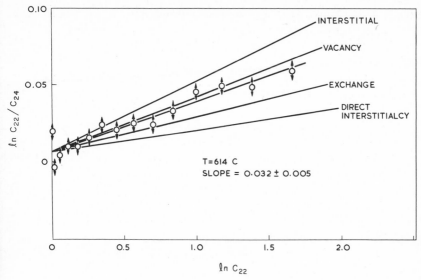

Fig. 1. Na²² and Na²⁴ diffusion in NaCl

Results

Isotope Effect in NaCl.   Figure 1 shows a plot of Eq 8 for NaCl and theoretical lines for the various mechanisms indicated. It is clear that diffusion in NaCl is by vacancies and that Eq 2 and 4 are closely obeyed. Because the vacancy mechanism of diffusion in NaCl was never seriously in doubt, the result is more strictly a verification of Eq 2 than a determination of f.

Isotope Effect in Na Metal.   The plots of ln C against x^2 obtained in this work are accurately linear. The only deviation, the point corresponding to the first section tends to lie high, indicates slight oxide blocking at the surface.

Figure 2 shows the values of D obtained in this work versus reciprocal of the absolute temperature and the earlier measurements of Nachtrieb et al. (14). The agreement between the two sets of measurements is excellent, particularly at the higher temperatures. This agreement is especially gratifying because different experimental conditions were used by Nachtrieb and his co-workers, namely two interdiffusing semi-infinite blocks.

The equation of the straight line shown in Fig. 2 is

$$D = 0.160 \pm 0.015 \exp\left[(-10,150 \pm 60)/RT\right]$$

This is to be compared with Nachtrieb's result of

$$D = 0.242 \exp\left[(-10{,}450 \pm 300)/RT\right]$$

It is interesting to note that if a line is fitted to Nachtrieb's high-temperature results only, the result

$$D = 0.14 \pm 0.03 \exp\left[(-10{,}070 \pm 140)/RT\right]$$

is obtained. It is clear from this that the slight discrepancy between Nachtrieb's best value and ours lies in the ice-point measurements. We hope to do more experiments between room temperature and about -30 C to resolve this.

The solid squares in Fig. 2 are results for which isotope-effect measurements were also made. A typical plot, using Eq 8, is shown in Fig. 3. Each of the three isotope-effect measurements yielded six determinations of

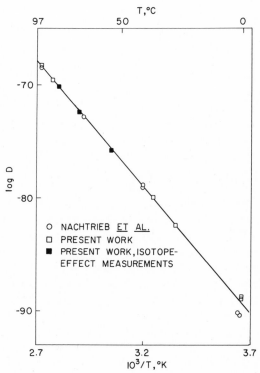

Fig. 2. D versus reciprocal absolute temperature for Na self-diffusion

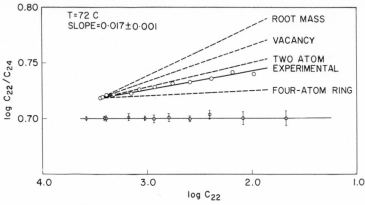

Fig. 3. Na^{24} and Na^{22} diffusion in Na

$[(D^\alpha/D^\beta) - 1]$. We consider that the best value for $[(D^\alpha/D^\beta) - 1]$ is

$$[(D^\alpha/D^\beta) - 1] = 0.016 \pm 0.002$$

and can find no sign of any variation of this result with temperature. This value is to be compared with the calculated values tabulated in Table 1 for Na metal.

Also shown in Fig. 3 is a line obtained by measuring the isotopic ratio on the stock solution deposited on the Na surface. The errors indicated are the actual experimental limits obtained by repeated counting. This line is, in effect, a zero line and verifies that our techniques for measuring isotopic ratios are satisfactory and independent of counting rate.

Discussion

A straightforward application of Eq 4 to the experimental data, that is, assuming ΔK equal to one, suggests that diffusion in Na is by interstitialcies. Interpretation of the data in this way has the merit of preserving Eq 4 and 5 but only at the expense of conflicting with some recent experimental evidence suggestive of a vacancy mechanism.

Because the maximum possible value of both f and ΔK is one, no mechanism having a slope lower than the experimental line in Fig. 3 can occur. The possibility of four-atom and higher rings is thus eliminated. Interstitial diffusion can almost certainly be eliminated by the small value of the isotope effect when taken in conjunction with the fact that all instances of interstitial diffusion so far investigated obey Eq 4 closely, with f equal to one (8).

Acceptance of the possibility of interstitialcy diffusion immediately raises the question of interstitial sites in bcc metals. This question has recently been extensively discussed, for α-Fe, by Johnson (15). Much of his treatment is relevant to Na.

The two obvious simple interstitial sites are the octahedral site in the center of each cube face and the tetrahedral sites, of which there are four on each cube face. The latter are the favored positions from the size point of view.

For the octahedral interstitials there are two interstitialcy jumps, first, the direct interstitialcy through the cube center to the site on the opposite face and, second, the indirect jump through the center and then at right angles to one of the octahedral sites on the other four faces. The direct interstitialcy resembles the crowdion mechanism of diffusion originally proposed for Na (16) and is a linear chain with zero correlation factor. The indirect interstitialcy has a correlation factor of one, hence the values given in Table 1.

In the instance of interstitialcy diffusion from tetrahedral sites, there are a large number of possible jumps, each with its appropriate correlation factor. These have not been calculated rigorously but appear to lie between 0.6 and 1.

The great difficulty in visualizing such interstitialcy diffusion mechanisms on a bcc lattice is that both octahedral and tetrahedral sites are adjacent to similar sites. It is not clear why interstitialcy should be preferred to interstitial diffusion. The latter is almost certainly ruled out by the small value of the isotope effect, as mentioned above.

Table 1. Correlation Factors and Isotope Effects

Mechanism	f	Calculated $[(D^{\alpha}/D^{\beta}) - 1]$
NaCl (fcc) Lattice		
Interstitial.........	1	0.0445
Vacancy...........	0.782	0.0347
Interstitialcy......	0.66 to 1	0.015 to 0.022
Two-atom ring.....	1	0.022
Four-atom ring.....	1	0.011
Na (bcc) Lattice		
Interstitial.........	1	0.0445
Vacancy...........	0.727	0.0325
Interstitialcy.......	0 or 1 (octahedral sites)	0 to 0.022
	0.66 to 1 (tetrahedral sites)	0.014 to 0.022
	≈ 1 (split interstitial)	0.022
Two-atom ring.....	1	0.022
Four-atom ring....	1	0.011

A more plausible configuration is a split interstitial at the body center. This was pointed out by Johnson to be the configuration of lowest energy when its axis is in the $\langle 110 \rangle$ direction. No correlation factors have been estimated for interstitialcies in this instance, but because of the number of possible jump directions and the feasibility of rotations, with consequent directional randomization, the correlation factor would be expected to be very close to one. If this were the mechanism, then on the basis of our experimental results the correlation factor would be 0.73. This mechanism of diffusion must therefore be considered a distinct possibility.

It would obviously be very interesting to have a verification of Eq 5 for interstitialcies. Because interstitialcy diffusion occurs definitely only in the Ag halides, a measurement of the Ag isotope effect in these substances is clearly desirable.

The recent experimental evidence favoring vacancy diffusion in Na, referred to earlier, is the work of Weymouth and Sullivan (17). By combining simultaneous measurements of lattice parameter and thermal expansion, these authors showed that the dominant defect in Na is a vacancy and that the formation energy is about 3.5 kcal/mole. This value for the formation energy is in fair agreement with the rough rule that the formation energy is about half the diffusion activation energy.

Measurements we have made of the diffusion of K in Na also provide evidence supporting the vacancy mechanism. The results are consistent with the vacancy model of diffusion interpreted by use of Le Claire's theory of homovalent impurity-vacancy diffusion (18). We should like to remark here that we have attempted measurements of the diffusion of Ca in Na to get data to compare with Le Claire's theory of heterovalent impurity diffusion (19) but with no success. There is apparently no Ca diffusion in Na. Whether this is due to the known low solubility of Ca in Na or to some other cause is not clear.

Another reason we have for seriously considering vacancies as the means of self-diffusion in Na lies in the pressure variation of the diffusion coefficient. The work of Nachtrieb and his co-workers (20) suggests that diffusion is by a strongly relaxed vacancy. The relative activation volume (the ratio of the activation to the molar volume) found by these workers was 0.52. It must be noted however, that if Johnson's calculations on α-Fe are taken as applicable to Na, a similar decrease of diffusion with increasing pressure would occur for interstitials.

If the evidence summarized above can be regarded as giving reasonable grounds for considering a vacancy mechanism, it is interesting to examine the low isotope effect in conjunction with the relaxed vacancy model.

There are three ways in which relaxed vacancies could be used to explain the low value of the isotope effect. First, it could be argued that in a very relaxed vacancy, a "relaxion" (21), the atomic configuration would cease to contain an entity recognizable as a vacant lattice site and that diffusion within the disordered region would be a cooperative phenomenon with a number of atoms involved in each jump. In this instance, Eq 5 might well apply and a low isotope effect would immediately follow. Our result requires n in Eq 5 to be 3.

Because "relaxions" have been hypothesized as the mechanism for diffusion in liquid Na, a possible experiment of interest would be to measure the isotope effect in liquid Na. We are attempting this experiment.

The second alternative is to argue that in the relaxed vacancy only one atom jumps, but, because of the relaxed environment, other atoms share in the motion and ΔK is substantially different from one.

Third, the possibility exists that in a highly relaxed vacancy the relaxation may not be the same for all the neighboring atoms. If some of the atoms were to relax further than the others, these atoms might be expected to interchange most often with the vacancy. Such lowered coordination around a vacancy has the effect of reducing the correlation factor (22). To a fair degree of accuracy, the correlation factor is given by the equation

$$f = 1 - (2/z)$$

where z is the coordination number. If, for example, z equaled two, a linear chain would result with f equal to zero.

A more plausible mode of relaxation, which could hold in a bcc lattice, is that suggested by Bradley and Thewlis (23, 24) for γ brass. Essentially the suggestion is that a tetragonal relaxation of four atoms might occur around a vacancy. This mode of relaxation produces a correlation factor of one half, which goes far to explain the low isotope effect reported here.

It should be noted that this tetrahedral model of a vacancy makes the agreement between theory and experiment for impurity diffusion in Na, mentioned above, more understandable than the "relaxion" model does. The latter has nothing in common with the model used by Le Claire in his calculations.

The explanations given above for the low isotope effect in Na on the basis of a vacancy model hinge essentially on justifying a low value for one of the factors on the right side of Eq 6. It is not clear how these factors can be resolved, but until this can be done, Eq 6 cannot be used to identify diffusion mechanisms except in favorable instances, for example, NaCl and interstitial diffusion, in which the measured values of $[(D^{\alpha}/D^{\beta}) - 1]$ are sufficiently large for the mechanism to be identified unambiguously.

Table 2. Activation Volumes and Isotope Effects

Element	Structure	Activation volume	ΔK	References
Cu...............	fcc	....	≥ 0.7(a)	13
Ag...............	fcc	0.90	≥ 0.7(a)(b)	25, 13
Au...............	fcc	0.70	....	26, 27
Pd...............	fcc	....	1.02 ± 0.04	28
Pb...............	fcc	0.77, 0.64	....	29, 30
NaCl............	fcc	....	0.93 ± 0.09	8
Na...............	bcc	0.52	0.50 ± 0.05	This work
P...............	cubic	0.44	....	31

(a) Deduced from Fe impurity diffusion in these metals.
(b) Dr. N. L. Peterson of the Argonne National Laboratory has obtained a preliminary value of 1.0 ± 0.05 for ΔK in Ag self-diffusion.

To return to the question of relaxed vacancies, it is interesting to collect existing data on isotope effects and relaxation volumes. This is done in Table 2. ΔK in Table 2 merely denotes the ratio $[(D^\alpha/D^\beta) - 1]/f[(m^\beta/m^\alpha)^{1/2} - 1]$; it is not necessarily intended to have any other significance.

Consideration of Table 2 shows two things, first, our ignorance of these quantities, and secondly the impossibility of ruling out a connection between low isotope effects and low activation volumes. Any of the mechanisms discussed above would suffice, and Table 2 suggests that these do not operate in the less relaxed fcc structures. It is intriguing to note that ΔK is one for interstitial diffusion in a wide range of lattices (8). This substantiates the idea that when the atoms neighboring the defect are not free to relax, ΔK is one.

In Table 2 no value is given for the relaxation volume of NaCl. There is evidence in this instance that the movement activation volume is large (32), and in the similar material KCl it is known that there is little relaxation around a vacancy (33). Certainly there is no reason to expect a relaxed vacancy mechanism of diffusion.

Table 2 provides a guide for future experiments. It is clearly desirable, for example, to have activation-volume measurements for Pd and isotope-effect measurements for Ag. However, at present such measurements in any material would be valuable.

In summary, it can be said that the isotope effect shows the mechanism of self-diffusion in Na is either a split interstitial, diffusing as an interstitialcy, or a relaxed vacancy and that Schoen's equation cannot, in general, be used in a straightforward way to identify, unambiguously, the mechanism of diffusion. When used in conjunction with other information, however, the isotope effect does offer the possibility of obtaining information about the fine details of atomic jumps and the nature of vacancies.

Acknowledgments. We would like to acknowledge many informative discussions with Mr. A. D. Le Claire and to thank him for his careful reading of the manuscript. We would also like to thank Dr. N. L. Peterson for a preprint of his paper and permission to quote his results.

References

1   J. Bardeen and C. Herring, Imperfections in Nearly Perfect Crystals, John Wiley & Sons, Inc., New York, 1952, p 261
2   K. Compaan and Y. Haven, Trans Faraday Soc, **52**, 786 (1956); **54**, 1498 (1958)
3   R. J. Friauf, Phys Rev, **105**, 843 (1957)
4   K. Compaan and Y. Haven, Proceedings of the Third International Conference on the Reactivity of Solids, 1956, p 255
5   A. S. Miller and R. J. Maurer, J Phys Chem Solids, **4**, 196 (1958)
6   A. B. Lidiard, Handbuch der Physik, Vol 20, Springer-Verlag, Berlin, 1957, p 246
7   A. H. Schoen, Phys Rev Letters, **1**, 524 (1958)
8   L. W. Barr, and A. D. Le Claire, Proc Brit Ceram Soc, **1**, 109 (July, 1964)
9   A. D. Le Claire and A. B. Lidiard, Phil Mag, **1**, 518 (1956)
10 J. R. Manning, Phys Rev, **116**, 825 (1959)
11 K. Tharmalingam and A. B. Lidiard, Phil Mag, **4**, 899 (1959)
12 G. H. Vineyard, J Phys Chem Solids, **3**, 121 (1957)
13 J. G. Mullen, Phys Rev, **121**, 1649 (1961)
14 N. H. Nachtrieb, E. Catalano and J. A. Weil, J Chem Phys, **20**, 1185 (1952)
15 R. A. Johnson, Phys Rev, **134**, 1329 (1964)
16 H. Paneth, Phys Rev, **80**, 708 (1950)
17 G. A. Sullivan and J. W. Weymouth, Phys Letters, **9**, 89 (1964)
18 A. D. Le Claire, Phil Mag, **10**, 641 (1964)
19 A. D. Le Claire, Phil Mag, **7**, 141 (1962)
20 N. H. Nachtrieb, J. A. Weil, E. Catalano and A. W. Lawson, J Chem Phys, **20**, 1189 (1952)
21 N. H. Nachtrieb and G. S. Handler, Acta Met, **2**, 797 (1954)
22 E. W. J. Mitchell, University of Reading, and A. B. Lidiard, Atomic Energy Research Establishment, private communication
23 A. J. Bradley and J. Thewlis, Proc Roy Soc London, Ser A, **112**, 678 (1926)
24 W. M. Lomer, Vacancies and Other Point Defects in Metals and Alloys, Institute of Metals, London, 1957, p 82
25 C. T. Tomizuka, Progress in Very High Pressure Research, John Wiley & Sons Inc., New York, 1961, p 266
26 R. P. Huebener and C. G. Homan, Phys Rev, **129**, 1162 (1962)
27 R. M. Emrick, Phys Rev, **122**, 1720 (1961)
28 N. L. Peterson, Phys Rev, **136**, A568 (1964)
29 J. B. Hudson and R. E. Hoffman, Trans AIME, **221**, 761 (1961)
30 N. H. Nachtrieb, H. A. Resing and S. A. Rice, J Chem Phys, **31**, 135 (1959)
31 N. H. Nachtrieb and G. S. Handler, J Chem Phys, **23**, 1187 (1955)
32 C. B. Pierce, Phys Rev, **123**, 744 (1961)
33 H. Pick and H. Weber, Z Physik, **128**, 409 (1950)

Chapter 12
Tracer Diffusion in Gamma Uranium

S. J. ROTHMAN AND N. L. PETERSON

The study of self-diffusion in α-U was begun at Argonne by R. Weil in 1953. In 1957, after we had had no success in getting a penetration curve for α-U, we switched to a study of self-diffusion in the γ phase. The results were very interesting, and so we started a study of the tracer diffusion of other elements (which we shall call "impurity diffusion") in γ-U. This chapter reviews the results of our experiments.

Experimental Techniques

We used U samples containing less than 100 ppm by weight of total impurity for our measurements. After the samples were cleaned by cathodic sputtering in purified A, radioactive tracers were deposited on them in thin layers by evaporation or sputtering (1, 2). The prepared samples were placed in Ta cups, and the cups, together with some Zr getter, were sealed in quartz tubing under a vacuum of 2×10^{-5} torr. Diffusion anneals were done in resistance-heated furnaces, with the annealing temperatures controlled and measured to ± 1 C. Chemical analysis of a sample stub left after sectioning showed no impurity pickup. Standard lathe sectioning and scintillation counting techniques (3) were used except for the measurements of self-diffusion (4) and the diffusion of Ni. In the first of these, U^{235} was used as the tracer, and the sections were analyzed by mass spectrography or fission counting (5, 6). The activity of Ni^{63} was measured by extracting it into a liquid scintillating solution and counting it there (7).

Results

Self-Diffusion. Penetration plots (plots of log concentration of in-diffused U^{235} versus x^2, where x is the distance of the center of the section from the original interface) are shown in Fig. 1, and the diffusion coefficients, D, calculated from them are plotted versus $1/T$ in Fig. 2.

The authors are with Argonne National Laboratory, Argonne, Ill.

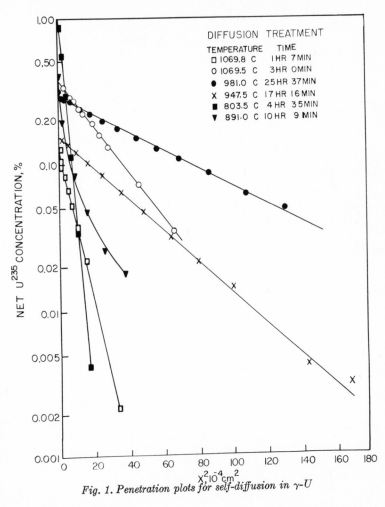

Fig. 1. Penetration plots for self-diffusion in γ-U

The maximum error in D is estimated to be 7%. Figure 2 also shows the earlier data of Bochvar et al. (8) and of Adda and Kirianenko (9). The agreement is quite good, no worse than a difference of 20% for values of D, and some of the disagreement can be explained by consideration of the purity of the metals used by the different investigators (see below). The values of the activation energy, Q, and the pre-exponential multiplier, D_0, are about 26.5 kcal/mole and 1.2×10^{-3} cm²/sec, respectively, which are much smaller than the 53 kcal/mole expected for Q from the melting-point correlation (10) and the 0.1 cm²/sec expected for D_0 from Zener's rule (11). It should be noted that the Arrhenius plot appears to be

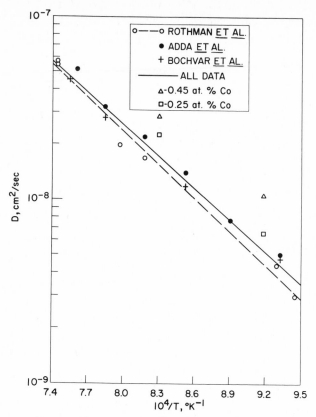

Fig. 2. Arrhenius plot for self-diffusion in γ-U

straight, unlike the plots for self-diffusion in bcc Zr (12) and Ti (13, 14). The points, however, are too scattered and the temperature range too limited to allow us to say that the Arrhenius plot for self-diffusion in γ-U is definitely straight.

The low values of Q and D_0 were the first indications that diffusion in γ-U is anomalous. Two of the common explanations for such anomalies can be discarded at once. The agreement among the data of three independent laboratories shows that experimental error is unlikely. The penetration plots and the large grain size of γ-U (4), as well as the auto-radiographic work of Bochvar *et al.* (8) indicate that grain-boundary diffusion is not the cause of the anomaly. The anomaly also is not due to rapid diffusion in the α or β phase during heating or cooling, because measurements of self-diffusion in α-U (15, 16) and β-U (17, 6) show that diffusion in these phases is very slow.

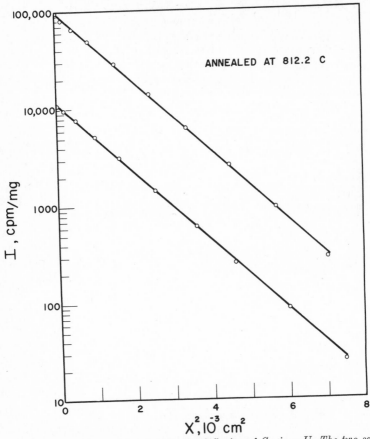

Fig. 3. Penetration plots for the diffusion of Cu in γ-U. The two samples were annealed simultaneously. The plots are separated along the ordinate by one decade for clarity

Impurity Diffusion. Two penetration plots for the diffusion of Cu in γ-U are shown in Fig. 3, and some plots for the diffusion of Co in γ-U are shown in Fig. 4. Values of D derived from plots similar to these for the diffusion of Cr, Mn, Fe, Co, Ni, Cu, Cb and Au are plotted versus $1/T$ in Fig. 5. The errors in D are no more than $\pm 3\%$, except for Mn (10%) and Au (7%). The Arrhenius plots are definitely curved.

Discussion

Curved Arrhenius Plots. Although we do not know the reason for the curvature of these Arrhenius plots, some reasons often suggested can

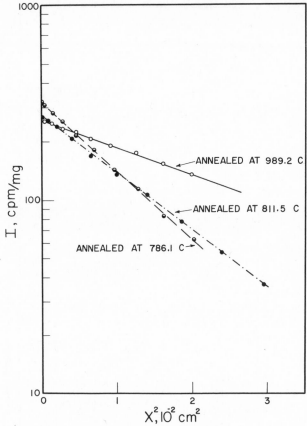

Fig. 4. Penetration plots for the diffusion of Co in γ-U

be eliminated. The data are reproducible enough to indicate that there are no major experimental errors, and grain-boundary diffusion can be eliminated for the reasons given above. Diffusion of Cr and Fe in the β phase is again much slower than that in the γ phase (18), and corrections were made for it.

Several workers have suggested that such curvature may be due to diffusion along dislocations (19), or some other defects introduced by the phase transformation (20). To investigate this point (21), we took a U sample with a thermocouple attached to the back, annealed it at 1098 C for 19.5 hr, lowered its temperature to 809 C, evaporated on a thin layer of Co^{60}, and diffused it for half an hour. The output of the thermocouple attached to the sample was recorded continuously and showed that the sample temperature stayed well above the β-γ transformation tempera-

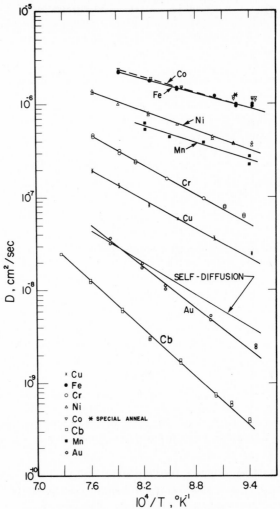

Fig. 5. Arrhenius plots for tracer diffusion in γ-U

ture. There was no undershoot. The value of D from this experiment is shown by the asterisk in Fig. 5; the agreement with D's from conventional experiments is within the experimental error. This result indicates that if defects introduced by the phase transformation were responsible for the curvature of the Arrhenius plots, these defects will not anneal out in a long anneal at 34 C below the melting point. We think that dislocations and nonequilibrium vacancies, as well as Gruzin's "surfaces of internal division," would have annealed out during the pre-anneal, and, therefore, that they are not responsible for the curved Arrhenius plots. Further evidence against nonequilibrium vacancies comes from a comparison of two runs for the diffusion of Co, one at 783.3 C for 2.67 $\times$ 10^3 sec and one at 786.1 C for 6.27 $\times$ 10^3 sec. The values of D from these runs are equal within the experimental error, indicating that the lifetime of the nonequilibrium vacancies is about several hours, which seems unreasonably long.

This argument does not apply if the defects, vacancies or dislocations, are locked by impurities. Such a mechanism has been proposed by Kidson (22), and we remark only that this mechanism does not fit the data for self-diffusion in γ-U, because the curvature of the Arrhenius plot, if it exists at all, is much smaller than the curvatures for diffusion of Co, Fe, Cu or Cr, although the effect should be just as large or larger.

Assuming that the curved Arrhenius plots are due to the simultaneous operation of two mechanisms, we have attempted to fit our data to the sum of two exponentials by use of a least-squares routine developed by Garbow (23). The results were unusual: Q for the high-temperature mechanism could be varied by almost a factor of three without appreciably changing the residual. This undoubtedly is due in part to the method of calculation and in part to the scatter of the data and the narrowness of the ranges in temperature and in D. Nevertheless, we do not attach much significance to the fact that the range of values includes the one predicted by the melting-point rule. One interesting number did come out of the calculation; D_0 for the low-temperature mechanism was always about 10^{-6} cm²/sec, which indicates either that this mechanism involves an extrinsic defect concentration or that it has a very large negative entropy of activation.

Mechanism of Diffusion. The mechanism of diffusion cannot be determined uniquely from tracer-diffusion data only. There are nevertheless strong indications that the vacancy mechanism is operative in γ-U.

Adda and co-workers (24–31) and Peterson and Ogilvie (32) have found marker movements in the interdiffusion of γ-U with Zr, Mo, Ti and Cb, which indicates that chemical diffusion in γ-U takes place by a defect mechanism. On the other hand, Pound *et al.* (33) and one of us (4) have argued that results from chemical-diffusion experiments do not necessarily apply to tracer diffusion because of the large chemical gradient and associated nonequilibrium effects in chemical diffusion. Therefore we carried out a Kirkendall-marker experiment in a very small concentration gradient, using a couple consisting of pure U and a U−0.407 at. % Co alloy. As shown in Fig. 6, marker movement definitely took place. This

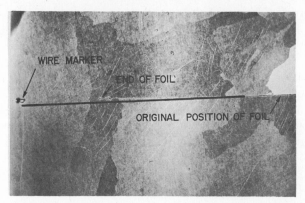

Fig. 6. Kirkendall marker movement during interdiffusion of pure U (bottom) and a U−0.407 at. % Co alloy (top). Polarized-light illumination.
41×

indicates that even in very dilute γ-U alloys, diffusion takes place by a defect mechanism.

From considerations of atomic sizes, we conclude that the defects themselves are vacancies. The smallest tracer used here has a Goldschmidt radius of 1.1 A (corrected for tetrahedral coordination) (34), whereas the tetrahedral holes in bcc γ-U have a radius of 0.424 A. It would be nice to eliminate interstitialcies as a diffusion mechanism more conclusively, but unfortunately, the existence of two solid-state transformations makes both quenching and Simmons-Balluffi experiments (35) impossible, and there are no isotopes suitable for an isotope-effect experiment. For lack of definite proof against it, we shall tentatively consider that diffusion in γ-U takes place by the vacancy mechanism.

Analysis of the Activation Energies for Impurity Diffusion (3). We have compared the activation energies from the high-temperature, straight-line parts of the Arrhenius plots for impurity diffusion (Table 1) with three theories based on the vacancy mechanism. The comparisons are not quantitative because there are so few data available on the physical properties and electronic structure of γ-U that a number of parameters had to be estimated.

The data agree with neither the theory of Turnbull and Hoffman (36), which is based on thermodynamics, nor the theory of Swalin (37), which is based on atomic size and elastic properties. Large size effects definitely are noticeable, because Au diffuses more slowly and with a higher activation energy than Cu, but when the size differences are small, the correlation with atomic size disappears.

Our attempts to fit these data to Le Claire's electrostatic theory (38)

Table 1. Parameters for Diffusion in γ-U

Diffusing element	Activation energy, kcal/mole	D_0, cm²/sec
U............	26.5	1.12×10^{-3} (a)
Cr...........	24.46 ± 0.43	$5.47 (+1.04, -0.87) \times 10^{-3}$
Mn..........	13.88 ± 1.66	$1.81 (+1.95, -0.94) \times 10^{-4}$
Fe...........	12.01 ± 0.34	$2.69 (+0.43, -0.37) \times 10^{-4}$
Co...........	12.57 ± 0.58	$3.51 (+0.95, -0.75) \times 10^{-4}$
Ni...........	15.66 ± 0.35	$5.36 (+0.86, -0.74) \times 10^{-4}$
Cu...........	24.06 ± 0.40	$1.96 (+0.35, -0.30) \times 10^{-3}$
Cb...........	39.65 ± 0.50	$4.87 (+1.18, -0.94) \times 10^{-2}$
Au...........	33.8	2.05×10^{-2}

(a) Least-squares fit of the data of Ref 4, 8 and 9.

were slightly more successful. There are serious difficulties in applying this model; that is, the screening constant q, which appears in the exponent of all the energy terms, can be estimated only roughly, and there is also a great deal of uncertainty about the "excess valences" of transition metal solutes in γ-U. Assuming that there is only one screening electron ($q = 1A^{-1}$), and assuming the valences of $+1$ for Cr and Cu, $+2$ for Mn and Ni, $+3$ for Fe and Co and -1 for Cb, we obtained fairly good agreement between the theoretical and experimental values of $\Delta Q = Q_{imp} - Q_{self}$. The results are, however, inconsistent internally. For Fe and Co, ΔH_2, the difference between the activation energies for the exchange of a vacancy with a Co (or Fe) atom and its exchange with a U atom, is negative, and so large that the activation energy for the exchange of an Fe (or Co) atom and a vacancy becomes negative; the theoretical ΔQ is reasonable only because the temperature dependence of the correlation coefficient is also very large and negative. This failure of our calculations is undoubtedly due to an oversimplified model. We feel that the order-of-magnitude agreements are encouraging and that some useful results could ensue if the calculation were done properly. Such theoretical work is badly needed in this field.

Correlation Effects. The above calculations also suggested that very strong correlation effects are to be expected, especially for the fast diffusers Fe and Co. This can be deduced qualitatively from the D_{Co}/D_{self} ratios, which lie between 100 and 500. This indicates that the vacancy must be bonded to the impurity, because it is unlikely that random vacancy-impurity encounters would yield such a high D_{imp}/D_{self} ratio. In such a situation, a correlated motion of the vacancy must take place for the tracer to keep diffusing, and, because in a bcc lattice there are no solvent atoms that are simultaneously neighbors of a vacancy and its nearest-neighbor impurity, the correlated motion must involve next-nearest neighbors too. Thus the impurity-vacancy bond must extend at least to the position of the second-nearest neighbor. Further, in order for the vacancy-U exchanges not to slow down the diffusion of the tracer, the presence of the Co tracer must accelerate self-diffusion in γ-U. We have checked this deduction (39) experimentally by measuring the self-diffusion of U in dilute U-Co alloys at two temperatures. The results (Table 2 and Fig. 7) show that the prediction is indeed fulfilled.

At the higher temperature, 939.9 C, the self-diffusion coefficient depends linearly on the Co concentration

$$D = D^0(1 + bC) \qquad (1)$$

with $b = 197$, which is much larger than that found for fcc metals (40). A calculation of the correlation factor for the diffusion of Co in γ-U from

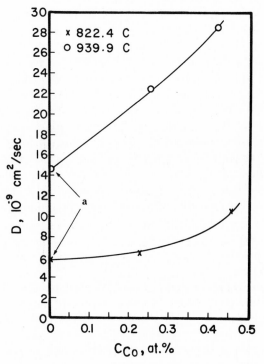

Fig. 7. *The effect of Co on self-diffusion in γ-U: plot of D_{self} versus Co concentration. Points labeled* a *from Ref 4.*

Table 2. Influence of Co on Self-Diffusion in γ-U

Co content, at. %	Annealing temp, °C	Annealing time, 10^3 sec	D, 10^{-9} cm^2/sec
0.457............	822.4	31.86	10.6
0.227............	822.4	31.86	6.53
0.420............	939.9	10.44	28.5
0.254............	939.9	10.44	22.5

these data, by use of Lidiard's theory (40) and a statistical mechanical calculation similar to Gibbs's (41), showed that the value of f depends on the form of the correlation factor that is used, that is which jump frequencies are used and which are ignored. Using the simplest form of f (42):

$$f = (2.35w_1 + 2.98k_1)/(2w_2 + 2.35w_1 + 2.98k_1) \qquad (2)$$

we find $f = 0.09$, which is reasonable and close to the value found by Gibbs *et al.* (14) for Fe diffusing in Ti. If a more rigorous form (43) is used for f, a negative value is obtained. At 822.4 C, where D_{self} does not depend linearly on the Co concentration, f is negative no matter which form is used. Thus, although Co does accelerate self-diffusion in γ-U as predicted from the impurity-diffusion data, a correlation coefficient cannot be calculated.

These results on the influence of solutes on self-diffusion help to explain the differences among the values of D_{self} reported by Bochvar *et al.*, Adda and Kirianenko, and us. From Fig. 2, D (Adda) $> D$ (Bochvar) $> D$ (Rothman). The French enriched U (sold to them by the U. S. Atomic Energy Commission) was the least pure; our U was the purest. The impurities in all the materials are not Co, but Al, Si and C, so the correlation cannot be made quantitative.

Conclusions

γ-U apparently belongs with Ti and Zr in the class of "anomalous diffusers." It is certain that diffusion in γ-U takes place by a defect mechanism, and very likely that the defects are vacancies. We consider that our experiments have shown that the anomaly is not due to grain-boundary diffusion, diffusion along dislocations, or nonequilibrium defects introduced by the phase transformation, providing such defects behave in γ-U as they behave in other metals.

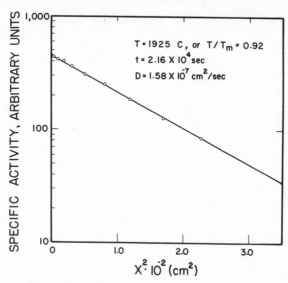

Fig. 8. *Penetration plot for self-diffusion in β-Hf*

The possibilities of finding the reason for the nonconventional diffusion behavior of γ-U are not too good. The critical experiments that have done so much to clear up the situation in fcc metals, that is, quenching studies, Simmons-Balluffi experiments and measurements of isotope effects in self-diffusion (44, 45), seem to be experimentally unfeasible for γ-U. The theoretical situation is equally gloomy, and there is no sign that anything is being done about it. Our belief is that further tracer-diffusion measurements in γ-U are useless. We have made a few measurements on other metals: one measurement of D for self-diffusion in β-Hf (Fig. 8), which, when plotted on a Sherby-Simnad-type plot (46), indicates that diffusion in this metal is anomalous, as one might expect, and two measurements on the diffusion of Hf in bcc Th (Fig. 9), which indicate that diffusion in Th is "normal." Classifying metals as "anomalous" or "normal" diffusers, in the hope of finding some unifying principle that will explain the anomaly, seems to be a roundabout and uncertain way of answering the basic question of why the diffusion behavior of γ-U, Ti and Zr differs from that of other metals.

Acknowledgments. Many members of the Argonne staff have helped in the experimental work and have discussed the work with us. Of them, John Hines and Elmar Koch deserve special acknowledgment. We are grateful to Alan Le Claire for some very useful discussions and for letting us see a number of his manuscripts before publication, and to

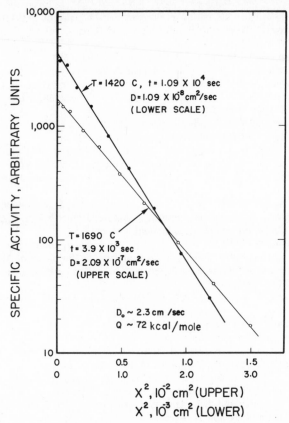

Fig. 9. Penetration plots for the diffusion of Hf[181] in bcc Th

G. B. Gibbs for access to his thesis. This work was supported by the U. S. Atomic Energy Commission.

References

1   S. J. Rothman, J Nucl Mater, **3**, 77 (1961); also ANL-6127, 1960
2   R. Weil, S. J. Rothman and L. T. Lloyd, Rev Sci Instr, **30**, 541 (1959)
3   N. L. Peterson and S. J. Rothman, ANL-6568, in preparation
4   S. J. Rothman, L. T. Lloyd and A. L. Harkness, Trans AIME, **218**, 605 (1960); **227**, 265 (1963)
5   J. Gray, Jr., and F. Hagemann, Rev Sci Instr, **33**, 1258 (1962)
6   S. J. Rothman, J. Gray, Jr., J. P. Hughes and A. L. Harkness, J Nucl Mater, **3**, 72 (1961)
7   John Hines, private communication

8   A. Bochvar, V. Kuznetsova and V. Sergeev, Self-Diffusion of Uranium in Gamma Phase, Transactions of the Second Geneva Conference, Vol VI, United Nations, Geneva, 1958, p 68

9   Y. Adda and A. Kirianenko, J Nucl Mater, **1**, 120 (1959)

10 G. V. Kidson and R. Ross, Self-Diffusion in Pure Polycrystalline Platinum, in Radioisotopes in Scientific Research (Proceedings First Unesco International Conference, Paris, 1957), Pergamon Press, New York, 1958, p 185

11 C. Zener, J Appl Phys, **22**, 372 (1951)

12 J. I. Federer and T. S. Lundy, Trans AIME, **227**, 592 (1963)

13 J. F. Murdock and T. S. Lundy, J Metals, **15**, 69 (1963)

14 G. B. Gibbs, D. Graham and D. H. Tomlin, Phil Mag, **8**, 1269 (1963)

15 Y. Adda, A. Kirianenko and C. Mairy, Compt Rend, **253**, 445 (1961)

16 S. J. Rothman, J. J. Hines, J. Gray, Jr., and A. L. Harkness, J Appl Phys, **33**, 2113 (1962)

17 Y. Adda, A. Kirianenko and C. Mairy, J Nucl Mater, **1**, 300 (1959)

18 S. J. Rothman, N. L. Peterson and S. A. Moore, J Nucl Mater, **7**, 212 (1962)

19 A. D. Le Claire, private communication

20 P. L. Gruzin, E. V. Kuznetsov and G. V. Kurdyumov, Influence of Intra-Grain Structure of Austenite on Self-Diffusion of Iron, in Problems of Metallography and the Physics of Metals, Fourth Symposium, edited by B. Y. Lyubov, Moscow, 1955; AEC-tr-2924, p 343

21 W. C. Hagel, Trans AIME, **227**, 267 (1963); A. D. Le Claire, private communication

22 G. V. Kidson, Can J Phys, **41**, 1563 (1963)

23 B. Garbow, private communication

24 Y. Adda and J. Philibert, Second Geneva Conference, paper 1160, 1958

25 Y. Adda and J. Philibert, Compt Rend, **242**, 3081 (1956)

26 Y. Adda, J. Philibert and C. Mairy, Compt Rend, **243**, 1115 (1956)

27 Y. Adda and J. Philibert, Compt Rend, **246**, 113 (1958)

28 Y. Adda, C. Mairy and J. L. Andreu, Compt Rend, **249**, 2775 (1960)

29 Y. Adda, J. Philibert and H. Faraggi, Rev Met, **54**, 597 (1957)

30 Y. Adda, C. Mairy and J. L. Andreu, Rev Met, **57**, 549 (1960)

31 Y. Adda and J. Philibert, Acta Met, **8**, 700 (1960)

32 N. L. Peterson and R. E. Ogilvie, Trans AIME, **227**, 1083 (1963)

33 G. M. Pound, W. R. Bitler and H. W. Paxton, Phil Mag, **6**, 473 (1963)

34 L. S. Darken and R. W. Gurry, Physical Chemistry of Metals, McGraw-Hill, New York, 1953

35 R. O. Simmons, J. S. Koehler and R. W. Balluffi, Radiation Damage in Solids, Vol 1, IAEA, Vienna, 1962, p 154

36 D. Turnbull and R. E. Hoffman, Acta Met, **7**, 407 (1959)

37 R. A. Swalin, Acta Met, **5**, 443 (1957)

38 A. D. Le Claire, Phil Mag, **7**, 141 (1962)

39 L. Slifkin, private communication

40 A. B. Lidiard, Phil Mag, **5**, 1171 (1960)

41 G. B. Gibbs, Thesis, University of Reading, 1962

42 J. R. Manning, Phys Rev, **116**, 819 (1959)

43 A. D. Le Claire, private communication

44 L. W. Barr and A. D. Le Claire, Trans Brit Ceram Soc, to be published

45 N. L. Peterson, Phys Rev, to be published

46 O. D. Sherby and M. Simnad, Trans ASM, **54**, 227 (1961)

Chapter 13
Re-examination of Silver Diffusion in
Silver-Rich AgMg

W. C. HAGEL AND J. H. WESTBROOK

Much effort is currently being directed toward development of inter-metallic compounds as new materials for structural, heat-resisting and energy-conversion applications. Because these compounds display a wide variety of crystal structures, lattice defects and bonding types, studies of their mechanical properties and diffusion mechanisms also are of funda-mental value. Each of the authors has provided extensive reviews (1, 2) treating both areas of research.

The compound β-AgMg was chosen for intensive investigations because of its simple, ordered CsCl-type crystal structure up to moderate melting temperatures and its broad solubilities for the component elements. At first, the hardness (3) and tensile behavior (4) of β-AgMg suggested the possibility that the greater strengthening and lower activation energies for flow stress observed among Mg-rich alloys of β-AgMg, when com-pared with Ag-rich alloys, resulted from a large concentration of vacancies similar to those appearing in Al-rich β-NiAl (5). Although part of the effect was later found to result from grain-boundary hardening (6), we (7) measured the diffusion of Ag^{110} in three β-AgMg alloys containing 45.8, 49.8 and 52.0 at. % Mg and determined lattice parameters and densities for a wider range of compositions and for a more numerous assortment. The primary conclusion was that only substitutional defects are present on both sides of stoichiometry.

Domian and Aaronson (8) next presented data for the diffusion of Ag^{110} in seven β-AgMg alloys containing on the average 41.1, 43.6, 48.5, 48.7, 52.8, 57.1 and 60.9 at. % Mg. Although different counting methods were used, coefficients from the two laboratories are reasonably close—except at lower temperatures. By invoking Elcock's six-jump cycle (9) as the mechanism of diffusion in CsCl-type compounds, Domian and Aaronson calculated theoretical values of Q that showed fair agreement

The authors are with the General Electric Research Laboratory, Schenectady, N.Y.

with their temperature dependence. Question was raised about the proper variation of activation energy with composition for Ag-rich β-AgMg, and the purpose of this work is to provide further determinations on the region where some uncertainty exists.

Experimental Procedure

Alloys were prepared by induction melting of selected fine Ag (99.95) and low-Fe Mg (99.95)* in magnesia crucibles under one atmosphere of A. Melts were poured under A into graphite molds providing $1\frac{1}{8}$-in.-diam by 4-in.-long ingots. These were homogenized in evacuated and A-filled fused-silica capsules by heating for 16 hr at 750 C. In contrast to previous experience, several ingots were lost until we realized that untarnished resting surfaces could become contaminated with Si unless they were placed upon alumina plaques (10). Three 1-in.-diam by $\frac{3}{4}$-in.-long cylinders were machined from the midportion of each cast bar for diffusion measurements. Three alloys, analyzing 43.6, 43.8 and 45.0 at. % Mg, were taken as representing compositions of interest. The first two were intended to duplicate one of the compositions employed by Domian and Aaronson. The third is intermediate between this composition and the most Ag-rich alloy previously studied by us.

The plane surfaces of each diffusion cylinder were ground flat and parallel and to a fine finish. After a light etch (H_2SO_4, CrO_3 and H_2O) was applied to clean the face, an average grain diameter of no less than 5 mm was noted. This is believed to be sufficiently coarse to avoid the complications of grain-boundary diffusion. However, extruded specimens received from Domian and Aaronson did show significantly smaller grain sizes than we had ever encountered in castings (Fig. 1), and considerable effort was expended in attempts to detect nonuniform penetration with high-resolution autoradiography. Even though tantalizing traces might appear after diffusing Ag^{110} for 120 hr at 500 C, there was no unequivocal evidence of boundary short-circuiting. Boundary short-circuiting might have accounted for Domian and Aaronson's higher D values at lower temperatures despite their indirect evidence that such a contribution did not take place.

Radioactive Ag^{110}, which decays by emitting β-particles (0.53 mev) and γ-rays over a half-life of 270 days, was obtained from the Oak Ridge National Laboratory as a 7.5 mc-ml^{-1} solution of $AgNO_3$ in HNO_3. The solution was added to an aqueous electrolyte containing KOH, K_2CO_3 and KCN. At low current densities, thin layers of the isotope, a few

* Supplied by Handy & Harman and Dow Chemical Co., respectively.

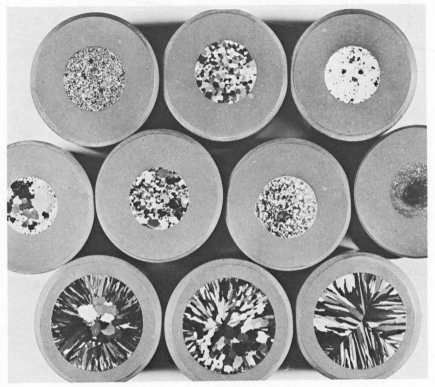

Fig. 1. Macrographs of extruded samples (first and second rows) used by Domian and Aaronson (8) and of three cast samples (third row) used in early work (7). Ag content decreases on going from left to right. Actual size

hundred Angstroms thick, were deposited uniformly onto one of the flat faces of each specimen. Paraffin was used to eliminate deposition elsewhere. After electroplating, each specimen was thoroughly washed and lightly buffed to remove any unevenness. The amount of isotope remaining was too small to have any influence on alloy composition. The plated cylinders were sealed in evacuated and A-filled fused-silica capsules (with precautionary alumina plaques) and diffusion annealed in Nichrome-wound resistance furnaces where temperatures from 500 to 700 C were maintained constant within ± 2 C for times up to 120 hr. Specimen temperatures in a 4-in. constant-temperature zone were measured with Pt/Pt–10 Rh thermocouples; annealing was commenced and terminated by pushing the capsules to and from this zone. Surface oxidation and evaporation were minimized by placing plated and unplated cylinders of the same composition face to face in a capsule.

A sequence of layers varying from 0.0002 to 0.0020 in. thick, as determined by a fixed-position dial gage, was machined in a lathe from the radioactive face of each specimen. This involved mounting the specimen face exactly 90° to the lathe axis, turning off a $\frac{1}{16}$-in. layer from the cylindrical surface to eliminate surface-diffusion effects, and capturing chips and dust by suction. Measurements of total cylinder length before and after all sections were removed showed close agreement with the sum of dial-gage readings. A reproducible counting configuration was maintained by placing the counter on the tool mount so that it could be brought in line with the lathe axis after each section was removed. Plastic positioning cups, without and with an Al β absorber, kept the counter window a constant distance ($\frac{1}{8}$ in.) from the specimen face. Counting rate was digitally recorded by use of a Nuclear-Instrument Autoscaler with a dual timer.

Although Ag-rich alloys are more machinable than the brittle ones containing high Mg, we preferred for reliability purposes still to use the Gruzin technique (11) as we did in our early work (in contrast to the layer-counting technique used by Domian and Aaronson). Here the remaining activity in the specimen is measured after each layer has been removed. If I is the activity of the specimen face after a section of thickness x has been removed, then the appropriate solution to Fick's law is

$$I - \frac{1}{\mu} \frac{\partial I}{\partial x} = \frac{K}{(\pi Dt)^{1/2}} \exp\left(-x^2/4Dt\right) \tag{1}$$

where μ is the linear absorption coefficient, D is the diffusion coefficient, K is a constant and t is the time of isothermal diffusion. I is taken as the difference in counts per minute (corrected for dead-time coincidence) measured without and with a β absorber, that is, it is only the β activity of the specimen surfaces; this double-counting procedure necessitates no background correction. By counting the activity of two specimens individually and jointly, we found a dead time (τ) of 100 microseconds at the plateau voltage (1275 v) of the Anton mica-window counter tube employed. The coincidence-corrected count equals the measured count N divided by $(1 - \tau N)$. Depending on initial specimen activity and the accuracy required, I varied from 50,000 to 20 counts per minute. With the source, counter tube and configuration chosen, the counts through a series of 1.73 to 210 mg-cm^{-2} Al absorbers, corrected for air and mica absorption, showed that a 0.015-in. Al sheet should effectively absorb all β radiation. Because the half-life of Ag^{110} is relatively long, no decay corrections were applied to a series of counts extending over one or two days. In keeping with the early work, we used a μ of 800 cm^{-1}.

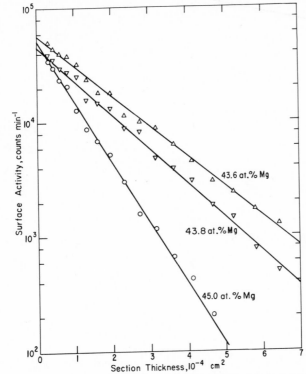

Fig. 2. Typical experimental results for Ag^{110} diffusion in Ag-rich AgMg alloys after 72 hr at 600 C showing β activity of specimen surface as a function of section thickness squared

To a first approximation, one can assume that the I in Eq 1 is $\gg (1/\mu)(\partial I/\partial x)$ and can write

$$I = K' \exp (-x^2/4D't) \tag{2}$$

Then, when $\ln I$ is plotted versus x^2, a straight line whose slope is $-1/4D't$ should result. As shown by the examples of Fig. 2 and all plotted penetration curves, this assumption holds true; however, a more exact value of D comes from evaluating $(1/\mu)(\partial I/\partial x)$. This is achieved by differentiating Eq (2) and substituting particular values of I and x into the relation

$$\partial I/\partial x = -xI/2D't \tag{3}$$

One can now plot $\ln [I - (1/\mu)(\partial I/\partial x)]$ versus x^2 to get a new corrected slope and a better value for D. The procedure can be repeated if neces-

Table 1. Diffusion Data for Ag^{110} in AgMg

Mg content, at. %	Temp, °C	Time, hr	D', cm^2 sec^{-1}	D, cm^2 sec^{-1}
43.6.........	700	10.8	1.42×10^{-9}	1.49×10^{-9}
	650	14.5	5.73×10^{-10}	5.98×10^{-10}
	600	72	1.61×10^{-10}	1.69×10^{-10}
	550	96	4.80×10^{-11}	5.01×10^{-11}
	500	120	3.20×10^{-11}	3.40×10^{-11}
	500	120	1.60×10^{-11}	1.80×10^{-11}
43.8..........	700	10.8	1.61×10^{-9}	1.68×10^{-9}
	650	72	5.10×10^{-10}	5.30×10^{-10}
	600	72	1.41×10^{-10}	1.50×10^{-10}
	550	120	5.45×10^{-11}	5.73×10^{-11}
	500	120	2.85×10^{-11}	3.12×10^{-11}
45.0..........	700	10.0	8.76×10^{-10}	9.19×10^{-10}
	650	14.5	2.50×10^{-10}	2.68×10^{-10}
	600	72	7.96×10^{-11}	8.48×10^{-11}
	550	96	3.04×10^{-11}	3.19×10^{-11}
	500	120	1.05×10^{-11}	1.20×10^{-11}
	500	120	1.28×10^{-11}	1.39×10^{-11}

sary, although for these specimens a third correction was found to give a negligible change in D. Table 1 gives the D' and D values determined in this manner for the three alloys.

Results and Discussion

Figure 3 shows a semilogarithmic plot of diffusion coefficients recorded in Table 1 versus the reciprocal of absolute temperature. There is a slight curvature caused by data points at 500 and 550 C. Little difference could be distinguished between D values for the 43.6 and 43.8 at. % Mg alloys. Passing two straight lines through points at 600 C and above gives the approximate Arrhenius relations:

$$D_{Ag} \text{ (43.6 and 43.8 at. % Mg)} = 0.309 \exp(-36{,}900/RT) \text{ cm}^2\text{-sec}^{-1} \quad (4)$$
$$D_{Ag} \text{ (45.0 at. % Mg)} = 0.686 \exp(-39{,}600/RT) \text{ cm}^2\text{-sec}^{-1} \quad (5)$$

The same data and those obtained in the early work can also be depicted as a function of atomic per cent Mg (Fig. 4). From the investigation of Berkowitz *et al.* (12) for the diffusion of Co^{60} in six β-NiAl alloys and the

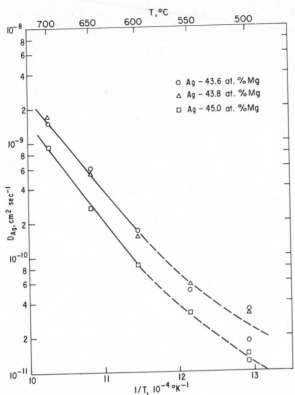

Fig. 3. D_{Ag} versus $1/T$ for Ag-rich AgMg

unpublished calculations of R. Kikuchi and H. Sato,* there is reason to expect a definite inverse cusping to converge on the stoichiometric composition. A fair estimate of the sum of possible errors in measuring composition, radiation, section thickness, temperature and time for each diffusion coefficient is about 10%. This was confirmed by several repeat runs, although at 500 C the reproducibility appears to be considerably less.

It is of interest to note that the Q calculations of Domian and Aaronson do show a small increase of about 600 cal/g-atom, on going from 500 to 700 C. Yet, the curvature seen here is greater and may be created by the presence of some free Ag at low temperatures. The maximum solubility limit of Ag-rich β-AgMg is unfortunately not well defined. Thermal analyses performed by Zemczuzny (13) set a limit of 37.4 at. % Mg; the

* Theory of Substitutional Diffusion in an Ordered Phase, talk presented at 93rd AIME Annual Meeting, February 17, 1964.

hardness and resistivity data of Smirnov and Kurnakov (14) indicate 40.0 at. % Mg at 400 C. From x-ray and metallographic studies, Ageev and Kuznetzov (15) give a value of 44.0 at. % Mg at 500 C. Letner and Sidhu (16) claim the limit at 525 C to be 47.0 at. % Mg, but their lattice-parameter data indicate that 42.0 at. % Mg is more likely. In our early work, we avoided this compositional region of doubt by setting our minimum Mg content at 45.8 at. %. The apparently low D value in Fig. 4 for that alloy at 500 C has been cross-checked many times. No error can be found, and another possibility is that there is a real discontinuity between 45.0 and 45.8 at. % Mg. The data of Domian and Aaronson are also too sparse to afford a check of this.

In Fig. 5, all the activation energies determined thus far are assembled as a function of composition. A conservative error limit of ±1.3 kcal/g-atom has been assigned to each. On the Mg-rich side of stoichiometry, a

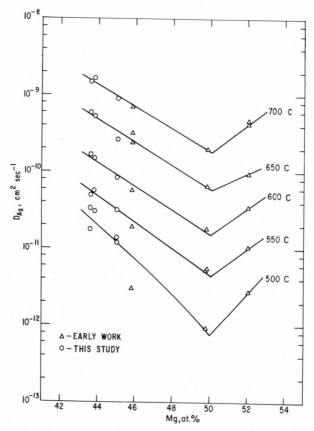

Fig. 4. Variation of D_{Ag} with composition at five temperatures investigated

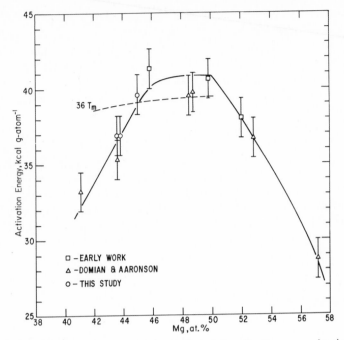

Fig. 5. Combined results (7, 8) for variation of the activation energy for Ag diffusion in AgMg with Mg content

single steep line can be drawn through the data of both sets of investigators. Compared with Hansen's (17) solidus temperatures for these compositions, this line falls more sharply than it should (assuming a simple correlation of Q with melting point); however, Domian's (8) redetermination of the Mg-rich solidus probably provides a closer correlation. On the Ag-rich side, there are three possible interpretations: (a) a maximum exists somewhere between 46 and 50 at. % Mg; (b) a single straight line goes through the triangular points up to 50 at. % Mg; or (c) the relation is as shown. A maximum off stoichiometry is unexpected, although Gupta's (18) study of the simultaneous self-diffusion of Au[195] and Cd[109] in single-crystal β-AuCd samples suggests a curved peak at 49 at. % Cd.

Domian and Aaronson have passed straight lines through their plots of log D versus at. % Mg, log D versus $1/T$, Q versus at. % Mg, log D_0 versus at. % Mg and calculated Q versus at. % Mg. In the instance of calculated Q versus at. % Mg, for which a linearly symmetric maximum was shown at 50 at. % Mg, the compositional dependence is determined to a large extent by a term ΔH_{0_i} (defined as the local disordering component of activation enthalpy required to bring a vacancy to position three of the jth six-jump cycle). For j's above 20, the sequence chosen gives unrealistically low ΔH_{0j} values, which in turn would cause lower Q's than expected. Also, their development requires knowing quantities for the sums of ΔH_f and ΔH_m (that is, the enthalpies for vacancy formation and motion) for both Mg and Ag in *disordered* β-AgMg. Because β-AgMg is ordered up to its melting temperature, and no real data can be obtained; they used β-CuZn containing 47 to 48 at. % Zn. Then it was assumed that ratios for $Q_{Zn}/T_m(\beta\text{-CuZn})$ and $Q_{Cu}/T_m(\beta\text{-CuZn})$ equaled the disordered $(\Delta H_f + \Delta H_m)_{Mg}/T_m(\beta\text{-AgMg})$ and disordered $(\Delta H_f + \Delta H_m)_{Ag}/T_m(\beta\text{-AgMg})$, respectively. When the many investigations on intermetallic compounds (2) are reviewed, it appears that diffusion in Zn-containing compounds is unusually fast and provides abnormally low Q values, which should therefore not be used as standards for other systems. Thus, the estimation procedure employed by Domian and Aaronson may not be valid.

As shown by the dashed line in Fig. 5, where Q is approximated by the empirical product (19) of 36 cal/g-atom-°K times the melting or solidus temperature (T_m), a fair correlation does exist from 45 to 50 at. % Mg. The presence of Arrhenius curvature and the drop-off in Q for alloys below 45 at. % Mg leads one to suspect some bias from low-temperature runs on samples that are not completely single phase or that possess other paths for high diffusivity.

Acknowledgments.   The authors are indebted to L. S. Butler for his assistance in sectioning and counting the diffusion specimens, and to W. F. Moore for preparation of the alloys.

References

1   J. H. Westbrook, Mechanical Properties of Intermetallic Compounds—A Review of the Literature, in Mechanical Properties of Intermetallic Compounds, edited by J. H. Westbrook, John Wiley & Sons, Inc., New York, 1960, p 1

2   W. C. Hagel, Diffusion in Intermetallic Compounds, General Electric Report No. 63-RL-3320M

3   J. H. Westbrook, Defect Structure and Temperature Dependence of Hardness of an Intermetallic Compound, J Electrochem Soc, **104**, 369 (1957)

4   D. L. Wood and J. H. Westbrook, Tensile Behavior of the Intermetallic Compound AgMg, Trans AIME, **224**, 1024 (1962)

5   A. J. Bradley and A. Taylor, An X-ray Analysis of the Nickel-Aluminum System, Proc Roy Soc, **159**, 56 (1937)

6   J. H. Westbrook and D. L. Wood, A Source of Grain-Boundary Embrittlement in Intermetallics, J Inst Metals, **91**, 174 (1963)

7   W. C. Hagel and J. H. Westbrook, Silver Diffusion in the Intermetallic Compound AgMg, Trans AIME, **221**, 951 (1961)

8 H. A. Domian and H. I. Aaronson, Self-diffusion of Silver in Beta-AgMg, Trans AIME, **230**, 44 (1964)

9 E. W. Elcock, Vacancy Diffusion in Ordered Alloys, Proc Roy Soc, **73**, 250 (1959)

10 J. H. Westbrook and W. C. Hagel, Silicon Contamination of AgMg, Trans AIME, **227**, 793 (1963)

11 P. L. Gruzin, Application of Artifically Radioactive Indicators in the Study of Diffusion and Self-Diffusion in Alloys, Self-Diffusion in Cobalt, Dokl Akad Nauk SSSR, **86**, 289 (1952)

12 A. E. Berkowitz, F. E. Jaumot and F. C. Nix, Diffusion of ^{60}Co in Some Ni-Al Alloys Containing Excess Vacancies, Phys Rev, **95**, 1185 (1954)

13 S. F. Zemczuzny, Solubility of Mg in Ag—The Equilibrium Diagram, Z Anorg Allgem Chem, **49**, 400 (1906)

14 W. Smirnov and N. Kurnakov, Silver-Magnesium, Z Anorg Allgem Chem, **72**, 31 (1911)

15 N. Ageev and V. G. Kuznetsov, X-Ray Study of Alloys of Mg and Ag, Bull Acad Sci USSR, 1937, p 289

16 H. R. Letner and S. S. Sidhu, An X-Ray Diffraction Study of the Silver-Magnesium Alloy System, J Appl Phys, **18**, 833 (1947)

17 M. Hansen, Constitution of Binary Alloys, McGraw-Hill Book Co., Inc., New York, 1958, p 30

18 D. Gupta, Self-Diffusion Studies in β-Phase Ordered Alloys of Au-Cd by Radioactive Tracer Technique, PhD Thesis, University of Illinois, 1961

19 P. G. Shewmon, Diffusion in Solids, McGraw-Hill Book Co., Inc., New York, 1963, p 65

Chapter 14

Simultaneous Diffusion of Silver and Magnesium in Stoichiometric Monocrystalline β-AgMg

H. A. DOMIAN AND H. I. AARONSON

Intermetallic compounds with an ordered bcc crystal structure of the CsCl type, such as β-AgMg, β'-CuZn and β-AuCd, consist of two inter-penetrating simple cubic sublattices, each of which is populated exclu-sively (if thermal disorder can be ignored) by atoms of one species at the stoichiometric composition. On the assumption that the unit process of diffusion in this type of lattice structure is the interchange between a vacancy* and a nearest neighboring atom, Huntington (4) and Elcock and McCombie (5, 6) have proposed that the principal diffusion mecha-nism is a closed cycle of six successive vacancy-atom exchanges. This cycle, some examples of which are illustrated in Fig. 1, requires the mini-mum number of individual exchanges or jumps to effect net mass trans-port without changing the level of long-range order in the alloy upon completion of the cycle. As the Monte Carlo calculations of Beeler (7) illustrate, the six-jump cycle consists of six *net* jumps along the path of the cycle; "excursions" developing into other types of jump configuration are energetically more costly and are thus usually retraced.

Studies of the self-diffusion of Ag[110] in polycrystalline β-AgMg have been previously reported by Hagel and Westbrook (3) and by us (8). The experimental data on the activation energy for self-diffusion have been rationalized in terms of a random-walk treatment of the six-jump cycle (8). Although the agreement obtained between theory and experiment is encouraging, the considerations of Elcock and McCombie (5, 6) and Huntington *et al.* (9) clearly indicate that a more critical appraisal of the applicability of this mechanism can be made on the basis of comparative measurements of the self-diffusivities of both Ag and Mg. Such an appraisal is most conveniently made on an alloy of stoichiometric composition.

The authors are with the Scientific Laboratory, Ford Motor Co., Dearborn, Mich.

* At least in β-AgMg, all vacancies are formed by thermal activation; none are present as a result of deviations from the stoichiometric composition (1–3).

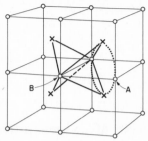

Fig. 1. Examples of the six-jump cycle. Circles and crosses represent different atomic species; square represents a vacancy. Vacancy exchanges sites with "circle" atom A at end of $2^{1/2}a_0$ cycle (dotted ellipse) and with "circle" atom B at end of any outlined a_0 cycle. "Cross" atoms participating in cycle also exchange positions upon completion.

Experimental Procedure

A single crystal of β-AgMg was grown by a modified Bridgman technique. Equiatomic proportions of Ag and Mg, both of 99.98% purity, were enclosed in an evacuated capsule fabricated from high-purity Fe. This capsule was protected from atmospheric oxidation by enclosure in an evacuated Inconel capsule. The composite capsule was then lowered through a temperature gradient of 30 C/cm at 2.7 mm/hr. The single crystal thus grown was 2.4 cm in diameter and 6.5 cm long. Following homogenization for 96 hr at 750 C, the crystal was reduced to a diameter of 2.2 cm by etching and sliced into disk-shaped diffusion specimens 3 mm thick with a spark-cutter. Electron-microprobe analysis showed that variations in composition across a given disk were less than 0.05 at. % Mg. The average composition of all the disks was 50.07 ± 0.08 at. % Mg.

In order to make the measured diffusivities of Mg and of Ag more accurately comparable, the approach used by Gupta (10) was adopted: radio-isotopes of both elements were plated onto each specimen and simultaneously diffused. Ag^{110} was electrodeposited from a cyanide solution; Mg^{28} was then evaporated onto the Ag plate by the technique of Shewmon and Rhines (11).

Diffusion specimens were encapsulated in Fe under an equivalent atmosphere of purified He; the Fe capsules were enclosed in He-filled, internally gettered Vycor capsules. Diffusion times ranged from 1.5 to 60 hr; temperatures, from 800 to 550 C at intervals of about 50 C. Corrections were made to the diffusion times for the heating and cooling cycles.

Following diffusion, from 10 to 20 sections, each 2 to 9 μ thick, were dissolved electrolytically from each specimen. An electrolyte of Na thiocyanate in a mixture of butyl cellosolve and ethyl alcohol was used at a potential of 4 v in conjunction with an Al anode. A mask with an aperture 1.8 cm in diameter prevented dissolution of material from the cylindrical surfaces and served as a reference plane for the measurement of section thickness. Appropriate compensation was made for the decrease in the average diameter of the sections that accompanied increasing depth of sectioning.

Both the electrolyte and the anode used for each section were counted in a well-type scintillation counter. Corrections were made for section thickness (12), coincidence, background, decay and counting efficiencies of both isotopes. Because counts were made from two rather closely spaced γ-ray peaks, 0.31 mev in Ag^{110} and 0.40 mev in Mg^{28}, the procedure adopted was to count each section twice—initially as soon as the sections were taken and again about a week later, when most of the Mg^{28} had decayed. Knowing the decay constants of both isotopes, we developed, from the considerations of Evans (13), the following relations to determine the counting rates of Mg, M_0, and of Ag, A_0, extrapolated to a zero time common to all sections of a particular diffusion specimen:

$$M_0 = \frac{(C_1 - B_1)K_{A_2} \exp(-\lambda_A t_2) - (C_2 - B_2)K_{A_1} \exp(-\lambda_A t_1)}{Z_1 K_{M_1} K_{A_2} \exp[-(\lambda_M t_1 + \lambda_A t_2)] - Z_2 K_{A_1} K_{M_2} \exp[-(\lambda_M t_2 + \lambda_A t_1)]} \tag{1}$$

$$A_0 = [(C_1 - B_1) - M_0 Z_1 K_{M_1} \exp(-\lambda_M t_1)]/K_{A_1} \exp(-\lambda_A t_1) \tag{2}$$

$$Z_1 = [\lambda_M \cdot \Delta t_i \exp(-\tfrac{1}{2}\lambda_M \cdot \Delta t_i)]/[1 - \exp(-\lambda_M \cdot \Delta t_i)] \tag{3}$$

In these equations, the subscripts refer to the first or the second counting "pass," Z_i is the correction for decay during counting (necessary only for Mg), C_i is the coincidence-corrected counting rate, λ_M and λ_A are decay constants for Mg and Ag, K_{M_i} and K_{A_i} are the detection efficiencies of the two species, B_i is the background counting rate, Δt_i is the time interval during which a section was counted, and t_i is the interval between zero time and the midpoint in time during the counting of a particular section. At least two pairs of counting passes were made on the sections taken from each specimen.

A program developed for the Philco 211 computer was used to calculate M_0 and A_0 for the individual sections and to determine the self-diffusivities of Mg, D_{Mg}, and Ag, D_{Ag}, from least-squares treatments of the variation of ln M_0 and ln A_0 with the square of the penetration distance (x^2). The program then examined each data point for conformance with Chauvenet's criterion (14) for acceptability. If the ratio of the difference between the experimental value of ln M_0 or ln A_0, obtained from Eq 1 or 2, and the value of this quantity (at the same x^2) predicted by the least-

squares treatment to the standard error of the experimental value wa
greater than Chauvenet's ratio (this ratio increases from 1.15 for tw
sections to 2.33 for 25 sections), the data point was rejected. Both th
least squares and the Chauvenet calculations were repeated until th
diffusivity became constant, that is, until no more data were rejected
The number of points rejected varied from none to two, and averaged les
than one. Following Davies (15), the t-test was then applied to evaluat
the significance of the difference between D_{Mg} and D_{Ag} for each pair o
diffusivities determined.

Results

The variation of the logarithm of the counting rates of Ag^{110} and Mg^{2}
with the square of the penetration distance into the same specimen i
typically illustrated in Fig. 2. Scatter about the least-squares regressio
lines through these data is somewhat greater than that obtained whe

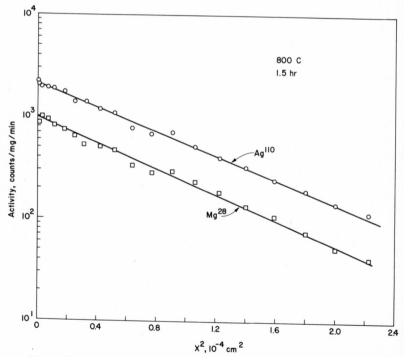

*Fig. 2. Variation of activity of Ag^{110} and Mg^{28} with square of penetration
distance*

Table 1. Diffusion Data

Composition, at. % Mg	Diffusion temp, °C	Diffusion time, hr	D_{Ag}, cm²/sec	D_{Mg}, cm²/sec	D_{Mg}/D_{Ag}	Null hypothesis probability(a)	Significance of probability(b)
50.03	549.6	39.7	5.81×10^{-12}	5.16×10^{-12}	0.89	<0.9	HS
49.99	599.3	31.8	2.68×10^{-11}	1.97×10^{-11}	0.73	≪0.1	HS
50.06	650.2	11.9	1.32×10^{-10}	8.82×10^{-11}	0.67	<0.1	HS
49.97	650.8	10.9	1.52×10^{-10}	1.36×10^{-10}	0.89	15	NS
50.08	700.0	6.5	4.02×10^{-10}	4.50×10^{-10}	1.12	0.8	HS
50.03	751.2	2.0	1.45×10^{-9}	1.80×10^{-9}	1.24	5	S
50.19	800.6	1.5	3.50×10^{-9}	3.36×10^{-9}	0.96	<0.1	HS

(a) Null hypothesis probability is the probability that there is no significant difference between D_{Ag} and D_{Mg}.
(b) Code used is as follows: HS, highly significant; NS, not significant; S, significant.

only Ag[110] was diffused, and the more accurate, conventional sectioning technique could be applied (compare Fig. 1 of Ref 8). For several sections, the counting rates of both isotopes are seen to fall above or below the regression lines, indicating that inaccuracies in section thickness are probably the principal source of the additional scatter.

The values of all of the diffusivities determined, together with the temperatures and times of the diffusion anneals and the average composition of the portion of the single crystal on which each pair of measurements was made, are recorded in Table 1. The results on the two specimens diffused at 650 C indicate that the error in D_{Mg} is probably somewhat larger than that in D_{Ag}, presumably as a result of the high decay rate of Mg[28] and the difficulties encountered in the deposition of this isotope.

The logarithms of D_{Ag} and D_{Mg} are plotted as functions of the reciprocal of the absolute diffusion temperature in Fig. 3. The following values of the activation energy, Q, and the pre-exponential factor, D_0, were obtained from least-squares analyses of these plots:

$$Q_{Ag} = 45.1 \pm 1.0 \text{ kcal/mole} \qquad D_{0_{Ag}} = 0.17 \pm 0.03 \text{ cm}^2/\text{sec}$$
$$Q_{Mg} = 47.5 \pm 1.8 \text{ kcal/mole} \qquad D_{0_{Mg}} = 0.051 \pm 0.015 \text{ cm}^2/\text{sec}$$

Statistical studies show that significant differences exist between the Q's and the D_0's, but that the magnitudes of these differences, particularly in the instance of Q, have not been precisely established.

The values of Q_{Ag} and $D_{0_{Ag}}$ are about 4.4 kcal/mole higher and a factor

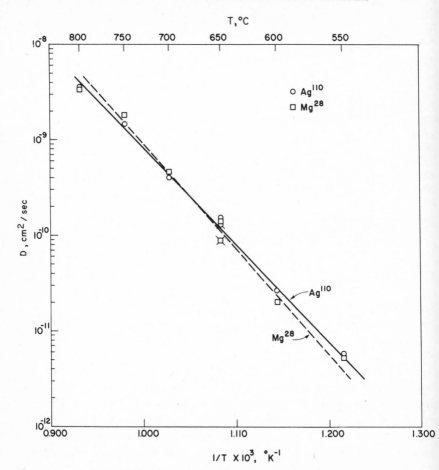

Fig. 3. Activation plots for D_{Ag} and D_{Mg}

of 1.5 to 3 smaller, respectively, than those previously reported from studies of the self-diffusion of Ag^{110} in polycrystalline alloys on the basis of direct measurement at a composition close to the stoichiometric (3) and extrapolation to this composition (8). These levels of agreement are not unreasonable when the differences in technique and in the nature of the specimens are considered.

Figure 4 illustrates the variation of the ratio D_{Mg}/D_{Ag} with temperature. Despite the scatter, two important generalizations can be made: this ratio increases with increasing temperature and is within the range $2/3$ to $4/3$ in the temperature region investigated.

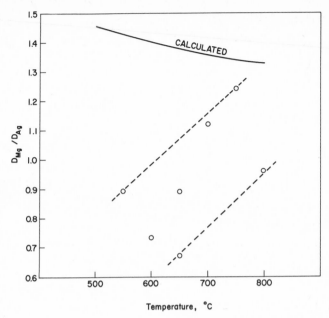

Fig. 4. Influence of temperature on measured and calculated values of D_{Mg}/D_{Ag}

Discussion

Although the average composition of the crystals deviated slightly from that of the stoichiometric, both experiment and prior theory (8) indicate that this variation is unlikely to produce substantial changes in any of the quantities under consideration. In order to permit certain points in the following treatment to be displayed more clearly, the assumption will therefore be made that we are dealing with an alloy of precisely stoichiometric composition.

The random-walk treatment previously presented for the diffusivity of Ag in β-AgMg by six-jump cycles (8) will now be reviewed in abbreviated form and some points not previously discussed will be emphasized. This treatment will then be extended to the diffusivity of Mg and to numerical determination of the ratios (though not the individual values) of the diffusivities and the D_0's. This treatment utilizes diffusion in a hypothetical disordered β-AgMg alloy (of the same composition) as a "base," and then takes account, in explicit form, of the effect of the imposition of long-range order upon the enthalpies of activation for vacancy formation and for the movement of vacancies by the six-jump cycle. In the ordered alloy, the six-jump cycle, rather than the individual vacancy-atom interchange, is considered the unit diffusion process. The general equation for the diffusivity of either species by this mechanism is

$$D = \frac{1}{6} \sum_{i=1}^{2} \sum_{j=1}^{3} \beta_j l_i^2 \nu_j N_{v_{Ag}} \exp\left(-\Delta F_{m_j}/RT\right)$$

$$+ \frac{1}{6} \sum_{i=1}^{2} \sum_{j=21}^{23} \beta_j l_i^2 \nu_j N_{v_{Mg}} \exp\left(-\Delta F_{m_j}/RT\right) \quad (4$$

where l_i is the *net* jump distance covered by a particular six-jump cycle ($l_i = 2^{1/2}a_0$ when $i = 1$ and $l_i = a_0$ when $i = 2$), ν_j is the atomic vibration frequency in the direction of the j'th cycle at the metastable energy peak of this cycle (position three in Fig. 7 of Ref 8), $N_{v_{Ag}}$ and $N_{v_{Mg}}$ are the concentrations of vacancies on the Ag and on the Mg sublattices, ΔF_{m_j} is the free energy of activation for the movement of a vacancy by j-type six jump cycles which are energetically indistinguishable and traverse the same l_i, β_j is the multiplicity factor for these cycles and gives the number of cycles with the same ΔF_{m_j} and l_i, and R and T are the gas constant and the absolute diffusion temperature. Three cycles are initiated on each sublattice (Table 2). The exponential of the free energy of activation for the movement of a vacancy can be decomposed into

$$\exp\left(-\Delta F_{m_j}/RT\right) = \exp\left(\Delta S_m/R\right) \exp\left[-(\Delta H_m' + \Delta H_{0_j})/RT\right] \quad (5$$

where ΔS_m is the entropy of activation for the movement of a vacancy in ordered β-AgMg, $\Delta H_m'$ is the enthalpy of activation for vacancy movement in disordered β-AgMg, and ΔH_{0_j} is the additional enthalpy of activa

Table 2. Description of Six-Jump Cycles in Stoichiometric β-AgMg(a)

j (b)	i (c)	Net V_{AgMg} (d), bonds broken	Net V_{AgAg} (d), bonds formed	Net V_{MgMg} (d), bonds formed	ΔH_{0_j}, cal/mole 500 C	800 C
1........ 1		9.5	3	6.5	32,410	33,25
2........ 2		10	3.5	6.5	32,140	32,98
3........ 2		10.5	3.5	7	34,755	35,66
21........ 1		9.5	6.5	3	12,195	12,58
22........ 2		10	6.5	3.5	14,810	15,27
23........ 2		10.5	7	3.5	14,540	15,00

(a) Condensed from Ref 8

(b) Cycle identification number. Cycles 4 through 20 and 24 through 40 appear at off-stoichiometric compositions.

(c) $i = 1$ refers to effective jump distance $l_i = 2^{1/2}a_0$; $i = 2$ refers to effective vacancy jump distance $l_i = a_0$.

(d) Nearest neighbor bond energies: $V_{AgMg} = -11,560$ cal/mole; $V_{AgAg} = -12,100$ cal/mole; $V_{MgMg} = -6325$ cal/mole at 500 C, -6195 cal/mole at 800 C.

tion required to move a vacancy by the six-jump cycle in ordered β-AgMg. (Thus $\Delta H_{m_j} \equiv \Delta H_m' + \Delta H_{0_j}$, where $\Delta H_m'$ is considered to have an average value, rather than a spectrum of discrete values.) Similarly, the vacancy concentration on the k'th sublattice is

$$N_{v_k} = \exp\left(\Delta S_{f_k}/R\right) \exp\left(-\Delta H_{f_k}/RT\right)$$
$$= \exp\left(\Delta S_{f_k}/R\right) \exp\left[-(\Delta H_f' + \Delta_k)/RT\right] \quad (6)$$

where ΔS_{f_k} and ΔH_{f_k} are the entropy and enthalpy of activation, respectively, for the formation of vacancies on this sublattice in the ordered alloy, $\Delta H_f'$ is the average enthalpy of activation for vacancy formation in disordered β-AgMg, and Δ_k is the additional enthalpy of activation required to form vacancies on the k'th sublattice. At the stoichiometric composition (8),

$$\Delta_{Ag} = -\tfrac{5}{4}(V_{AgMg} - V_{AgAg}) \quad (7a)$$
$$\Delta_{Mg} = -\tfrac{5}{4}(V_{AgMg} - V_{MgMg}) \quad (7b)$$

where V_{AgMg}, V_{AgAg} and V_{MgMg} are the enthalpies of formation of Ag-Mg, Ag-Ag and Mg-Mg bonds. In Ref 8, an empirical scaling rule was applied to obtain $\Delta H_{f+m_{Ag}}'$ and $\Delta H_{f+m_{Mg}}'$ as a function of composition from their counterparts in disordered β-CuZn. It is now convenient to collect certain exponential terms by defining two new quantities. At the stoichiometric composition:

$$Y_{Ag} \equiv \Delta H_{f+m_{Ag}}' + \Delta_{Ag} = 21{,}040 - \tfrac{5}{4}(V_{AgMg} - V_{AgAg}) \quad (8a)$$
$$Y_{Mg} \equiv \Delta H_{f+m_{Mg}}' + \Delta_{Mg} = 17{,}850 - \tfrac{5}{4}(V_{AgMg} - V_{MgMg}) \quad (8b)$$

In terms of the foregoing, Eq 4 is rewritten as

$$D = \tfrac{1}{6}\nu \exp\left[(\Delta S_f + \Delta S_m)/R\right] \left[\sum_{i=1}^{2}\sum_{j=1}^{3} \exp\left(-Y_{Ag}/RT\right) \beta_j l_i^2 \times \right.$$
$$\left. \exp\left(-\Delta H_{0_j}/RT\right) + \sum_{i=1}^{2}\sum_{j=21}^{23} \exp\left(-Y_{Mg}/RT\right) \beta_j l_i^2 \exp\left(-\Delta H_{0_j}/RT\right) \right] \quad (9)$$

All values of ν_j have been necessarily assumed equal to ν. Similarly, the differences in the entropies of formation and movement of vacancies on the Mg and the Ag sublattices have necessarily been ignored. The latter approximation, however, should have negligible numerical influence upon the results, because the first group of summed terms is found to have a much smaller value than the second group.

We now apply Eq 9 to D_{Ag} and D_{Mg} on the basis of the finding (8) that a vacancy can reach 12 other sites on the same sublattice upon completion of a single six-jump cycle for which $l_i = 2^{1/2}a_0$ and six additional sites on this sublattice through cycles with $l_i = a_0$. Inspection of Fig. 1 shows that the $2^{1/2}a_0$ cycles can be executed in two different ways and that the a_0 cycles can be completed by traversing 12 distinguishable paths.

Computation of ΔH_{0_i} was performed on the basis of the net number of Ag-Mg bonds broken and the net numbers of Ag-Ag and Mg-Mg bonds formed* as the vacancy travels from its initial position to the peak metastable energy position of the cycle. The ΔH_{0_i}'s are identical for the two $2^{1/2}a_0$ cycles in Fig. 1; the four planar a_0 cycles exhibit a second ΔH_{0_i}, and the eight "bent" a_0 cycles are characterized by a third value. The net numbers of bonds formed and broken, and the values of ΔH_{0_i} at two temperatures, based on the listed bond energies, are given in Table 2 for the three energetically distinguishable cycles initiated on each sublattice.

With regard to the l_i terms associated with the various ΔH_{0_i}'s, Fig. 1 shows that when the vacancy and a "circle" atom exchange positions by means of a $2^{1/2}a_0$ cycle, $l_i = 2^{1/2}a_0$, whereas the two "cross" atoms that simultaneously exchange positions are displaced by $l_i = a_0$. When a vacancy and a "circle" atom exchange by one of the twelve a_0 cycles, the "circle" atom is displaced by $l_i = a_0$, whereas the "cross" atoms are moved $l_i = 2^{1/2}a_0$ by the four planar cycles and $l_i = a_0$ by the eight bent cycles.

In terms of the individual diffusivities, Eq 9 now becomes

$$
\begin{aligned}
D_{\mathrm{Ag}} = {} & \tfrac{1}{6}\nu \exp\left[(\Delta S_f + \Delta S_m)/R\right] \{\exp\left(-Y_{\mathrm{Ag}}/RT\right)\,[24 \\
& \qquad\qquad\qquad\qquad\qquad\qquad\qquad \times 2a_0{}^2 \exp\left(-\Delta H_{0_1}/RT\right) \\
& + 24 \times a_0{}^2 \exp\left(-\Delta H_{0_2}/RT\right) + 48 \times a_0{}^2 \exp\left(-\Delta H_{0_3}/RT\right)] \\
& + \exp\left(-Y_{\mathrm{Mg}}/RT\right)\,[24 \times a_0{}^2 \exp\left(-\Delta H_{0_{21}}/RT\right) \\
& + 24 \times 2a_0{}^2 \exp\left(-\Delta H_{0_{22}}/RT\right) + 48 \times a_0{}^2 \exp\left(-\Delta H_{0_{23}}/RT\right)]\} \\
= {} & 4a_0{}^2\nu \exp\left[(\Delta S_f + \Delta S_m)/R\right] \{\exp\left(-Y_{\mathrm{Ag}}/RT\right)\,[2\exp\left(-\Delta H_{0_1}/RT\right) \\
& + \exp\left(-\Delta H_{0_2}/RT\right) + 2\exp\left(-\Delta H_{0_3}/RT\right)] \\
& + \exp\left(-Y_{\mathrm{Mg}}/RT\right)\,[\exp\left(-\Delta H_{0_{21}}/RT\right) + \exp\left(-\Delta H_{0_{22}}/RT\right) \\
& + 2\exp\left(-\Delta H_{0_{23}}/RT\right)]\}
\end{aligned}
\tag{10}
$$

$$
\begin{aligned}
D_{\mathrm{Mg}} = {} & \tfrac{1}{6}\nu \exp\left[(\Delta S_f + \Delta S_m)/R\right] \{\exp\left(-Y_{\mathrm{Ag}}/RT\right)\,[24 \\
& \qquad\qquad\qquad\qquad\qquad\qquad\qquad \times a_0{}^2 \exp\left(-\Delta H_{0_1}/RT\right) \\
& + 24 \times 2a_0{}^2 \exp\left(-\Delta H_{0_2}/RT\right) + 48 \times a_0{}^2 \exp\left(-\Delta H_{0_3}/RT\right)] \\
& + \exp\left(-Y_{\mathrm{Mg}}/RT\right)\,[24 \times 2a_0{}^2 \exp\left(-\Delta H_{0_{21}}/RT\right) \\
& + 24 \times a_0{}^2 \exp\left(-\Delta H_{0_{22}}/RT\right) + 48 \times a_0{}^2 \exp\left(-\Delta H_{0_{23}}/RT\right)]\} \\
= {} & 4a_0{}^2\nu \exp\left[(\Delta S_f + \Delta S_m)/R\right] \{\exp\left(-Y_{\mathrm{Ag}}/RT\right)\,[\exp\left(-\Delta H_{0_1}/RT\right) \\
& + 2\exp\left(-\Delta H_{0_2}/RT\right) + 2\exp\left(-\Delta H_{0_3}/RT\right)] \\
& + \exp\left(-Y_{\mathrm{Mg}}/RT\right)\,[2\exp\left(-\Delta H_{0_{21}}/RT\right) + \exp\left(-\Delta H_{0_{22}}/RT\right) \\
& + 2\exp\left(-\Delta H_{0_{22}}/RT\right)]\}
\end{aligned}
\tag{11}
$$

* Taking the second nearest neighboring bond enthalpy as half the nearest neighboring enthalpy for a bond of the same type (16–18).

Comparison of Eq 10 and 11 shows that the difference between D_{Ag} and D_{Mg} is ascribed, in this approximation, solely to the difference in the l_i^2 terms. Unlike previous theories (5, 6), a multiplying factor of two is not applied to the jump frequencies corresponding to the net interchange of two "cross" atoms in Fig. 1, even though only one "circle" atom is simultaneously displaced. As Zener (19) has pointed out, the jump frequency, Γ_i, in the elementary random-walk equation, $D = (\frac{1}{6}) \sum_i \Gamma_i l_i^2$, represents the rate at which an individual atom makes the particular jump i associated with the displacement l_i. If other atoms are simultaneously displaced, their contribution to D will also be individually assessed by the summation process. Thus, if diffusion takes place in a bcc metal by means of Zener's four-atom ring, which is formally somewhat similar to the six-jump cycle, $D = (\frac{1}{6}) \times 8 \times 3 \times (3^{\frac{1}{2}}a_0/2)^2 \times \nu \exp(-\Delta F_m/RT)$, where the number of sites attainable by rotation of such a ring is 8, the number of rings by which a given site can be reached is 3, and the effective jump distance is $3^{\frac{1}{2}}a_0/2$.

On this basis, the ratio of the diffusivities of the two atomic species will not necessarily follow directly from considerations of lattice configuration even when effectively all generation and/or movement of vacancies is initiated from one sublattice. Computation of this ratio also requires knowledge of the enthalpies of activation for the operation of the various six-jump cycles.

From the relation $[\partial \ln D/\partial(1/T)] = -Q/R$, the over-all activation energy, Q, for the diffusion of either Ag or Mg can be written

$$Q = \frac{\begin{aligned}&\exp(-Y_{Ag}/RT) \sum_{j=1}^{3} \gamma_{k,j}(\Delta H_{0_j} + Y_{Ag}) \exp(-\Delta H_{0_j}/RT) \\ &\quad + \exp(-Y_{Mg}/RT) \sum_{j=21}^{23} \gamma_{k,j}(\Delta H_{0_j} + Y_{Mg}) \exp(-\Delta H_{0_j}/RT)\end{aligned}}{\begin{aligned}&\exp(-Y_{Ag}/RT) \sum_{j=1}^{3} \gamma_{k,j} \exp(-\Delta H_{0_j}/RT) \\ &\quad + \exp(-Y_{Mg}/RT) \sum_{j=21}^{23} \gamma_{k,j} \exp(-\Delta H_{0_j}/RT)\end{aligned}}$$

(12)

where $k = 1$ refers to Q_{Ag} and $k = 2$ to Q_{Mg}, and the various $\gamma_{k,j} \equiv \beta_{k,j} \times l_i^2$ and ΔH_{0_j} are as given in Eq 10 and 11.

Numerical evaluation of this equation, made on the bases of Eq 8a and 8b and Table 2, yields values of Q_{Ag} that vary from 37.7 to 38.5 kcal/mole as the diffusion temperature is increased from 500 to 800 C and values of Q_{Mg} that similarly increase from 37.2 to 37.9 kcal/mole. The average calculated values are

$$\bar{Q}_{Ag} = 38.1 \text{ kcal/mole}$$
$$\bar{Q}_{Mg} = 37.5 \text{ kcal/mole}$$

Although the absolute values of these energies are appreciably lower than the experimental values, the calculated ratio $\bar{Q}_{Mg}/\bar{Q}_{Ag} = 0.984$ is quite close to the experimental ratio of 1.053, and within even the one-standard-error (68% confidence limit) range of this ratio.

Even though $D_{0_{Ag}}$ and $D_{0_{Mg}}$ cannot be separately evaluated because sufficiently accurate estimates of ΔS_f and ΔS_m are not yet feasible, the ratio of the D_0's can be determined from the relations

$$D_{0_{Mg}}/D_{0_{Ag}} = \exp\left[\ln \Psi_{Mg} - \ln \Psi_{Ag} + (\bar{Q}_{Mg} - \bar{Q}_{Ag})/RT\right] \tag{13}$$

$$\Psi_k = \exp\left(-Y_{Ag}/RT\right) \sum_{j=1}^{3} \gamma_{k,j} \exp\left(-\Delta H_{0_j}/RT\right)$$

$$+ \exp\left(-Y_{Mg}/RT\right) \sum_{j=21}^{23} \gamma_{k,j} \exp\left(-\Delta H_{0_j}/RT\right)$$

Similarly, the ratio of D_{Mg} to D_{Ag} at a given temperature is

$$D_{Mg}/D_{Ag} = \Psi_{Mg}/\Psi_{Ag} \tag{14}$$

The difference between the ratio $D_{0_{Mg}}/D_{0_{Ag}} = 0.30$ measured experimentally and the calculated ratio of 1.01 can perhaps be regarded as significant. The discrepancies between the experimental and the computed values of D_{Mg}/D_{Ag}, shown in Fig. 4, are clearly appreciable. Both of these differences, as well as the result that $\bar{Q}_{Mg}/\bar{Q}_{Ag}$ is a little less than unity, instead of slightly greater, appear to stem largely from a single common cause. This factor may be clearly identified by means of the following approximation. Because $\bar{Q}_{Mg}$ and $\bar{Q}_{Ag}$ are only minutely changed by the elimination of Ag-sublattice vacancies but are raised about 15 kcal/mole when the contribution of Mg-sublattice vacancies is ignored, only a very small error is introduced by assuming that $Y_{Ag} = \infty$. Thus

$$\frac{D_{Mg}}{D_{Ag}} = \frac{2 \exp\left(-\Delta H_{0_{21}}/RT\right) + \exp\left(-\Delta H_{0_{22}}/RT\right) + 2 \exp\left(-\Delta H_{0_{23}}/RT\right)}{\exp\left(-\Delta H_{0_{21}}/RT\right) + 2 \exp\left(-\Delta H_{0_{22}}/RT\right) + 2 \exp\left(-\Delta H_{0_{23}}/RT\right)} \tag{15}$$

Although the data in Table 2 show $\Delta H_{0_{21}} < \Delta H_{0_{22}}$, the experimental results in Fig. 4 indicate that $\Delta H_{0_{21}} > \Delta H_{0_{22}}$. The calculated difference in these enthalpies, about 2650 cal/mole, is not a large one, however, and quite possibly lies below the "limit of resolution" of the bond-breaking-and-forming model upon which these computations are based. The form of Eq 15 is such, however, that the magnitude, and especially the sign of this difference, have a crucial effect on D_{Mg}/D_{Ag}. The ratio $D_{0_{Mg}}/D_{0_{Ag}}$ is similarly affected, through the influence of these quantities upon Ψ_{Mg}. In the instance of Q_{Mg}/Q_{Ag} (Eq 12), however, the $(\Delta H_{0_j} + Y_{Mg})$ term largely damps small changes in ΔH_{0_j}; this ratio is thus insensitive to the differences under consideration.

An assessment of the validity of this approach, which is not dependent upon a detailed evaluation of ΔH_{0_j}, is now clearly desirable. This is readily made on the basis of Eq 15 by taking the extremum relative values of ΔH_{0_j}. Thus, if $\Delta H_{0_{21}} \ll \Delta H_{0_{22}} \sim \Delta H_{0_{23}}$, then $D_{Mg}/D_{Ag} \sim 2$; if $\Delta H_{0_{22}} \ll \Delta H_{0_{21}} \sim \Delta H_{0_{23}}$, then $D_{Mg}/D_{Ag} \sim \frac{1}{2}$; if $\Delta H_{0_{23}} \ll \Delta H_{0_{21}} \sim \Delta H_{0_{22}}$, then $D_{Mg}/D_{Ag} \sim 1$. The outer limits of these ratios, $\frac{1}{2} < D_{Mg}/D_{Ag} < 2$,* are seen to be consistent with the experimental data. This result provides basic support for the conclusion that the six-jump cycle is the dominant mechanism of diffusion in β-AgMg.

Huntington *et al.* (9) report that $D_{Cd}/D_{Au} \sim 1.35$ in stoichiometric β-AuCd. The diffusivity ratio calculated on the same basis used for β-AgMg is 1.52 at 450 C, the middle of the experimental diffusion range. This much better agreement suggests that the bond-breaking-and-forming model may be a more satisfactory approximation in the instance of β-AuCd.

Although the quasi-chemical model does not seem to be generally accurate for CsCl-type compounds—hardly a novel conclusion—it nonetheless seems worthwhile to examine further some over-all aspects of the particular form of this model used here. Calculations made in this paper and Ref 8, in which this model is invoked, have been performed on the basis of both first and second nearest neighbor interactions. The conventional qualitative argument that screening of an atom from neighbors more distant than nearest is significantly less complete in bcc than in fcc structures forms, of course, part of the justification for the adoption of this model. A further supporting argument is that transformation of a lattice from the fcc to the bcc structure requires that the bond energy be increased by 50% on an entirely first-nearest-neighbors model, but by only about 9% when both first and second nearest neighbors are considered in the bcc lattice. Because Kaufman (20) calculates that the

* These limits may be compared with the $\frac{2}{3}$-to-$\frac{3}{2}$ range predicted by Elcock (6).

enthalpy change associated with an fcc $\rightleftarrows$ bcc transformation is often about 1% of the enthalpy of sublimation, the model used here would appear to be appreciably less inaccurate.

When only nearest neighbors are considered, $N_{v_{Ag}} = N_{v_{Mg}}$ (21); inclusion of second-nearest-neighbor interactions, however, inevitably destroys this equality. If N_v is computed solely on a bond-breaking model

$$N_{v_{Mg}}/N_{v_{Ag}} = \exp\left[(\Delta S_{f_{Mg}} - \Delta S_{f_{Ag}})/R\right] \exp\left[-3(V_{AgAg} - V_{MgMg})/RT\right] \quad (16)$$

Because $V_{AgAg} \sim 1.9 V_{MgMg}$, $N_{v_{Mg}} > N_{v_{Ag}}$ unless the difference in entropies of formation is exceedingly large. A strictly bond-breaking model, however, tends greatly to overestimate ΔH_f (22). The semiempirically modified approach used here and in Ref 8 yields, less pronouncedly, $N_{v_{Ag}} > N_{v_{Mg}}$. Because the ΔH_{0_j}'s are much less for Mg-sublattice vacancies (Table 2), however, virtually all of the vacancies that do move are those formed on this sublattice. This conclusion leads to the interesting prediction that the sum of the enthalpies of formation and movement of vacancies in β-AgMg and similar intermetallic compounds, as measured by quenching and annealing techniques, should not equal the enthalpy of activation for diffusion, as determined by the radiotracer technique. The results of Wayman et al. (23, 24) on stoichiometric β-AuCd tend to confirm this prediction, but were perhaps complicated by the use of rather thick wires and other problems. It would seem quite instructive to perform studies of this type on β-AgMg, in which advantage could be taken of the absence of a low-temperature transformation and a well-characterized defect structure.

Acknowledgments. Appreciation is expressed to E. T. Kennedy for assistance in the laboratory, to Dr. J. Cost and Dr. N. A. Gjostein for their comments on the manuscript, and to C. E. Carrig and A. Zold for discussions of computer programing.

References

1 N. V. Ageev and V. G. Kusnetsov, Bull Acad Sci USSR, 289 (1937)
2 H. R. Letner and S. S. Sidhu, J Appl Phys, **18**, 833 (1947)
3 W. C. Hagel and J. H. Westbrook, Trans AIME, **221**, 951 (1961)
4 H. B. Huntington, private communication to L. Slifkin, reported in Ref 5
5 E. W. Elcock and C. W. McCombie, Phys Rev, **109**, 605 (1958)
6 E. W. Elcock, Proc Phys Soc London, **73**, 250 (1959)
7 J. R. Beeler and J. A. Delaney, Phys Rev, **130**, 962 (1963)
8 H. A. Domian and H. I. Aaronson, Trans AIME, **230**, 44 (1964)
9 H. B. Huntington, N. C. Miller and V. Nerses, Acta Met, **9**, 749 (1961)
10 D. Gupta, Thesis, University of Illinois, 1961
11 P. G. Shewmon and F. N. Rhines, Trans AIME, **200**, 1021 (1954)

12 G. A. Shirn, E. S. Wadja and H. B. Huntington, Acta Met, **1**, 518 (1953)
13 R. D. Evans, The Atomic Nucleus, McGraw-Hill Book Co., New York, 1955
14 A. G. Worthing and J. Geffner, Treatment of Experimental Data, John Wiley & Sons, Inc., New York, 1943
15 O. L. Davies, Statistical Methods in Research and Production, Oliver and Boyd, London, 1949
16 I. N. Stranski and R. Suhrmann, Ann Physik, **1**, 153 (1947)
17 J. P. Hirth and G. M. Pound, J Chem Phys, **26**, 1216 (1957)
18 J. P. Barbour, F. M. Carbonnier, W. W. Dolan, W. P. Dyke, E. E. Martin and J. K. Trolan, Phys Rev, **117**, 1452 (1960)
19 C. Zener, Imperfections in Nearly Perfect Crystals, John Wiley & Sons, Inc., New York, 1952, p 289
20 L. Kaufman, Technical Report No. 2, Manufacturing Laboratories, Cambridge, Mass., 1959
21 L. A. Girifalco, J Phys Chem Solids, **24**, 323 (1964)
22 N. Brooks, Impurities and Imperfections, American Society for Metals, Metals Park, 1955, p 1
23 C. M. Wayman, K. M. Thein and N. Nakanishi, J Appl Phys, **34**, 2842 (1963)
24 N. Nakanishi, K. M. Thein and C. M. Wayman, J Appl Phys, **34**, 2847 (1963)

Chapter 15
Diffusion in Magnetic Materials

R. J. Borg

The diffusivity in several ferromagnetic metals and alloys is found to decrease more rapidly with decreasing temperature in the vicinity of T_c, the Curie temperature, than predicted by the Arrhenius relation. This departure from the customary linear relation between $\ln D$ and T^{-1} has been termed the "magnetic effect." It is illustrated in Fig. 1, which presents the results of diffusion in Fe and in an Fe-V alloy.

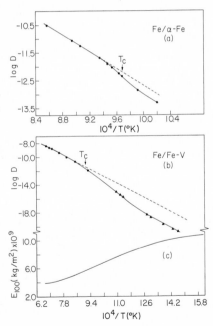

Fig. 1. (a) Self-diffusion coefficients for Fe and α-Fe (1). (b) Diffusion coefficients of Fe and Fe−18% V. The dashed lines are drawn to emphasize the lack of linearity in the region of the magnetic transformation (6). (c) Young's modulus as a function of temperature of Fe−3% Si.

The author is with the Lawrence Radiation Laboratory, University of California, Livermore, Calif.

Although the exact functional dependence of D upon T is somewhat obscured by the inherent impreciseness of diffusion measurements, two general features seem to characterize it wherever it is found: first, the departure from linearity occurs over a temperature range extending both above and below T_c; second, the diffusion coefficients below T_c are lower than predicted by extrapolation of the results from higher temperatures.

In discussing the possible causes and magnitude of the magnetic effect, it is first necessary to obtain some reliable estimate of the extent of the nonlinear behavior with respect to temperature. Lacking this, it is impossible to decide upon the proper values for diffusion in the region of complete spin disorder, and hence there is no basis upon which to evaluate the magnitude of the influence of magnetic order. In brief, one must first determine whether the material in question possesses a temperature range that is convenient for diffusion measurements and that is free of the influence of magnetism.

Measurements of the diffusion (12) of Fe and Co into δ-Fe yield activation energies almost 10 kcal less than those obtained by the same authors (1, 4) in the paramagnetic region of α-Fe. This was considered sufficient evidence to conclude that most of the paramagnetic region of α-Fe was still influenced by the short-range order of spins. Short-range order has been demonstrated to exist up to at least 850 C by means of neutron diffraction (18).

This conclusion has since been further verified by diffusion measurements in Fe−1.8 at. % V, an alloy that is bcc at all temperatures. These results are shown in Fig. 2 and for the linear portion, namely $T \gtrsim 900$ C, are well described by

$$D = 1.3 \exp\left(-56.5 \times 10^3/RT\right)$$

Because additional measurements are still in progress, the rates of D_0 and Q given above must be regarded as tentative. However, they are essentially identical with the values previously reported (12) for δ-Fe, namely

$$D = 1.9 \exp\left(-57.0 \times 10^3/RT\right)$$

Assuming Fe−1.8 at.% V to be nearly identical to pure Fe, with respect to diffusion, we may conclude that the effect of magnetism is prevalent and detectable up to some temperature between 875 and 900 C. The assumption that Fe and the alloy are indistinguishable in their diffusive behavior in the linear region has been demonstrated experimentally. Measurements on samples of Fe and the alloy simultaneously diffused at 1435 C and 871 C agreed to within 1%.

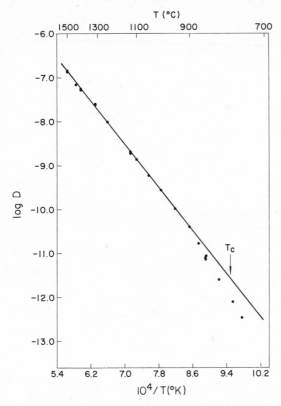

Fig. 2. The diffusion coefficients of Fe in Fe−1.8 at. % V

A value of about 57 kcal has been reported twice previously (2, 19) for the self-diffusion of Fe in the paramagnetic region. However, in neither instance was the range of temperatures sufficient to establish this result with any great accuracy or to establish the limit of the magnetic effect. Consequently, the agreement with the present results on Fe-V and with δ-Fe is regarded as somewhat fortuitous.

Although the upper limit of the influence of magnetism has now been determined, the lower bound remains uncertain. It is, furthermore, seemingly impossible to determine this limit at present, because of the small values of D below ∼700 C.

Unfortunately, as yet no other magnetic metals have been as thoroughly studied as Fe, and we know even less about the extent and strength of the influence of magnetic order. Table 1 lists the systems in which the magnetic effect has been thus far observed.

The evidence for the existence of a magnetic effect in connection with

Table 1. Systems in Which the Magnetic Effect Has Been Observed

Matrix	Diffusion element	Technique	Ref
Fe.....................	Fe	Tracer	1, 2
Fe.....................	Ni	Tracer	3, 4
Fe.....................	Co, Au	Tracer	4
Fe.....................	Cu	Chemical	5
Fe – 18 at. % V.........	Fe	Tracer plus internal friction	6
Fe – 1.8 at. % V........	Fe	Tracer	7
Co-Ni alloys...........	Co, Ni	Tracer	8

interstitial diffusion is less well substantiated. Recent measurements (9) of the diffusion of C in α-Fe have revealed a hitherto unsuspected lack of conformity with the Arrhenius relation. Unfortunately, the measurements do not extend to sufficiently high temperatures to permit separation of the paramagnetic region from the ferromagnetic. Smith (9) has critically reassessed all pertinent data and proposed the values shown in Fig. 3. The broken straight line through the high-temperature values serves to emphasize that linearity is not maintained over the entire range of temperature.

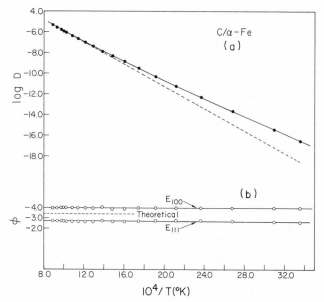

Fig. 3. (a) The diffusion of C in α-Fe (9). (b) Same data corrected for the temperature variation of the elastic properties.

The diffusion of C in Co and Co-rich Fe alloys (10) does not appear to deviate from the Arrhenius relation although a small departure would perhaps be hidden by the usual scatter of the measurements. It is interesting to note that the diffusion of Ni and Co in pure Co and Co-rich Ni alloys also failed to reveal the magnetic effect. However, in no investigation to date have the measurements in Co been extended over a sufficient temperature range both above and below T_c to rule out the possibility of a small but observable magnetic effect.

We now turn our attention to the possible causes of the magnetic effect, which we will discuss in terms of absolute-rate theory. The usual formulation in an obvious notation is

$$
\begin{aligned}
D &= \rho \nu l^2 \exp\left[-(\Delta G_m + \Delta G_f)/RT\right] \\
&= \rho \nu l^2 \exp\left[(\Delta S_m + \Delta S_f)/R\right] \exp\left[-(\Delta H_m + \Delta H_f)/RT\right]
\end{aligned} \tag{1}
$$

Assuming a vacancy mechanism, the subscripts m and f in Eq 1 refer to the motion and formation of the vacancy, respectively.

The first attempt to explain the effect of ferromagnetism (1) upon diffusion considered only the variation in ΔH_f. A possible variation in ΔG_m was ignored because the elastic-constant data at that time could not be reconciled with the diffusion data. ΔS_f was also neglected because it is not clear how this could be calculated, although the variation due to magnetism was believed to be small. Acknowledging these limitations, an estimate of the magnitude of the change in ΔH_f was made as follows: if an atom has Z nearest neighbors, X having like spin and Y unlike spin,

$$
Z = X + Y \tag{2}
$$

The exchange energy is $-J$ for a pair with like spin and is $+J$ for a pair with unlike spin. The difference between the internal energy of the state with short-range order E_0 and the internal energy of the state with random spins E_r is

$$
E_0 - E_r = -J(X - Y) \tag{3}
$$

for a pair of atoms. The energy per atom is, on the average, $(-J/2)$ $\times (X - Y)$. If a short-range order parameter is defined by

$$
s = (X - Y)/Z \tag{4}
$$

the energy change per atom is $-ZJs/2$. Because the total energy change involved in a magnetic transformation is about kT_c

$$
J \approx 2/Z(bkT_c) \tag{5}
$$

where b is a constant that is unity in the simple Bragg-Williams approximation or about 0.60 in a more detailed treatment of the bcc structure (13). A semi-empirical evaluation (14) gives $b = 0.44$, and an estimate based on spin wave theory (14) predicts $b = 0.72$.

The excess enthalpy of formation approximately equals the change in internal energy per atom that must be supplied in forming a vacancy. Combining Eq 3, 4 and 5, one has

$$\Delta H_f{}^x \approx bRT_c s \tag{6}$$

This treatment has been recently extended (20) in an attempt to explicitly calculate the temperature dependence of J.

However, one cannot account for the decrease in D completely by the vacancy-decrease model just presented. The model grossly overestimates the effect of magnetic order upon the equilibrium vacancy concentration but still accounts for a decrease in D by a factor of only three, whereas the results obtained from Fe-V (see Fig. 2) require a decrease from the extrapolated values by a factor of $\sim$160. Thus, we may conclude from a more or less strictly thermodynamic argument that, although a decrease in vacancy concentration does result from the loss of energy accompanying the magnetic transformation, it is insufficient to explain the entire magnetic effect. Consequently, we are forced to re-examine the effect of magnetism upon ΔG_m.

Young's modulus has been measured recently (15) for Fe–3% Si up to 1100 C. The results for the $\langle 100 \rangle$ direction are shown in Fig. 1 (c). Contrary to earlier measurements, the temperature dependence is now of the correct form to account for the magnetic effect, if the plastic behavior of Fe–3% Si is assumed to be nearly the same as that of pure Fe.

The elastic properties can be related to the diffusion coefficients by use of the model first proposed by Zener (16) and subsequently elaborated by Le Claire (17). In accordance with the model

$$\Delta G_m \cong kE \tag{7}$$

The constant k has the dimensions of volume and is equivalent to the term $k_2(M/\rho)$ in the Le Claire (17) derivation. Choosing Young's modulus E to be in a $\langle 100 \rangle$ direction, and substituting Eq 7 into Eq 1 and rearranging, one obtains

$$\Phi \equiv \ln D + (kE_{100}/RT) = \ln (\rho\nu l^2) - \Delta G_f/RT \tag{8}$$

Ignoring the small correction for thermal expansion and plotting against

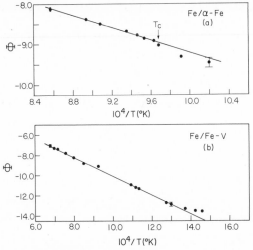

Fig. 4. The function Φ combines log D with Young's modulus according to the Zener-Le Claire model. (a) Data of Fig. 1(a) and (c) thus treated. (b) Data of Fig. 1(b) thus treated.

the reciprocal of temperature, one should obtain a straight line whose slope is proportional to ΔH_f. Such plots, shown in Fig. 4, use the data presented in Fig. 1. The values of k are selected solely to give the best fit of the data to Eq 8 and are 1.05 for α-Fe and 0.932 for Fe-V. A realistic estimate of the limits of error allows $\pm 10\%$ variation in D and 2% error in E_{100} at lower temperatures; at the higher temperatures the latter remains the same, and only $\pm 2\%$ variation in D is allowed. As can be seen in Fig. 4, the temperature variation of Φ is commensurate with the magnetic effect.

The slope, $d\Phi/d(1/T)$, is quite sensitive to the value of k, whereas the scatter of the individual measurements, which is the criterion for choosing k, is not. For this reason, as well as the inherent errors in the data, one cannot derive an accurate value of ΔH_f from Eq 8; however, it is of interest to calculate this quantity to discover whether it is reasonable or absurd. In fact, one calculates for ΔH_f, 35 kcal for δ-Fe and 43 kcal for the alloy, both of which are undoubtedly correct to within 50%.

Two objections can be raised to the foregoing analysis: first, one may question the choice of E_{100} rather than a more complex description of the deformation about the saddle point; and second, one may question the advisability of applying data pertinent to Fe–3% Si to Fe–18% V. With regard to the first point, it must be admitted that without a reliable description of diffusion in bcc structures E_{100} was selected mainly on the basis of inspection. It is expected that the temperature dependence of E, with which we are primarily concerned, is far less sensitive to direction and composition than its actual values are. The fact that Si lowers T_c but V raises it is a valid criticism; however, in this analysis the discrepancy is not detectable.

For interstitial diffusion one can apply the same analysis but with ΔG_f equal to zero and the correlation coefficient ρ equal to one. Rewriting Eq 8 one obtains

$$\Phi \equiv \ln D + kE/RT = \ln (l^2 \nu/6) \qquad (9)$$

Again, solely by minimizing the scatter, k is found to be 0.301 and 0.557 for $\langle 111 \rangle$ and $\langle 100 \rangle$ respectively; the resulting plots of Φ are shown in Fig. 3(b). It is apparent that Φ is a temperature-independent constant in accord with Eq 9, and the average values of $\langle \Phi_{100} \rangle$ and $\langle \Phi_{111} \rangle$ are -2.68 ± 0.04 and -3.95 ± 0.03, respectively. To determine a reasonable value for $\langle \Phi \rangle$ we can calculate the right side of Eq 9 independently. Taking ν equal to 1.3×10^{-3} sec^{-1}, as calculated by Wert and Zener (21), and substituting this value along with the square of the jump distance, one obtains $\langle \Phi \rangle = -3.36$. This value, as shown in Fig. 3(b), lies almost exactly midway between the two extreme values corresponding to $\langle 100 \rangle$ and $\langle 111 \rangle$. Thus, although a single direction for Young's modulus appears to be an oversimplification, the calculations tend to support the fundamental hypothesis.

In summary, both the decrease in vacancy concentration and the change in elastic properties contribute to the magnetic effect but the latter is dominant. This conclusion rests primarily upon the elastic behavior of Fe-Si and such inferences as can be made concerning the contribution of the magnetic energy to ΔH_f.

Certainly more measurements in other magnetic systems, especially of the elastic properties as well as the diffusion coefficients, are needed before one can finally resolve and quantify the underlying causes of the magnetic effect.

Acknowledgment.   This work was performed under the auspices of the U. S. Atomic Energy Commission.

References

1   R. J. Borg and C. E. Birchinall, Trans AIME, **218,** 980 (1960)
2   F. W. Buffington, K. Hirano and M. Cohen, Acta Met, **9,** 434 (1961)
3   K. Hirano, M. Cohen and B. L. Averbach, Acta Met, **9,** 440 (1961)
4   R. J. Borg and D. Y. F. Lai, Acta Met, **11,** 861 (1963)
5   G. R. Speich, private communication

6   J. Stanley and C. Wert, J Appl Phys, **32**, 267 (1961)

7   D. Y. F. Lai and R. J. Borg, to be published

8   K. Hirano, R. P. Agarwala, B. L. Averbach and M. Cohen, J Appl Phys, **33**, 3049 (1962)

9   R. P. Smith, Trans AIME, **224**, 105 (1962)

10 R. P. Smith, Trans AIME, **230**, 476 (1964)

11 R. J. Borg, J Appl Phys, **34**, 1562 (1963)

12 R. J. Borg, D. Y. F. Lai and O. H. Krikorian, Acta Met, **11**, 867 (1963)

13 P. R. Weiss, Phys Rev, **74**, 1493 (1948)

14 V. A. Hofmann, A. Paskin, K. J. Taver and R. J. Weiss, J Phys Chem Solids, **1**, 54 (1956)

15 J. L. Lytton, D. M. S. Report No. 62-4, Stanford University, April 23, 1962

16 C. Zener, Imperfections in Nearly Perfect Crystals, John Wiley & Sons, Inc., New York, 1950

17 A. D. Le Claire, Acta Met, **1**, 438 (1953)

18 M. K. Wilkinson and C. E. Shull, Phys Rev, **103**, 525 (1956)

19 D. Graham, and D. H. Tomlin, Phil Mag, **8**, 1581 (1963)

20 L. A. Girifalco, Phys Chem Solids, **23**, 1171 (1962)

21 C. Wert and C. Zener, Phys Rev, **76**, 1169 (1949)

Chapter 16
Vanadium Self-Diffusion

R. F. Peart

Recent publications (1–7) on tracer diffusion in bcc transition metals have emphasized that in general it is no longer sufficient to measure diffusion coefficients over limited temperature ranges in order to obtain meaningful diffusion parameters. In particular, the results for self-diffusion and impurity diffusion in β-Zr (3), β-Ti (1, 4), α-U (7) and Cr (5, 6) show that the parameters Q and D_0 in the Arrhenius equation $D = D_0 \exp(-Q/RT)$ are temperature dependent. Although most of the work reported is of good precision by current standards, it has not been found possible to uniquely determine the analytical form of this temperature dependence. The data for the diffusion of impurities in Ti (1) have been analyzed as the sum of two exponential functions and interpreted in terms of two competing mechanisms. For Zr (3) it has been suggested that the same mechanism is operative over the complete range of measurement and that the associated activation energy and frequency factor are temperature dependent. An alternative to these interpretations is that the temperature dependence can be described in terms of two exponential functions with an abrupt change of slope at a critical temperature. This possibility is admitted by the data for both Ti and Zr.

In addition to the above effects, the magnitude of both Q and D_0 corresponding to low-temperature measurements is very much smaller than that anticipated for a simple vacancy mechanism. The activation energies are less than half of the values given by the closely followed empirical relation $Q = 36T_m$, where T_m is the melting temperature, and the frequency factors have values in the range of 10^{-3} to 10^{-5} cm²/sec, which, when interpreted in terms of Zener's theory, often represent negative entropies of activation. These two aspects of diffusion in bcc metals have lead to speculation concerning the role of short-circuiting paths in producing enhanced diffusion at low temperatures (1, 4).

The author was formerly with the Materials Research Laboratory and the Dept. of Min., Met. & Pet. Eng., University of Illinois. His present address is T. J. Watson Research Center, International Business Machines, Yorktown Heights, N.Y.

Table 1. Diffusion Coefficients for V^{48} in V

Temp, °C	Type of diffusion specimen(a)	Sectioning technique	Diffusion coefficient (b,c), cm²/sec
880.......... 1		Chemical etching	3.85×10^{-15}(V)
977.......... 1		Chemical etching	3.67×10^{-15}
			4.69×10^{-14}
1028.......... 1		Lathe sectioning	4.76×10^{-14}
			1.49×10^{-13}
1097.......... 2		Lathe sectioning	1.50×10^{-13}
1112.......... 1		Lathe sectioning	6.42×10^{-13}
			8.12×10^{-13}(E)
1171.......... 4		Lathe sectioning	8.30×10^{-13}(V)
1190.......... 1		Lathe sectioning	2.64×10^{-12}
			3.76×10^{-12}
1199.......... 4		Lathe sectioning	3.75×10^{-12}
1229.......... 4		Lathe sectioning	4.62×10^{-12}
1238.......... 1		Lathe sectioning	6.62×10^{-12}
			8.25×10^{-12}
1262.......... 1		Chemical etching	7.58×10^{-12}
			1.084×10^{-11}
1297.......... 1		Lathe sectioning	1.120×10^{-11}
			2.01×10^{-11}(E)
1317.......... 4		Lathe sectioning	2.07×10^{-11}(V)
1356.......... 1		Lathe sectioning	2.66×10^{-11}
			4.78×10^{-11}
1378.......... 4		Lathe sectioning	4.75×10^{-11}
1392.......... 1		Lathe sectioning	7.07×10^{-11}
			9.13×10^{-11}
1421.......... 4		Lathe sectioning	9.20×10^{-11}
1465.......... 3		Lathe sectioning	1.64×10^{-10}
1560.......... 3		Lathe sectioning	3.04×10^{-10}
1630.......... 3		Lathe sectioning	1.28×10^{-9}
1682.......... 3		Lathe sectioning	2.99×10^{-9}
1795.......... 3		Lathe sectioning	5.55×10^{-9}
1833.......... 3		Lathe sectioning	2.46×10^{-8}
			3.52×10^{-8}

(a) Code is as follows: 1 indicates single crystal, single cylinder, diffused both ends; 2, single crystal, single cylinder, diffused one end; 3, single crystal, double cylinder, adjacent ends diffused; 4, polycrystal, single cylinder, diffused one end.
(b) Not corrected for thermal expansion.
(c) Method of depositing V^{48} is indicated parenthetically by E for electrodeposition and V for evaporation.

The present work was undertaken in an attempt to clarify these problems. V was chosen for this investigation for the following reasons. First, its proximity to Ti and Cr in the periodic table gives some hope for detecting these temperature-dependent effects in this metal. Second, the absence of a crystallographic change, which occurs in Ti, Zr and U, eliminates the possibility of enhanced diffusion due to structural defects retained from the lower phase and also enables, in principle at least, diffusion coefficients to be measured over a very wide temperature range. Last, high-purity single crystals of V are available, and V[48] is a readily produced and convenient radio-isotope for tracer diffusion measurements.

Data were obtained over a temperature range of about 950 C in 99.99% pure single crystals and in 99.9% pure polycrystalline specimens. Statistical analyses show that the results are best represented as two activation energies with a change of slope at 1356 C and preclude interpretation in terms of competing diffusion mechanisms or a single mechanism with temperature-dependent diffusion parameters.

Experimental Methods

Most of the results reported here were obtained by the use of well-established techniques that are adequately reported in the literature.

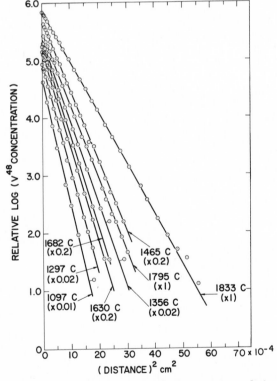

Fig. 1. Self-diffusion profiles obtained by lathe sectioning techniques for the diffusion of V[48] in V single crystals. Correction factors for the square of the distance are given parenthetically.

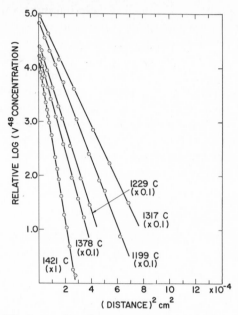

Fig. 2. Self-diffusion profiles obtained by lathe sectioning techniques for the diffusion of V^{48} in V polycrystals. Correction factors for the square of the distance are given parenthetically.

Some diffusion coefficients, particularly those less than 10^{-13} cm^2/sec, were measured by means of a chemical etching technique. This essentially involved the immersion of the radioactive face of the diffusion specimen in a solution of nitric acid, acetic acid and water and subsequent counting of the radioactivity removed. Distances were obtained by weighing the specimen before and after the removal of each section. More information concerning this technique as well as a detailed account of types of specimens, their preparation, heat treatment and radioactive analysis will be published elsewhere.

Results

Representative penetration profiles obtained by the lathe sectioning and chemical etching techniques for the diffusion of V^{48} in single and polycrystalline specimens of V are shown in Fig. 1 through 4. A summary of the diffusion coefficients is given in Table 1, and their temperature dependence is shown graphically in Fig. 5 and 6.

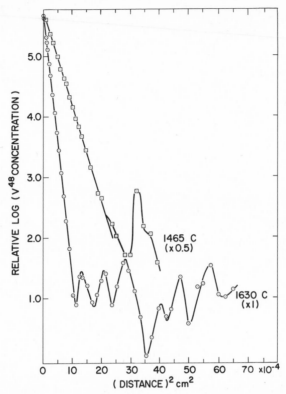

Fig. 3. Self-diffusion profiles obtained by lathe sectioning techniques for the diffusion of V^{48} in V single crystals and showing substructure effects. Correction factors for the square of the distance are given parenthetically.

Table 2. Results of Least-Squares Analysis of Diffusion Data

Temperature range, °C	Activation energy(a), kcal/mole	Frequency factor(a), cm²/sec
880–1229........	73.82 ± 0.23	0.39 ± 0.03
1112–1356........	73.67 ± 0.49	0.37 ± 0.06
880–1356........	73.65 ± 0.15	0.36 ± 0.02
1356–1682........	93.68 ± 0.51	$(1.88 ± 0.25)10^2$
1421–1833........	93.66 ± 0.55	$(1.86 ± 0.28)10^2$
1356–1833........	94.14 ± 0.33	$(2.14 ± 0.20)10^2$

(a) Data presented include plus or minus probable error.

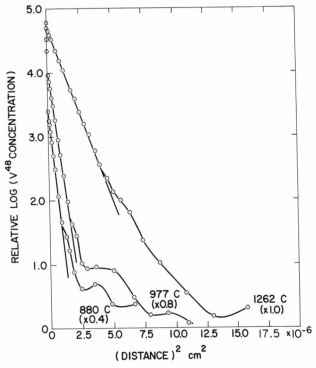

Fig. 4. Self-diffusion profiles obtained by chemical etching techniques for the diffusion of V^{48} in V single crystals and showing substructure effects. Correction factors for the square of the distance are given parenthetically.

Analysis and Accuracy of Data

A visual inspection of the data shown in Fig. 5 and 6 suggests that they can readily be represented by two straight lines. Least-squares analyses were therefore applied to the data in the temperature ranges of 880 to 1356 C and 1356 to 1833 C. The resulting equations are

$$D = (0.36 \pm 0.02) \exp \left[-(73.65 \pm 0.15)/RT\right] \text{ for 880 to 1356 C} \quad (1)$$
$$D = (2.14 \pm 0.20)10^2 \exp \left[-(94.14 \pm 0.33)/RT\right] \text{ for 1356 to 1833 C} \quad (2)$$

As a test for possible curvature in these Arrhenius plots, the top and bottom two thirds of the data in each of the above temperature ranges were also subjected to least-squares analysis. The results, given in Table 2, show no detectable departures from linearity and differ from the above equations by less than the quoted probable errors of about 0.4% on the activation energies and 10% on the frequency factors.

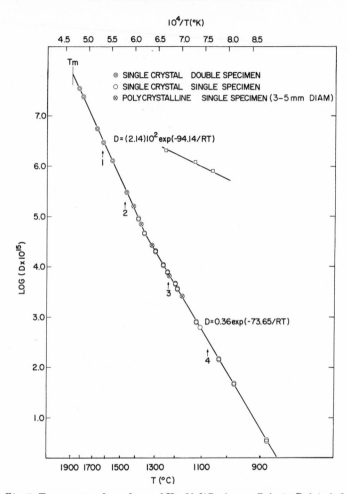

Fig. 5. Temperature dependence of V self-diffusion coefficients. Points 1, 2, 3 and 4 are the centers of mass of the data in the following temperature ranges: point 1, 880 to 1229 C; point 2, 1112 to 1356 C; point 3, 1356 to 1682 C; point 4, 1421 to 1833 C.

Additional evidence showing that the data are best represented by Eq 1 and 2 is given in Fig. 6. The dotted curve corresponds to the sum of two exponential functions that have been normalized to the points 1, 2, 3 and 4 shown in Fig. 5. These points are the centers of mass of the data in the temperature ranges 880 to 1229 C, 1112 to 1356 C, 1356 to 1682 C and 1421 to 1833 C, respectively (Table 2). This procedure yields the equation

$$D = D_L + D_H = 0.65 \exp\left(-69.5/RT\right) + 5 \cdot 10^2 \exp\left(-98.5/RT\right) \quad (3)$$

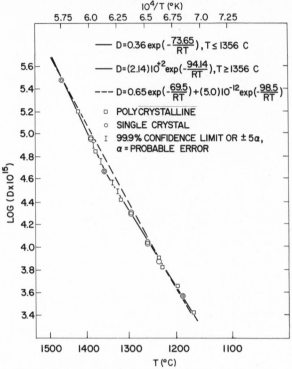

Fig. 6. Larger-scale graph of "knee" region shown in Fig. 5

where L and H refer to low and high temperatures, respectively. It is apparent from the 99.9% confidence limits shown in Fig. 6 that the data are more closely fitted by Eq 1 and 2.

The calculated probable error on the data is less than 1% on each diffusion coefficient. This value is significantly smaller than the estimated experimental random error of $\pm 2\%$ and $\pm 4\%$ on the low- and high-temperature, lathe-sectioned specimens, respectively, and $\pm 4\%$ on specimens that were sectioned by chemical etching, the larger error on the high-temperature data being a reflection of the accuracy of temperature measurement and control. In addition to these random errors, those of a systematic nature are expected to contribute errors of about the same magnitude. This variation of accuracy with temperature and sectioning technique was taken into account by the use of appropriate weighting factors in the least-squares analyses.

Discussion

In common with recent work (8–11) on diffusion in metals, the diffusion profiles shown in Fig. 4 have three distinct regions corresponding to diffusion in the surface layer of a few microns in thickness, normal lattice diffusion and enhanced diffusion along short-circuiting paths. Diffusion in the surface layer is invariably several orders of magnitude slower than bulk diffusion and is most likely due to the formation of an oxide layer or the presence of other impurities. The short-circuiting paths producing the "tails" shown in Fig. 3 and 4 are undoubtedly dislocations. When measurements were extensive enough, these "tails" showed a constant periodicity of about 25 microns, which is about the magnitude of grain diameters in a subgrain network revealed by etching the "single" crystals of V. This is considered a fortuitous coincidence because the network does not possess the necessary constancy of size or orientation to produce the observed diffusion profiles.

Any complete interpretation of the temperature dependence of the diffusion coefficients necessarily involves an explanation of the sharpness of the "knee" region of the data. Before this effect is discussed, let us first consider the characteristic features and possible mechanisms of the low-temperature diffusion. The possibility of dislocations playing a dominant role in diffusion in this region can be precluded for the following reasons. First, a dislocation density of 10^{10} to 10^{12} lines/cm^2 would be required in a well-annealed single crystal to account for the observed enhancement of diffusion. This value is to be compared with 10^9 lines/cm^2 reported by Edgington and Smallman (12) for 1 % deformed V crystals. Second, such an enhancement would produce a measurable curvature in the Arrhenius plot, whereas the data are closely linear over a range of about 500 C.

The work of Edgington and Smallman (12) provides strong evidence that the mechanism of diffusion producing the values $Q = 72.5$ kcal/mole and $D_0 = 0.36$ cm^2/sec is one involving a vacancy. These authors obtained the value 67 ± 5 kcal/mole for self-diffusion in V from the annealing out of vacancy dislocation loops in deformed V crystals at 700 to 800 C. In addition, the above values of Q and D_0 are consistent with the well-established pattern of vacancy diffusion in fcc metals.

The main feature of the high-temperature data is the frequency factor $D_0 = 200$ cm^2/sec. This value is about two orders of magnitude greater than those obtained for D_0 in other bcc metals for which the Arrhenius plots are found to be linear, and therefore appears closely tied to the reasons for the "transition" that occurs at 1356 C. Some evidence for a polymorphic transformation in 99.3 % V at about 1550 C is given by

Seybolt *et al.* (15), who found anomalies in the V-O phase diagram and in measurements of the thermal emf of a V/Mo thermocouple. Results obtained in this laboratory for the thermal emf of V/Mo and V/Pt thermocouples up to 1700 C show no effects attributable to such a transformation, but a preliminary investigation of the temperature dependence of the electrical resistivity in V did reveal some indication of a change of slope in the temperature range of 1300 to 1400 C. This result was not always reproducible and much further work is required to substantiate it.

Although it appears possible to eliminate a simple crystallographic phase change as an explanation of the present results on the grounds that all existing diffusion data in polymorphic metals show a discontinuity at the transition temperature, the possibility of an electronic transition cannot be neglected. Such a transition associated with an interchange of 4s and 3d electrons would explain the abnormalities in the physical properties of other bcc transition metals, in particular Cr (19) and Ti (20). In the present instance, if it is assumed that the decrease in resistivity shown in Fig. 9 is due to an increase in the number of conduction electrons, a $3d \rightarrow 4s$ transfer is required.

A final interpretation arises from the suggestion of Kidson (18) that the presence of interstitial gases in Ti and Zr produces an increase in the vacancy concentration that results in the observed fast diffusion rates. In the present instance a large increase in interstitial solubility from effectively zero concentration below 1356 C to several atomic per cent over a temperature range of several degrees would be required. The phase diagram of the V-O system by Seybolt (15) does show a significantly marked increase in O solubility around 1350 C, but the solubility limit of 3 at. % below this temperature tends to discredit this idea.

Conclusions

This investigation has shown that self-diffusion in V in the temperature range of 880 to 1833 C can be represented by two distinct activation energies above and below the temperature 1356 C. There is strong evidence that suggests that diffusion below 1356 C is the result of a simple vacancy mechanism.

No single explanation is offered for the "transition" temperature. Much work on the electrical and physical high-temperature properties of V is required in order to determine whether a phase change exists at this temperature.

Acknowledgments.   This work was supported in part by the U. S Atomic Energy Commission and the U. S. Air Force. The author would like to thank Professors C. Wert and D. Lazarus for their active interest and support of this investigation.

References

1 G. B. Gibbs, D. Graham and D. H. Tomlin, Phil Mag, **8,** 1269 (1963)
2 R. F. Peart and D. H. Tomlin, Acta Met, **10,** 123 (1962)
3 J. I. Federer and T. S. Lundy, Trans AIME, **227,** 592 (1963)
4 J. F. Murdock, T. S. Lundy and E. E. Stansbury, Acta Met, to be published
5 H. W. Paxton and E. G. Gondolf, Arch Eisenhuettenw, **30,** 55 (1959)
6 W. C. Hagel, Trans AIME **224** (3), 430 (1962)
7 S. J. Rothman, L. T. Lloyd and A. L. Harkness, Trans AIME, **218** (4), 605 (1960)
8 T. S. Lundy, PhD Thesis, University of Tennessee, 1964
9 R. E. Pawel and T. S. Lundy, ORNL TM 575 (May 1963)
10 D. L. Styris and C. T. Tomizuka, University of Arizona
11 G. P. Williams and L. Slifkin, Phys Rev Letters, **1,** 7 (1958)
12 J. W. Edginton and R. E. Smallman, J Australian Inst Met, **8,** 1 (1963)
13 R. F. Peart, D. Graham and D. H. Tomlin, Acta Met, **10,** 519 (1962)
14 J. Askill and D. H. Tomlin, Phil Mag, **8** (90), 997 (1963)
15 A. U. Seybolt and H. T. Sumsion, J Metals, **5,** 292 (1953)
16 R. Herman and C. A. Swenson, J Chem Phys, **29,** 398 (1958)
17 P. W. Bridgman, Proc Am Acad Arts Sci, **81,** 165 (1952)
18 G. V. Kidson, Can J Phys, **41,** 1563 (1963)

Chapter 17
Tracer-Diffusion Studies in Molybdenum

J. Askill

Several studies of the self-diffusion in Mo have been reported in the literature. None of the investigators used the standard method of analysis of serial sectioning by lathe, and none gave material purity. For these reasons the present experiments were carried out on high-purity poly-crystalline and single-crystal material, and the analysis was carried out by lathe sectioning. In view of the wide divergence of the results on tracer solute diffusion obtained by Peart et al. (1) and Borisov et al. (2), the present study includes experiments with the solutes Co^{60} and Cb^{95}.

Experimental Methods

Diffusion specimens 8 mm in diameter and 6 mm long were prepared from a $\frac{1}{2}$-in.-diam polycrystalline rod and a single crystal $\frac{1}{4}$ in. in diameter and 5 in. long of 99.99% purity. The main impurities in the polycrystalline rod were C (100 ppm), Fe (100 ppm) and Si (10 ppm). Grain growth anneals with the polycrystalline samples resulted in grain sizes of 1 to 2 mm after cycling operations from 1600 to 2200 C. The face on one end of each specimen was ground and etched flat, and the radio-isotope was applied by electrodeposition in an ammonium oxalate plating bath.

Pairs of specimens were placed face-to-face in a Mo crucible and heat treated in a vacuum at pressures between 10^{-4} and 10^{-5} mm Hg. Tempera-ture measurements with a calibrated optical pyrometer were considered accurate to about 20 C. From 8 to 15 sections were machined from each specimen after the diameter had been reduced by about 1 mm to remove surface-diffusion effects. The turnings were weighed, dissolved in aqua regia and assayed by use of a well-type scintillation counter.

The author was formerly with the Department of Physics, University of Reading, Berkshire, England. His present address is Oak Ridge National Laboratory, Oak Ridge, Tenn.

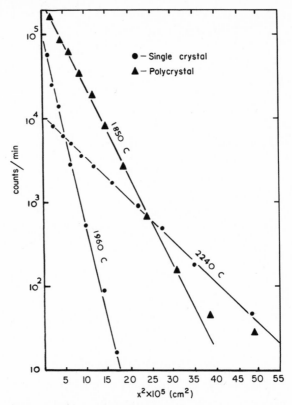

Fig. 1. Typical penetration plots for self-diffusion in Mo

Results and Discussion

Penetration plots for some of the self-diffusion runs are shown in Fig. 1. These are also typical of the penetration plots obtained when the solutes Co[60] and Cb[95] were used. Curvature at the lower ends was detected for some polycrystalline samples, at temperatures below 1900 C, and is associated with grain-boundary diffusion.

The self-diffusion results together with all other reported data on self-diffusion in Mo are shown in Fig. 2. The data for single crystals are expressed by

$$D = (0.1^{+0.1}_{-0.1}) \exp\left[-(92.2 \pm 2.6)/RT\right]$$

and the data for polycrystals, by

$$D = (0.5^{+0.7}_{-0.3}) \exp\left[-(96.9 \pm 4.4)/RT\right]$$

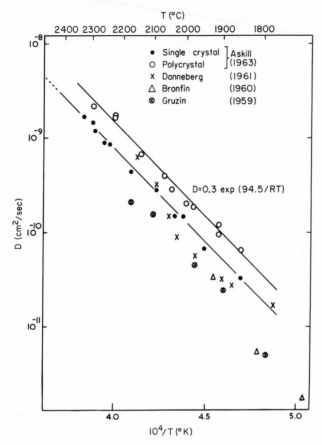

Fig. 2. Self-diffusion data

The solute data are expressed by

$$D_{Co^{60}} = (18^{+20}_{-9}) \exp\left[-(106.7 \pm 3.8)/RT\right]$$
$$D_{Cb^{95}} = (14^{+14}_{-7}) \exp\left[-(108.1 \pm 3.2)/RT\right]$$

Figure 3 shows the present self-diffusion results, the results for the solutes Co^{60} and Cb^{95} and the data of Borisov *et al.* (2) on the tracer diffusion of W^{185} in Mo. Table 1 summarizes the self-diffusion data of this and other studies, and Table 2 gives the data for tracer solute diffusion.

The value of $Q \approx 95$ kcal/mole for self-diffusion in Mo is in good agreement with the empirical melting-point rule of $34T_m$, and the value $D_0 = 0.5$ cm²/sec is in reasonable agreement with Zener's relation for

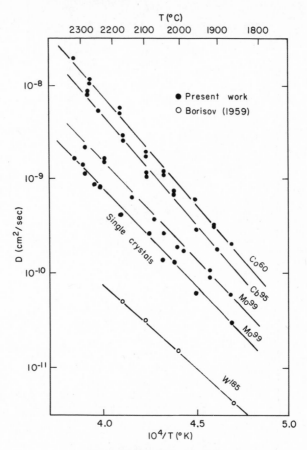

Fig. 3. Solute-diffusion data

Table 1. Self-Diffusion Data

Material	Temp range, °C	D_0, cm^2/sec	Q, kcal/mole	Reference
Single crystals.......	1850–2350	$0.1^{+0.1}_{-0.1}$	92.2 ± 2.6	This paper
Polycrystalline.......	1850–2350	$0.5^{+0.7}_{-0.3}$	96.9 ± 4.4	This paper
Polycrystalline.......	1700–1900	2.77	111	5
Polycrystalline.......	1800–2150	4.0	115	2
Polycrystalline.......	1870–2080	0.38	100.8	4

Table 2. Solute-Diffusion Data

Solute	Temp range, °C	D_0, cm²/sec	Q, kcal/mole	Reference
Co[60]	1850–2350	18^{+20}_{-9}	106.7 ± 3.8	This paper
Cb[95]	1850–2350	14^{+14}_{-7}	108.1 ± 3.2	This paper
W[185]	1750–2150	4×10^{-4}	78	2

D_0, which gives $D_0 = 0.8$ cm²/sec. The experimental values of Q and D_0 for self-diffusion are thus consistent with a vacancy mechanism of diffusion.

An unusual feature of the solute results is that the values of D_0 and Q for the tracer diffusion of Co[60] and Cb[95] are greater than the self-diffusion results. This trend is opposite to that found for solutes in Cb by Peart *et al.* (1). It is hoped to re-examine the W solute data in view of the low values of Q and D_0 given by Borisov.

Effect of an Argon Atmosphere on the Lattice and Grain-Boundary Diffusion Rates of Cobalt-60 in Molybdenum

Previous work on the tracer diffusion of Co[60] in Mo by Peart *et al.* (1), who used autoradiographic analysis and an A atmosphere for the heat treatments, gave lattice diffusion coefficients appreciably smaller than those found in the present work, and also showed very strong grain-boundary effects. Some further experiments were therefore carried out with an A atmosphere for the diffusion anneals and both autoradiographic and serial-sectioning analysis. The results, which are shown in Fig. 4, are expressed by the following relations:

Vacuum, Serial Sectioning	$D = 18 \exp(-106.7/RT)$
Argon, Serial Sectioning	$D = 45 \exp(-118/RT)$
Argon, Autoradiography	$D = 47 \exp(-116/RT)$

The effect of the A atmosphere is to decrease the lattice diffusion coefficients of Co[60] in Mo by a factor that varies from 6.3 at 1850 C to 2.8 at 2350 C, and also to considerably enhance grain-boundary diffusion. The A used in the present study and also in that of Peart was of 99.95% purity, the main impurity being N. It is thought that the N impurity resulted in this effect.

Previous studies by Graham (6) on the effect of an A atmosphere on the tracer diffusion of Fe[55] and Ni[63] in β-Ti, and by McCoy and Murdock

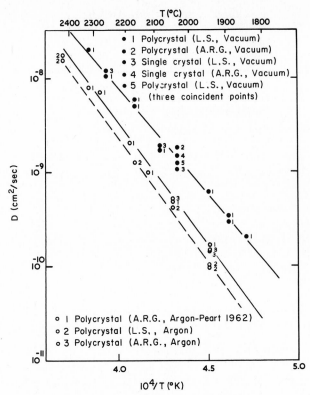

Fig. 4. Tracer diffusion of Co⁶⁰ in Mo

(7) on the effect of an atmosphere of A and H on the tracer diffusion of Co^{60} in Ni, have both shown no effect.

References

1   R. F. Peart, D. Graham and D. H. Tomlin, Acta Met, **10,** 519 (1962)
2   Y. V. Borisov, P. L. Gruzin and L. V. Pavlinov, Metal i Metalloved, **1,** 213 (1959);
     U. S. Report JPRS-5195
3   J. Askill and D. H. Tomlin, Phil Mag, **8** (90), 997 (1963)
4   W. Danneberg and E. Krautz, Z Naturforsch, **16a,** 854 (1961)
5   M. B. Bronfin, S. Z. Bokshtein and A. A. Zhukhovitsky, Zavodsk Lab, **26** (7), 828
     (1960)
6   D. Graham, Ph D Thesis, Reading University, England, 1962
7   H. E. McCoy and J. F. Murdock, ASM Trans Quart, **56,** 11 (1963)

Chapter 18
Self-Diffusion in Chromium

J. ASKILL

In a number of recent studies of self-diffusion and solute diffusion in the bcc transition metals Ti and Zr, Arrhenius plots representing the results have been found to be nonlinear. Several studies of self-diffusion in Cr have been reported and are shown in Fig. 1. Of these data two sets, those of Paxton and Gondolf (5) and Hagel (2), suggest that self-diffusion in Cr may also not be represented by the normal relation

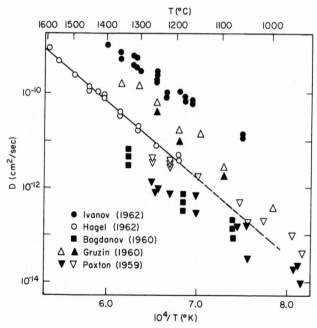

Fig. 1. Published data on self-diffusion in Cr

The author was formerly with the Department of Physics, University of Reading, Berkshire, England. His present address is Oak Ridge National Laboratory, Oak Ridge, Tenn.

253

$D = D_0 \exp(-Q/RT)$ with constant values of the activation energy Q and the frequency factor D_0.

The aim of the present study is to determine whether Cr has anomalous diffusion characteristics similar to those of Ti and Zr or whether the self-diffusion results over the combined temperature range of both Paxton and Hagel can be represented by constant values of Q and D_0.

Experimental Methods and Results

Cylindrical specimens about 1.2 cm in diameter and 0.8 cm long were prepared from a 99.98% purity Cr rod. Grain growth anneals at temperatures around 1400 C resulted in grain sizes of 1 to 3 mm. The face of one end of each specimen was prepared by grinding on various grades of

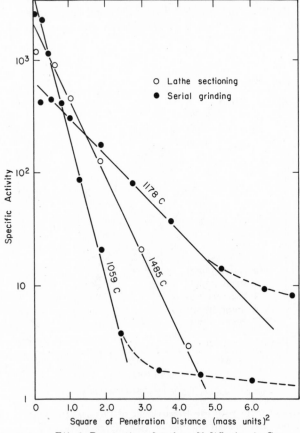

Fig. 2. Penetration plots for self-diffusion in Cr

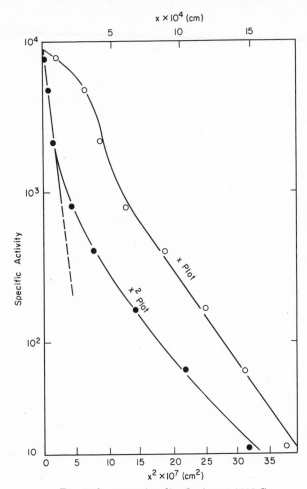

Fig. 3. Concentration distribution at 1028 C

Carborundum paper and by etching with a solution of one part H_3PO_4 to one part concentrated H_2SO_4. A thin layer of high-specific-activity Cr^{51} was then deposited on the face of one end by electrolysis in a bath of saturated ammonium oxalate solution. Diffusion heat treatments were carried out in a Crucilite element furnace that was temperature controlled to ± 1 C. The experiments below 1250 C were carried out in a vacuum at pressures of about 5×10^{-6} mm Hg; those above 1250 C, under a pressure of half an atmosphere of A.

Because of the small values of the diffusion coefficient, hand grinding was used as the method of analysis for experiments carried out in the

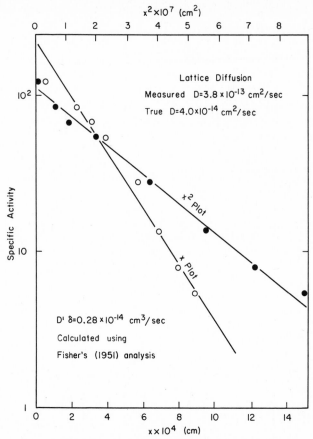

Fig. 4. Grain-boundary penetration plot for self-diffusion in Cr at 998 C

lower end of the temperature range. Successive layers of the diffusion
zone about 1 μ thick were removed by grinding on 4-cm-diam disks of
320-grade Carborundum paper held in a brass frame. The activity on
each disk was then measured by use of a scintillation counter and a
single-channel analyzer. At temperatures above 1300 C, diffusion zones
suitable for standard lathe sectioning were obtained. For heat treatments
at 1326 and 1485 C, one of each of the pairs of specimens was analyzed by
lathe sectioning, and the other was analyzed by grinding, so that the two
methods could be compared.

Penetration plots for three samples, one analyzed by lathe sectioning
and two by serial grinding, are shown in Fig. 2. The deviation from
linearity at the low-concentration end could be due to grain-boundary

effects or to the possible transference of small amounts of active material from one exposed face to the next during the grinding operations. At temperatures below 1100 C the penetration plots gave definite indication of effects of grain-boundary diffusion. This is shown in Fig. 3. The results showed a transition from an x^2 penetration dependence at high temperatures (volume diffusion) to a linear dependence on x at lower temperatures (grain-boundary diffusion). The penetration plot for one experiment at 998 C (shown in Fig. 4) is associated almost entirely with grain-

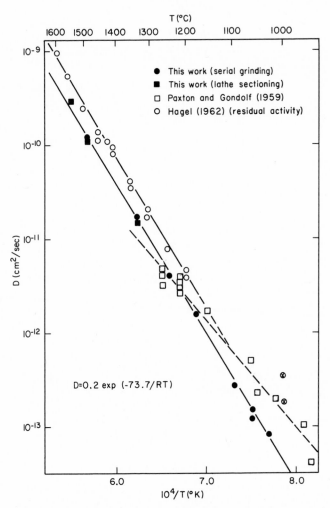

Fig. 5. Self-diffusion in Cr. Circled X represents apparent diffusion coefficient deduced from experiment at 998 C (Fig. 4)

Table 1. Summary of Data for Self-Diffusion in Cr

Temp range, °C	D_0, cm²/sec	Q, kcal/mole	Reference	Year
1100–1350............	....	76	7	1957
1000–1250............	1.5×10^{-4}	52.7	5	1959
	2.3×10^{-5}	51.3	5	1959
1000–1350............	45	85	4	1959
1080–1320............	1.65×10^{-3}	62.4	3	1960
1050–1400............	6.47×10^{-2}	59.2	1	1962
1200–1600............	0.28	73.2	2	1962
1030–1550............	0.2	73.7	This paper	....

boundary diffusion. It is interesting to note that the plots of both log c versus x^2 and log c versus x in Fig. 4 are reasonably fitted by straight lines. The apparent diffusion coefficient deduced from the former is appreciably greater than the values expected by extrapolation of the high-temperature data (see Fig. 5).

The results of the present study at temperatures below 1150 C suggest that those of Paxton and Gondolf (5) may well have been influenced by effects of grain-boundary diffusion, particularly between 1000 and 1150 C.

Figure 5 shows the present results together with those of Hagel (2) and Paxton and Gondolf (5). The agreement between grinding and lathe-sectioning methods of analysis is seen to be quite satisfactory, and the temperature dependence $D = D_0 \exp(-Q/RT)$ is exhibited over the temperature range of 1030 to 1545 C with constant values of the activation energy and frequency factor.

$$D = (0.2^{+0.1}_{-0.05}) \exp(-73.7/RT) \text{ cm}^2/\text{sec}$$

A summary of data is given in Table 1.

Diffusion in Cr, therefore, should no longer be grouped with the "anomalous" bcc metals—Ti, Zr and U—but with the "normal" bcc metals—Cb, Ta, Mo and W.

References

1   L. I. Ivanov, M. P. Matveeva, V. A. Morozov and D. A. Prokoshkin, Russ Met Fuels English Transl, **2**, 63 (1962)

2   W. C. Hagel, Trans AIME, **224**, 430 (1962)

3   N. A. Bogdanov, Russ Met Fuels English Transl, **3**, 95 (1960)

4 P. L. Gruzin, L. V. Pavlinov and A. D. Tyutyunnik, Izv Akad Nauk SSSR, **5**, 155 (1959)
5 H. W. Paxton and E. G. Gondolf, Archiv Eisenhuettenw, **30**, 55 (1959)
6 J. C. Fisher, J Appl Phys, **22**, 74 (1951)
7 S. Z. Bokshtein, S. T. Kishkin and L. M. Moroz, Zavodsk Lab, **23**, 316 (1957)
8 J. I. Federer and T. S. Lundy, Trans AIME, **227**, 592 (1963)
9 G. B. Gibbs, D. Graham and D. H. Tomlin, Phil Mag, **8**, 1269 (1963)
10 J. E. Murdock, T. S. Lundy and E. E. Stansbury, Acta Met, **12**, 1033 (1964)
11 R. F. Peart and D. H. Tomlin, Acta Met, **10**, 132 (1962)

Chapter 19

Diffusion of Titanium-44 and Vanadium-48 in Titanium

J. F. MURDOCK

After Federer and Lundy (1) first noted curved Arrhenius-type plots for diffusion in β-Zr, an extensive program to study diffusion in bcc metals was begun at Oak Ridge National Laboratory to try to characterize this anomaly. Earlier studies of diffusion in Zr (2–6) and in Ti (7) did not span a sufficient temperature interval to reveal the inconstancy of Q and D_0. In fact, differences in reported (2–6) activation energies and frequency factors for self-diffusion in Zr were resolved by Federer and Lundy in terms of the temperature interval studied and their curved ln D versus T^{-1} plot for this system.

Availability of suitable isotopes, Ti^{44} and V^{48}, led us to this experiment.

A plane-source semi-infinite-medium specimen was used. The activity versus depth profile was determined by lathe sectioning and gamma spectrometry. Further details of the experimental procedure can be found in an earlier publication (8).

The solution to Fick's second law that applies to diffusion of a plane source into a semi-infinite medium is (9)

$$A(x, t) = [M/(\pi Dt)^{1/2}] \exp{(-x^2/4Dt)} \tag{1}$$

where $A(x, t) = $ the activity per unit volume at a penetration distance x, the specimen at time t, $M = $ the activity per unit area initially deposited at $x = 0$, $D = $ the diffusion coefficient.

The diffusion coefficients can readily be calculated from penetration plots of ln $A(x, t)$ versus x^2. A computer program written by Winslow (10) was used to calculate the diffusion coefficients from the basic data.

The author is with the Metals and Ceramics Division, Oak Ridge National Laboratory, Oak Ridge, Tenn.

Results

Penetration plots for Ti[44] annealed at 1200, 1337 and 1540 C are shown in Fig. 1; plots for V[48] at 1050, 1154 and 1370 C are shown in Fig. 2. A plot of ln D versus $1/T$ for each diffusing isotope is shown in Fig. 3.

Discussion of Results

Federer and Lundy (1) and Graham (11) have discussed various methods of considering nonlinear behavior in an Arrhenius plot. That the data may be fitted by continuously curving lines over the entire temperature range is compatible with all three of the possible explanations that have resulted. These ideas are

1. The same mechanism may apply over the entire temperature range with the activation energy being temperature dependent. As Federer and Lundy (1) pointed out, the fact that activation energies of diffusion have

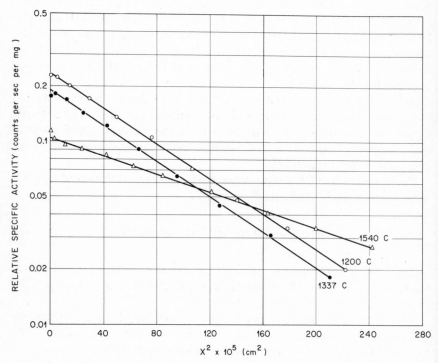

Fig. 1. Penetration plots for the diffusion of Ti[44] in Ti at 1200, 1337 and 1540 C

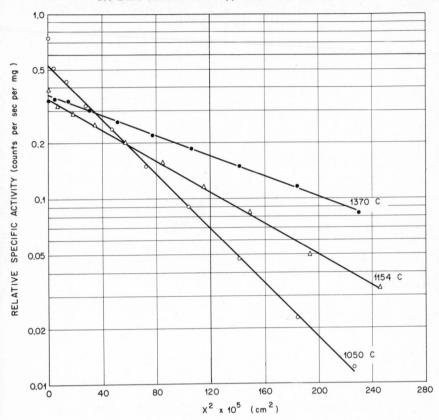

Fig. 2. Penetration plots for the diffusion of V^{48} in Ti at 1050, 1154 and 1370 C

previously been found to be constant with temperature is only empirical and must be demonstrated by experiment in each instance. For diffusion in Ti for any sufficiently narrow temperature range, the activation energy appears to be constant. Only this study and previous ones covering wide temperature intervals have resulted in variations of Q with temperature.

2. The data at high temperatures may result from pure volume diffusion; that at low temperatures, from diffusion predominantly by short-circuit paths such as grain boundaries or dislocations. The experiments by Peart and Tomlin (7) and by Graham (11) using the autoradiographic technique tend to exclude the short-circuit paths as a basis for explaining the magnitude of the curvature.

3. Two or more volume diffusion processes may compete. Kidson (12) has postulated that diffusion in Zr may be divided into two regions—

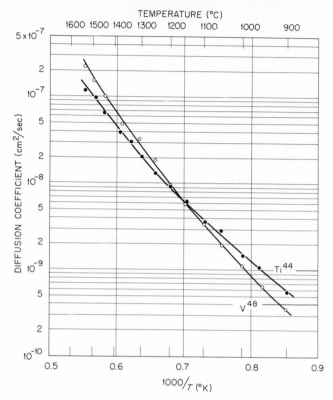

Fig. 3. Temperature dependence of the diffusion of Ti^{44} and V^{48} in Ti

"extrinsic" and "intrinsic." He attributes the low-temperature extrinsic region to the presence of a temperature-independent concentration of vacancies due to the presence of some impurity (possibly O). Further, he considers the extrinsic concentration of vacancies much greater than the concentration of thermal vacancies (intrinsic) at low temperatures.

Kidson treated the Zr data as the sum of two exponential terms, one representing the extrinsic region, the other representing the intrinsic region. By use of this approach, the Ti^{44} and V^{48} data were graphically fit to the sum of two exponential terms. A program was written for the IBM-7090 computer, which used the method of nonlinear least squares to yield the best fit of the sum of two exponential terms to the experimental data. The resulting equations are

$$D_{Ti^{44}} = 3.58 \times 10^{-4} \exp{(-31,200/RT)} + 1.09 \exp{(-60,000/RT)} \quad (2)$$
$$D_{V^{48}} = 3.10 \times 10^{-4} \exp{(-32,200/RT)} + 1.37 \exp{(-57,200/RT)} \quad (3)$$

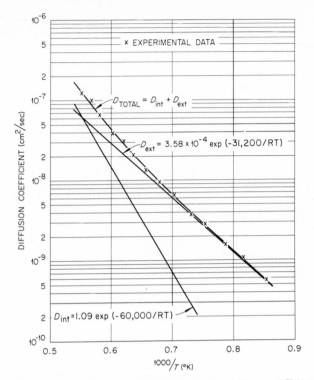

Fig. 4. Computer fit of the experimental data for the diffusion of Ti^{44} in Ti to the model proposed by Kidson

Diffusion coefficients calculated from these equations are compared with the experimental data in Fig. 4 and 5. Plots of each term of the sum on a semilogarithmic scale with $1/T$ as the linear coordinate are linear; plots of the sum form a continuous curve.

Equations 2 and 3 are of the form

$$D = C_A \exp\left(-Q_A/RT\right) + C_B \exp\left(-Q_B/RT\right) \tag{4}$$

Differentiating the logarithm of Eq 4 with respect to $1/T$ yields

$$\frac{d \ln D}{d(1/T)} = \frac{-C_A \dfrac{Q_A}{R} \exp\left(-Q_A/RT\right) - C_B \dfrac{Q_A}{R} \exp\left(-Q_B/RT\right)}{C_A \exp\left(-Q_A/RT\right) + C_B \exp\left(-Q_B/RT\right)} \tag{5}$$

Multiplying Eq 5 by $-R$ gives a parameter that was called the "apparent activation energy" by Federer and Lundy (1) and Kidson (12). Plots

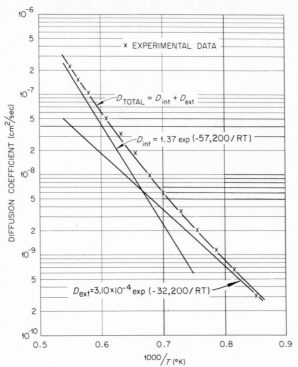

Fig. 5. Computer fit of the experimental data for the diffusion of V^{48} in Ti
to the model proposed by Kidson

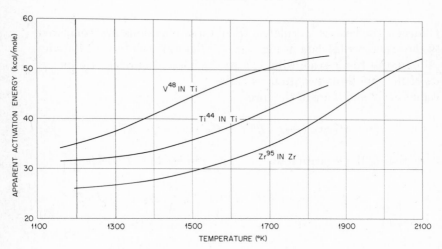

Fig. 6. Temperature dependence of the apparent activation energy for the
diffusion of Ti^{44} and V^{48} in Ti and Zr^{95} in Zr. Data for Zr are from Ref 12.

of the apparent activation energy as a function of temperature for Ti^{44} and V^{48} diffusing in Ti are shown in Fig. 6. The results of Kidson's treatment of the Zr data also are shown in Fig. 6 for qualitative comparison.

In conclusion, the Arrhenius-type equation with constant D_0 and Q was found to be inapplicable for completely describing the data for diffusion in Ti. This further substantiates the results of Federer and Lundy (1) and of Graham (11). Three possible explanations have been offered: (1) the activation energy is a temperature-dependent function for a single mechanism, (2) diffusion along short-circuit paths predominates at low temperatures, and (3) two or more volume-diffusion mechanisms compete. The proposed model of Kidson is seen to qualitatively explain the data. However, with the presently available data, no single explanation of the observed anomaly can as yet be ruled correct.

Acknowledgments. Thanks are extended to F. R. Winslow for his discussions of the data and for his aid in programing for the computer and to J. H. Terry and R. A. Padgett for performing much of the experimental work. The work of A. A. Brooks and Mrs. Kyleen Franz of the Oak Ridge Gaseous Diffusion Plant in computer fitting the experimental data was greatly appreciated. This research was sponsored by the U. S. Atomic Energy Commission under contract with the Union Carbide Corporation.

References

1   J. I. Federer and T. S. Lundy, Trans AIME, **227,** 592 (1963)
2   G. B. Fedorov and V. D. Gulyakin, Production and Physical Metallurgy of Pure Metals, No. 1, Moscow, 1959, p 170
3   G. Kidson and J. McGurn, Can J Phys, **39,** 1146 (1961)
4   V. S. Lyashenko, V. N. Bykov and L. B. Pavlinov, Phys Metals Metallogr USSR English Transl, **8,** 362 (1959)
5   D. Volokoff, S. May and Y. Adda, Compt Rend, **251,** 2341 (1960)
6   Ye. V. Borisov, Study of Diffusion in Zirconium and in Certain Alloys with a Zirconium Base, NP-TR-448, F-TS-9849/V, p 196 (1958)
7   R. F. Peart and D. H. Tomlin, Acta Met, **10,** 123 (1962)
8   J. F. Murdock, Diffusion of Titanium-44 and Vanadium-48 in Titanium, ORNL-3616 (1964); to be published in Acta Met
9   J. Crank, The Mathematics of Diffusion, Oxford University Press, New York, 1956, p 9
10   F. R. Winslow, A Fortran Program for Calculating Diffusion Coefficients and Plotting Penetration Curves, ORNL-TM-726 (1963)
11   D. Graham, PhD Thesis, University of Reading, England, 1962; G. B. Gibbs, D. Graham and D. H. Tomlin, Phil Mag, **8,** 1269 (1963)
12   G. Kidson, Can J Phys, **41,** 1563 (1963)

Chapter 20
The Analysis of Diffusion Data

David Y. F. Lai

In the determination of diffusion data, sufficient care should be exercised in the experiments to minimize or eliminate any error due to the technique itself. However, it would be most instructive to know what these errors are and to establish at least a first approximation of their magnitudes.

Some of these errors will be enumerated along with their effect on the results in tracer diffusion studies that involve use of the sectioning and residual counting technique.

A brief review of the experimental technique may be in order here. The sample is either a rectangular slab or a circular disk. The large faces are flattened and made parallel and then vapor-plated with the appropriate radioactive isotope. The sample is then encapsulated in a quartz ampoule and annealed at the selected temperature for a given length of time. Sections are taken off by grinding and the residual activity counted. The thickness of each section is calculated from the loss of weight of the sample, the cross-sectional area and the density of the material.

In this instance of diffusion of a plane source into a semi-infinite medium, one expression for the volume diffusion process is

$$\ln c/c_0 = -x^2/4Dt \tag{1}$$

When $\ln c$ is plotted against x^2, the slope of the resulting straight line is $-1/4Dt$.

An alternate expression is

$$a_x/a_0 = \frac{\int_x^\infty \exp\left(-x^2/4Dt\right) dx}{(\pi Dt)^{1/2}}$$
$$= \operatorname{erfc}\left[x/2(Dt)^{1/2}\right] = \operatorname{erfc}(\alpha) \tag{2}$$

The author is with the Lawrence Radiation Laboratory, University of California, Livermore, Calif.

Plotting x against a_x/a_0 on a modified probability graph or an error function complement graph will yield a straight line. By use of this equation, the intercept of the resulting straight line, and a table of error functions, D may be calculated. The commercially available probability paper may be used for this purpose but only half of the graph may be used. In order to increase the resolution by expanding the scale, an error function complement graph paper was designed and printed especially for this use.

Because the possible errors involved in these two methods of analysis are so numerous as to require a monograph, only a few of these will be described. These are the heat-up time correction, and errors due to incorrect area measurement, constant background, and incorrect reference plane.

As written in the previous equations, D is considered a constant. This is true only if the sample is instantaneously brought to the anneal temperature and after the anneal period quenched instantly.

If the sample has been at temperatures other than the ambient and anneal temperatures, a correction should be made for the diffusion that occurs at these temperatures. If this is not considered, then the true D for the anneal temperature will be compromised by the smaller D's for the lower temperatures. The result is a smaller D being assigned to the anneal temperature.

It should be remembered of course that although the error will always be present, it may be so small as to be insignificant as in the instance of a rise to the anneal temperature that is rapid compared with the anneal duration. Then it would not be worth the time to calculate any correction. This is true also with the other errors encountered.

When D is determined from the previous equations, t is the only variable conveniently changed. This t is the time the sample must be held at the anneal temperature to give the same concentration profile as the actual run.

Consider a sample that has been brought up to the anneal temperature by instantaneously raising its temperature after each time period Δt such that the corresponding D's are a function of t.

After the time period from 0 to t_1, the concentration profile is represented by

$$C = C_0 \exp\left(-x^2/4D_0 t\right) = C_0 \exp\left(-x^2/4D_0\,\Delta t\right) \tag{3}$$

If the sample had been at D_1 instead, the time period necessary to give the same profile is given by

$$C_0 \exp\left(-x^2/4D_0 t_1\right) = C_0 \exp\left(-x^2/4D_1 t_1'\right) \tag{4}$$

and $$D t_1' = D_0\,\Delta t \tag{5}$$

After the sample is held at D_1 an additional Δt, the profile becomes

$$C = C_0 \exp\left[-x^2/4D_1(t_1' + \Delta t)\right] \tag{6}$$

Applying the same argument as before

$$D_2 t_2' = D_1(t_1' + \Delta t) = D_0 \Delta t + D_1 \Delta t \tag{7}$$

By repeating this process, we obtain

$$D_{n+1}t_{n+1}' = \sum_{n=0}^{n} D_n \Delta t \tag{8}$$

When each time period becomes infinitely small and D becomes a continuous function of t,

$$D_{n+1}t_{n+1}' = \int_0^n D \, dt = \int_0^n f(t) \, dt \tag{9}$$

$$t_{n+1}' = [1/f(\infty)] \int_0^n f(t) \, dt \tag{10}$$

Because D is being sought, evaluation of Eq 10 is a little difficult. This may be circumvented by use of the relation

$$D = D_0 \exp\left(-Q/RT\right) \tag{11}$$

Then $\quad t_{n+1}' = [1/D_0 \exp\left(-Q/RT\right)] \int_0^t D_0 \exp\left(-Q/RT_i\right) dt$

$$= \frac{\int_0^t \exp\left(-Q/RT_i\right) dt}{\exp\left(-Q/RT\right)} \tag{12}$$

If the temperature of the sample has been followed closely at the beginning of the anneal until it has stabilized, then $\exp\left(-Q/RT_i\right)$ may be plotted against t (see Fig. 1). The integral of the preceding equation is represented by the area under the curve from 0 to t in Fig. 1. t_c is such that the shaded area has the same value as that under the curve. t_c then becomes the corrected time.

The time correction is estimated by use of an appropriate Q. After a more accurate value of Q is determined, the correction may be re-evaluated as many times as necessary to obtain the necessary precision.

As has been mentioned earlier, the cross-sectional area of the sample is used to determine the thickness of the section removed. Any error in

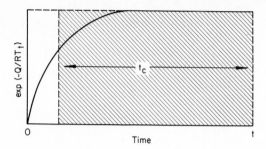

Fig. 1. Time versus exp $(-Q/RT_i)$

determining the area will result in a linear error in distance. The distance is given by

$$x = W/\rho A \tag{13}$$

where W is the weight of material removed, ρ is the density of the material, and A is the cross-sectional area. If the error is δA, then this equation becomes

$$x' = W/\rho(A + \delta A) = W/\rho A' = (A/A')x \tag{14}$$

In the instance of error function complement plotting, the equation previously given becomes

$$\alpha = x'/2(D't)^{1/2} = [A/2A'(D't)^{1/2}]x \tag{15}$$

Because $\alpha = x/2(Dt)^{1/2}$, then

$$D' = (A/A')^2 D \tag{16}$$

Thus the erroneous plot remains linear, and therefore any error in area measurement cannot be detected from the curvature of the plot. The error, nevertheless, gives a wrong D, as expressed in the last equation.

A similar error will occur in the x^2 plot. The modified equation is

$$\ln c/c_0 = (1/4Dt)(A'/A)^2 x'^2 \tag{17}$$

This plot also gives a straight line, thereby making the detection of this type of error from the curvature impossible. The diffusion coefficient is then determined from this plot by use of

$$\ln c/c_0 = (1/4D't)x'^2 \tag{18}$$

These two equations give the relation

$$D' = (A/A')^2 D \tag{19}$$

which is the same as in the previous instance.

When the origin of the distance axis is incorrectly assigned, as in the instance of error in the initial weighing, both plots will be affected. In the error function complement plot, the modified equation is

$$\alpha = (x + \delta x)/2(Dt)^{1/2} = x/2(Dt)^{1/2} + k \tag{20}$$

The resulting curve will be a straight line with the same slope as before, but intersecting the vertical axis at k instead of at the origin.

When a constant error is applied to the distance in the x^2 plotting, the curve is no longer straight. The modified equation is

$$\ln c/c_0 = -(x' - \delta x)^2/4Dt = -(1/4Dt)(x'^2 - 2x'\delta x + \delta x^2) \tag{21}$$

The slope S_n' of the resulting curve at distance x_n' is given by

$$(d \ln c_n/c_0)/dx'^2 = (1/4Dt)(1 - \delta x/x_n') = S_n' \tag{22}$$

where c_n is the concentration at x_n'.

D is then given by

$$D = -(1/4tS_n')(1 - \delta x/x_n') \tag{23}$$

When the apparent distance is mistaken for the true distance, the apparent D is given by

$$D_n' = -1/4tS_n' \tag{24}$$

The error in D is

$$(D - D_n')/D = -\delta x/(x_n' - \delta x) \tag{25}$$

The distance error may be calculated from the slopes determined at two distances, x_1' and x_2'.

$$S_1' = -(1/4Dt)(1 - \delta x/x_1') \tag{26}$$
$$S_2' = -(1/4Dt)(1 - \delta x/x_2') \tag{27}$$

Combining and simplifying these two equations gives

$$\delta x = x_1'x_2'(S_1' - S_2')/(x_1'S_1' - x_2'S_2') \tag{28}$$

Equation 22 indicates that a concave curve is due to a negative error and a convex curve a positive error.

The activity determined by the counter after each sectioning is corrected by subtracting a constant chamber background. Even after this correction, there may still remain a constant error in each count due to an error in determining the chamber background or due to activity remaining on the back or sides of the sample.

In the x^2 plot, this error is eliminated because only the differences between successive counts are used.

In the error function complement plot, however, a curved line will result from this error. An equivalent form of Eq 1 is

$$a_x/a_0 = (2/\pi^{1/2}) \int_\alpha^\infty \exp (-\alpha^2) \, d\alpha \tag{29}$$

With a constant background ba_0, this equation becomes

$$\frac{a_x + ba_0}{a_0(1 + b)} = \frac{2 \int_\alpha^\infty \exp (-\alpha^2) \, d\alpha + b\pi^{1/2}}{(1 + b)(\pi)^{1/2}} \tag{30}$$

When the experimental data are first plotted, the following relation is assumed:

$$\frac{a_x'}{a_0'} = \frac{a_x + ba_0}{a_0(1 + b)} = \frac{2 \int_\alpha^\infty \exp (-\alpha^2) \, d\alpha + b\pi^{1/2}}{(1 + b)\pi^{1/2}}$$

$$= (2/\pi^{1/2}) \int_{\alpha'}^\infty \exp (-\alpha^2) \, d\alpha \tag{31}$$

The plot then is that of x' versus x.

When the sectioning is carried far enough such that $a_x \to 0$, Eq 31 becomes

$$a_\infty'/a_0' = b/(1 + b) \tag{32}$$

The curve will asymptotically approach the value $b/(1 + b)$. When Eq 32 is substituted back into Eq 31, then

$$a_x/a_0 = (a_x' - a')/(a_0' - a') \tag{33}$$

This equation may be used to replot all points to obtain the true curve.

Only a very few errors have been presented. The experimenter must, of course, consider all possible sources of errors both in the experimental technique and in the analysis of the resulting data. If an error is considered significant, then a correction, which may be exact or approximate, should be made.

Acknowledgment.   This work was performed under the auspices of the U. S. Atomic Energy Commission.

Chapter 21

Correlation of Diffusion Data as a Periodic Function of Atomic Number

R. H. MOORE

It is quite generally held that the activation energy for self-diffusion is the sum of the activation energies for vacancy formation and mobility, that is

$$Q_0 = Q_v + Q_m \tag{1}$$

Upon introduction of minute quantities of an alloying element, the activation energy for solute diffusion, Q_2, is found to differ from Q_0, sometimes appreciably.

It is unlikely that minute concentrations of alloying elements will have much effect on Q_v, which is a solvent property, but there must be significant differences between the interaction of solute atoms with migrating vacancies within the solvent metal and the interaction of solvent atoms with these vacancies. Thus within a given solvent metal, Q_2 is a function of some solute property.

Q_2 varies periodically with atomic number, and it might be expected to be proportional to some other property that also varies periodically with atomic number. If size of the solute atom is important, then atomic volume should be a suitable correlating parameter, and it is observed that the dependence of $\log Q_2$ on V_2 is exponential in character. Thus a plot of $\log Q_2$ versus $\log V_2$ yields a straight line with the equation

$$\log Q_2 = b - a \log V_2 \tag{2}$$

or

$$Q_2 = k V_2^{-a} \tag{3}$$

Because the values of Q_2 vary over a relatively small range, an alternative function is

$$Q = b' - a' \log V_2 \tag{4}$$

The author is with the Hanford Atomic Products Operation, General Electric Co., Richland, Wash.

275

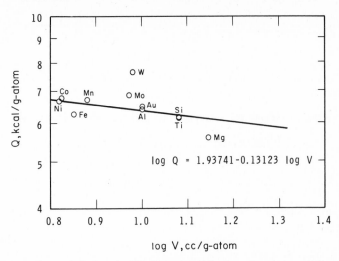

Fig. 1. Solute diffusion in Ni. Data for diffusion of various metals were obtained from the following references: Ni, Ref 1; Au, Ref 2; Co, Ref, 3; Fe, Ref 4; Mg and Si; Ref 5; Ti, Al, Mn and W, Ref 6. Open circles represent experimental data.

or

$$\exp(Q) = k'V^{-\alpha'} \tag{5}$$

Figure 1 shows the data for solute diffusion in Ni. The equation of the curve was obtained by use of least-squares analysis and a high-speed digital computer. The equation of the curve is

$$\log Q = 1.93741 - 0.13123 \log V \tag{6}$$

This equation fits the data for Ni, Au, Co, Fe, Ti, Si, Al and Mn to within 1.8%. The relative errors for Mg, Mo and W were 9.1, 6.4 and 16.1%, respectively.

Figure 2 shows data for solute diffusion in Cu. This curve exhibits a break near the volume of the solvent metal. Elements like Fe, Ni and Co, which on passing over the activation barrier may become negative ions (and therefore would expand), diffuse with higher activation energy than the solvent atoms. Elements that would yield positive ions and would contract diffuse with lower activation energies than the solvent atoms.

For the nontransition elements, the equation of the line determined by least-squares analysis is

$$\log Q = 1.75483 - 0.096013 \log V \tag{7}$$

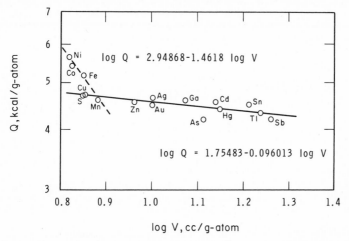

Fig. 2. Solute diffusion in Cu. Data for diffusion of various elements were obtained from the following references: Cu, Zn, Ga, Au, Hg and Tl, Ref 7; As, Ag and Cd, Ref 8; S, Ref 9; Sn, Ref 10; Sb, Ref 11; Fe, Co, Ni and Mn, Ref 12.

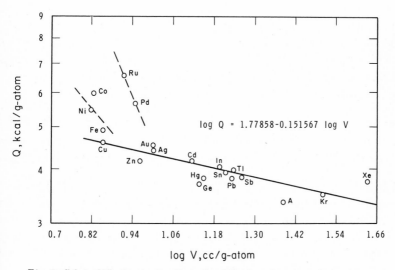

Fig. 3. Solute diffusion in Ag. Data for diffusion of various elements were obtained from the following references: Au, Cd, Cu, Hg, In, Pb, Ru, Sb, Sn, Tl and Zn, Ref 8; Pd, Ref 13; Ag, Ref 14; A, Ref 15; Xi and Kr, Ref 16; Fe, Ref 17; Co and Ni, Ref 18; Ge, Ref 19.

The equation for the 3-d transition elements, determined from the plotted data, is

$$\log Q = 2.94868 - 1.4618 \log V \qquad (8)$$

With the exception of As, for which the relative error was $+5.9\%$, Eq 7 fits the data for the nontransition elements to within $\pm 2.0\%$. Equation 8 predicts the data for the 3-d transition elements to within $\pm 2.0\%$.

Data for Pd (Ref 13) were not included, and as will be shown shortly, the 4-d transition elements correlate along a third line.

Figure 3 shows data for solute diffusion in Ag. Here again the curve separates into distinct curves for the 3-d and 4-d transition elements and the nontransition elements. For the nontransition elements, the equation of the curve was determined by least-squares analysis, that is

$$\log Q = 1.77858 - 0.151567 \log V \qquad (9)$$

This equation fits the data to within $\pm 3.0\%$ with exception of data for Ge, A, Au and Xe for which the relative errors were $+11.0$, $+10.1$, -7.0 and -9.3%, respectively.

Data for the 3-d and 4-d transition elements are not sufficient to permit determination of the equations for these curves with any degree of confidence.

Figure 4 illustrates the periodic dependence of Q_2 on atomic number of the diffusing solute and the internal consistency of observed and predicted data.

Figure 5 shows the data for diffusion in β-Ti. It is generally held that O, N, B and C diffuse interstitially in β-Ti. It appears this may also be true for P^{24} diffusion. There are not really enough points to establish that interstitial diffusion also obeys this correlation, but the results are fairly satisfactory.

Plots for the diffusion of 3-d transition elements in β-Ti lie along a line of slightly positive slope. Although Cb is a 4-d transition element, it also falls on this line. Mo, also a 4-d transition element, is off this curve. Sn, a nontransition element, also is off this curve. From evidence for the fcc systems, there is no reason to expect the 4-d transition elements and nontransition elements to correlate on the same line and thus differ from the 3-d transition elements and the nontransition elements. There are insufficient data to establish curves for the 4-d transition elements and the nontransition elements.

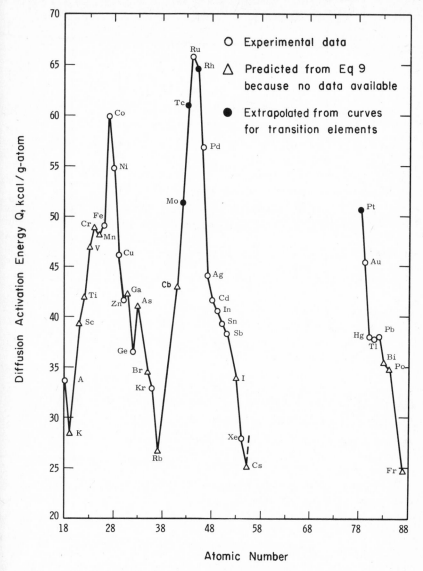

Fig. 4. Periodic dependence of diffusion activation energy on atomic number for diffusion in Ag

For the 3-d transition elements the equation of the curve is

$$\log Q = 0.18116 + 0.3509 \log V \qquad (10)$$

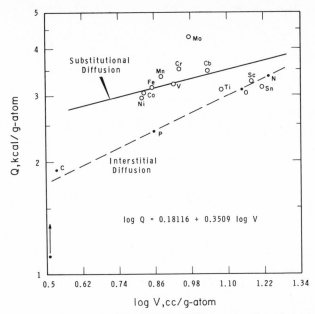

Fig. 5. Solute diffusion in β-Ti. Data for diffusion of various elements were obtained from the following references: Fe, Ni, Co and Cb, Ref 20; P, Sc, Ti, V, Cr, Mn, Mo and Sn, Ref 21.

This equation fits the data for these elements to within about 5% except for Ti and Sc, which exhibit relative errors of +16.3 and +20.2%.

Summary and Conclusions

It has been shown that data for solute diffusion in Ag, Cu, Ni and β-Ti accurately obey the relation

$$Q = kV^a$$

where V^a is a measure of the size effect and k, the proportionality constant, takes into account the forces of electric attraction and repulsion, which must necessarily be present.

This correlation is sufficiently accurate to permit an evaluation of the internal consistency of the data. It will also serve to predict the activation energy for diffusion when data are lacking.

Acknowledgment. This work was performed under Contract No. AT(45-1)-1350 for the Atomic Energy Commission.

References

1 K. Hirano, R. P. Agarwala and M. Cohen, J Appl Phys, **33**, 3049 (1962)

2 D. Turnbull and R. E. Hoffman, Acta Met, **7**, 407 (1959)

3 R. C. Ruder and C. E. Birchnall, J Metals, **3**, 142 (1951)

4 R. A. Swalin, University Microfilms Publication No. 10043, Ann Arbor, Michigan

5 R. A. Swalin, Acta Met, **5**, 443 (1957)

6 R. A. Swalin and A. Martin, Trans AIME, **206**, 567 (1956)

7 S. Komura and N. Kunitomi, J Phys Soc Japan, **18**, Supplement II, 208 (1963)

8 D. Lazarus, Solid State Physics, Vol 10, Academic Press, New York–London, 1960, p 71–126.

9 M. M. Pavlyuchenko, I. E. Kanonyuk and A. D. Markin, Abstr J Metals, 3/4 Pt. A, No. 30 (1962)

10 L. C. C. da Silva and R. F. Mehl, Trans AIME, **191**, 155 (1951)

11 M. C. Inman and L. W. Barr, Acta Met, **8**, 112 (1960)

12 C. A. Mackliet, Phys Rev, **109**, 1964 (1958)

13 N. L. Petersen, Phys Rev, **132**, 2471 (1963)

14 C. T. Tomizuka and E. Sonder, Phys Rev, **103**, 1182 (1956)

15 A. D. Le Claire and A. H. Rowe, Rev Met, **52**, 94 (1955)

16 J. M. Tobin, Acta Met, **7**, 701 (1959)

17 J. G. Mullen, Phys Rev, **121**, 1649 (1961)

18 T. Hirone, *et al.*, J Phys Soc Japan, **18**, Supplement II, 213 (1963)

19 R. E. Hoffman, Acta Met, **6**, 95 (1958)

20 R. F. Peart and D. H. Tomlin, Acta Met, **10**, 123 (1962)

21 D. Graham, Chapter 2 in this volume

Chapter 22

Investigations of Diffusion of Carbon in Three Refractory Metals Over a Wide Range of Temperatures

I. I. Kovenskii

The dependence of the diffusion coefficients on absolute temperature may be written in the usual form $D = D_0 \exp(-\epsilon/kT)$, if one assumes that the activation energy of a diffusion process, ϵ, is not a function of temperature. However, that assumption, even though it is supported by many experiments, is adequate only for a rather narrow temperature range, in most investigations not including more than about 300 degrees. Apparently, it would be interesting to see whether a nonconstant value of ϵ would be detected if this interval were increased. A convenient subject of such experiments would be the refractory metals, because in these metals it is possible to extend the measurements over the widest possible temperature range. On the other hand, for such experiments, it is necessary that the mobility of the diffusing elements be sufficiently high to insure reasonable precision in the results even at the lowest temperatures investigated in a selected range. Also, it is certainly necessary that throughout the temperature range of the measurements, no phase transformation occurs.

All of these conditions are satisfied for alloys of Ti, Ta and W with C to a concentration of about 0.1% (by weight). In the temperature ranges of 950 to 1650, 600 to 2600 and 1800 to 2800 C, respectively, these alloys are solid solutions and do not undergo any kind of phase transformation (1–3). On the other hand, in the literature known to us, there are no data on C diffusion in the C solid solutions with Ti, although there are data on diffusion in the carbide (4), and investigations of diffusion of C in Ta and W refer to rather narrow ranges of temperature (5, 6). Therefore we began our experiments, because it appeared that this study would be of considerable interest.

This paper was translated and presented by Dr. G. Love of the Oak Ridge National Laboratory, Oak Ridge, Tenn. The author is with the Academy of Sciences of the Ukraine, Kiev, USSR.

The experiments were carried out on wire samples about 70 mm long and 0.5 mm in diameter. The chemical composition (in weight per cent) of the samples was as follows: for the Ti-base samples, 99.86 Ti, 0.11 C, 0.002 W, 0.001 Ni, 0.001 Cb, 0.001 Ta, 0.002 Zr, 0.002 Cr, 0.004 O; for the Ta-base samples, 99.78 Ta, 0.12 C, 0.060 Cb, 0.002 W, 0.001 Mg, 0.002 Mo, 0.001 Ni, 0.004 Ti; for the W-base samples, 99.86 W, 0.09 C, 0.001 Cu, 0.001 Zn, 0.006 Fe, 0.001 Si, 0.001 S, 0.001 P, 0.004 O.

A length of sample wire about 10 mm long in the middle of the sample was doped with C^{14} in such a fashion that the radioactive zone was sharply bounded. A plot of the distribution of activity versus length on the sample has a π-shaped appearance. Activity was measured by use of an end window meter and recorded at each 0.1 mm of length on the sample by use of a diaphragm with a slit width of 0.1 mm. The distribution of the C^{14} isotope in the cross section of the active zone was measured, and the C concentration versus length on the sample axis was the same as the concentration versus length on the sample diameter.

Diffusion annealing of the samples was carried out in an atmosphere of purified A by use of direct heating with an alternating current. Temperatures were controlled with an optical pyrometer having an accuracy of ± 5 to 7 C. The experiments at 600 C were performed in a furnace, and the sample temperature was measured with a thermocouple.

After annealing, the distribution of radioactivity versus length on the sample was measured a second time. The data obtained were plotted on graphs from which diffusivities were calculated.

The experimental techniques were chosen to guarantee agreement with the conditions for application of Fick's equations for diffusion in one dimension into an infinite solid body. The expression for these conditions is

$$2C/C_0 = \text{erf } Z$$

where $Z = x/2(Dt)^{1/2}$, x being the distance of the point on the sample at which is measured the concentration C of the radio-isotope from the edge of the initial radioactive zone. C_0 is the concentration of C^{14} in this zone. Uniformly, the ratio C/C_0 is taken to be equal to the ratio of the relative activities.

In order to calculate diffusion coefficients, activity measurements from six points, x, on each sample were used; duplicate samples were run at each temperature. The average values of the diffusion coefficients thus obtained are given in Table 1.

In all instances several successive layers were etched off the samples, and the measurements of the distribution of radioactivity with distance were repeated. By this method it was demonstrated that preferential

Table 1. Diffusion Coefficients

Temp, °C	D, cm²/sec	Temp, °C	D, cm²/sec	Temp, °C	D, cm²/sec
C in Ti		**C in W**		**C in Ta**	
950.........	1.23×10^{-6}	1800.......	5.02×10^{-7}	600.......	2.18×10^{-9}
1000........	1.77×10^{-6}	1850.......	5.49×10^{-7}	800........	2.76×10^{-8}
1050........	2.21×10^{-6}	1900.......	7.24×10^{-7}	1000........	1.38×10^{-7}
1150........	4.09×10^{-6}	2000.......	1.17×10^{-6}	1200........	5.80×10^{-7}
1250........	6.42×10^{-6}	2100.......	1.77×10^{-6}	1400........	1.89×10^{-6}
1350........	8.48×10^{-6}	2200.......	2.75×10^{-6}	1800........	9.54×10^{-6}
1450........	1.24×10^{-5}	2300.......	3.15×10^{-6}	2200........	3.01×10^{-5}
1550........	1.58×10^{-5}	2400.......	4.51×10^{-6}	2600........	6.58×10^{-5}
1650........	2.40×10^{-5}	2500.......	5.87×10^{-6}		
		2600.......	8.74×10^{-6}		
		2700.......	1.12×10^{-5}		
		2800.......	1.41×10^{-5}		

surface diffusion did not occur, that is, that the data of Table 1 represent volume diffusion.

For the solid solution of C in Ti, the usual variation of the diffusion coefficient with temperature was observed to within the limits of error of our measurements (see Fig. 1). Its parameters are given in Table 2.

The observed temperature dependence of the diffusion coefficient of C in W is shown in Fig. 2. As is evident from this graph, in the temperature range 1800 to 2600 C there is good agreement with the usual linear relation between $\ln D$ and $(1/T)$. The parameters of this dependence are

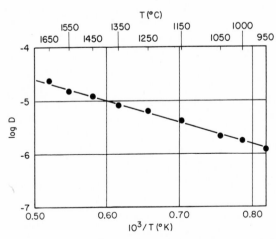

Fig. 1. Temperature dependence of the diffusion coefficient of C in Ti

Table 2. Diffusion Parameters

Alloy	D_0, cm^2/sec	ϵ, kcal/mole
Ti-C..............	3.18×10^{-3}	18.9
Ta-C..............	2.78×10^{-3}	24.6
W-C..............	9.22×10^{-3}	40.4

listed in Table 2. However, in the range of 2600 to 2800 C there is visible deviation from this dependence. Between 1800 and 2600 C the difference between experimental values of the diffusion coefficient and values calculated with the formula $D = D_0 \exp\left(-\epsilon/kT\right)$ fluctuates in the range of 4 to 11% (only at 2200 C this difference amounts to 14.6%). However at 2600, 2700 and 2800 C the differences amount to 15, 16.3 and 17.5%, respectively.

As is evident from Table 2, the temperature range for the investigation of the diffusion of C in Ta was 2000 C. In the region of 600 to 1400 C, the usual linear dependence of $\ln D$ on $(1/T)$ is observed (see Fig. 3). The calculated diffusion parameters in this temperature range are listed in Table 2.

Beginning at the point corresponding to 1800 C, there are increasing deviations from the equation derived above. The maximum deviation between the experimental values of the diffusion coefficients and the derived curve in the region below 1400 C is approximately 18.5%. At 1800, 2200 and 2600 C the deviations are 37.7, 64.5 and 78.8%, respectively.

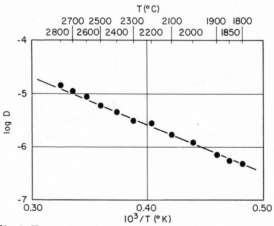

Fig. 2. Temperature dependence of the diffusion coefficient of C in W

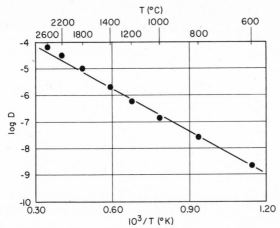

Fig. 3. Temperature dependence of the diffusion coefficient of C in Ta

Because it is evident from the plots that no phase transformation occurs in the temperature range investigated, the observed deviations for the W-base and Ta-base systems indicate that it is necessary to take the temperature dependence of the activation energy into account whenever the temperature range exceeds 800 C.

Before it will be possible to reach definite quantitative conclusions on this point, which is of great theoretical interest in the field of diffusion, it is necessary to accumulate a sufficiently large amount of experimental data obtained over large temperature ranges.

References

1   M. Hansen, Constitution of Binary Alloys, McGraw-Hill Book Co., Inc., New York, 1958
2   V. I. Smirnova and B. F. Ormont, Dokl Akad Nauk SSSR, **96,** 557 (1954)
3   Metals Handbook, American Society for Metals, Metals Park, 1948
4   G. B. Samsonov, Tech Pub Moscow Inst for Light Metals and Copper, No. 30, 192 (1957); G. B. Samsonov, Proc of Conf on the Chem of Boron and Its Compounds, p 74 (1958); G. B. Samsonov and V. P. Latsheva, Dokl Akad Nauk SSSR, **109,** 582 (1956)
5   C. A. Wert, J Appl Phys, **21,** 1196 (1950)
6   M. Pirani and Y. Sandor, J Inst Metals, **73,** 385 (1947)

PART 5

Enhancement of Diffusion

Chapter 23
Radiation Effects, Diffusion and Body-Centered Cubic Metals

M. S. WECHSLER

The purpose of this paper is to review the state of knowledge on the effect of radiation on the bcc metals and to emphasize those aspects bearing on diffusion and diffusion-controlled phenomena. As is true of the study of diffusion in metals, the fcc metals have received the greatest attention in radiation experiments in the past, and it is only relatively recently that some effort is being devoted to the bcc metals.

Production of Point Defects by Radiation

The principal interconnection between radiation effects and diffusion lies, of course, in the fact that point defects, which provide mechanisms for diffusion, are created as a result of bombardment by high-energy particles. The point defects are chiefly vacancies and interstitials, and they occur when struck atoms are displaced from their lattice sites. Displacements may also be produced by γ-rays (chiefly through the action of energetic electrons resulting from the Compton effect) or by atom recoil following neutron absorption and the emission of a capture γ-ray, but we shall confine our discussion to defects produced by collisions with bombarding particles.

In most calculations of the displacement production rate, no attempt is made to incorporate any dependence on the lattice arrangement of the atoms in the crystal. In the usual formulation (1, 2), the displacement production rate, K, is given by

$$K = \sigma_d \phi \tag{1}$$

where K is the number of displacements per lattice site produced per

The author is with the Solid State Division, Oak Ridge National Laboratory, Oak Ridge, Tenn.

second, σ_d is the displacement cross section and ϕ is the flux of bombarding particles. The displacement cross section depends upon three factors:

1. The differential scattering cross section $d\sigma$ (E,T). This factor expresses the relative likelihood that the bombarding particle of energy E will transfer energy T to the struck atom.

2. The displacement probability, $p(T)$, that is, the probability that the struck atom will be displaced after receiving energy T.

3. The displacement multiplication function $\nu(T)$, that is, the total number of displacements produced in the collision cascade in which the primary struck atom partitions its energy among other atoms in the crystal.

The displacement cross section for projectile particles of energy E is then given by

$$\sigma_d = \int_0^{T_m(E)} \nu(T)p(T)[d\sigma \ (E,T)/dT] \, dT \tag{2}$$

where $T_m(E)$ is the maximum energy that can be transferred. The maximum energy transferred corresponds to a head-on collision. For heavy particles, conservation of energy and momentum leads to the result

$$T_m(E) = [4mM/(m + M)^2]E$$

where m and M are the masses of the projectile and target atoms, respectively. For electrons, which are relativistic particles in the energy ranges of interest, the expression becomes

$$T_m(E) = 2(E + 2mc^2)E/Mc^2$$

where c is the speed of light. If the projectile particles are distributed in energy, as is always true for reactor neutron irradiations, then the differential flux, $\phi'(E)$, must be used and Eq 1 becomes

$$K = \int_0^\infty \sigma_d(E)\phi'(E) \, dE$$

where $\sigma_d(E)$ is given by Eq 2.

Among the three factors contributing to σ_d in Eq 2, the differential scattering cross section is least likely to be affected by the lattice arrangement, because it depends on the interaction between projectile and target particles at short distances. For charged-particle bombardments, $d\sigma$ (E,T) follows Rutherford scattering for which

$$d\sigma \ (E,T) \propto dT/T^2$$

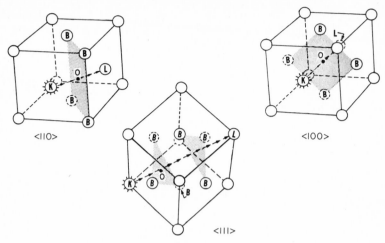

Fig. 1. Diagrams for fcc lattice showing path of knock-on, K, before striking atom, L. Knock-on passes at O between barrier atoms, B. (After Sosin, Ref 2)

or its relativistic equivalent (3). The $1/T^2$ factor indicates that low energy transfers (glancing collisions) are greatly favored. For neutron bombardment, the scattering is more nearly isotropic and we have simply

$$d\sigma\ (E,T)\ \propto\ dT$$

However, the second factor in the integrand of Eq 2, the displacement probability, $p(T)$, may depend sensitively on the lattice arrangement. This is especially true for low T, for which the energy transferred is barely sufficient to displace the atom. The directions for easy displacement of the struck atom for the fcc crystal are shown in Fig. 1. In a machine calculation for a simulated Cu crystal (4), it was found that the displacement threshold energies were 25, 25 to 30, and 85 ev for atoms set in motion at low energies along the $\langle 100 \rangle$, $\langle 110 \rangle$ and $\langle 111 \rangle$ directions, respectively.

The corresponding situation for the bcc crystal is shown in Fig. 2. The knocked-on atom moving in the $\langle 111 \rangle$ direction (atom K, Fig. 2a) must pass through two rings of barrier atoms (A_1, A_2 and A_3; and B_1, B_2 and B_3) in equilateral-triangle configurations before it strikes the next lattice atom (atom L), whereas there is only one ring of barrier atoms for the $\langle 100 \rangle$ and $\langle 110 \rangle$ directions (Fig. 2b and c). This is also true for the fcc crystal, but the $\langle 111 \rangle$ direction, which is the nearest-neighbor direction for bcc crystals, is not the nearest-neighbor direction for fcc crystals. In the machine calculation for a simulated bcc Fe crystal (5), the displace-

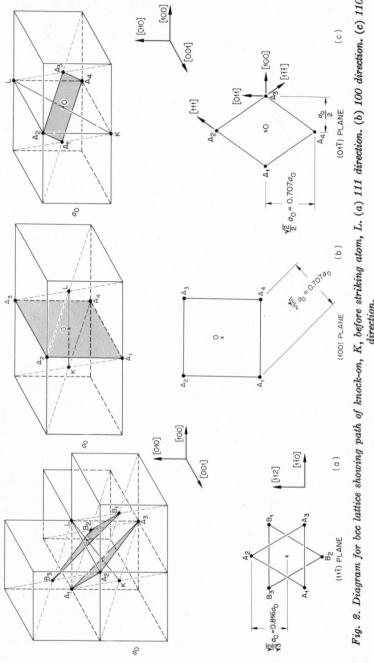

Fig. 2. Diagram for bcc lattice showing path of knock-on, K, before striking atom, L. (a) 111 direction. (b) 100 direction. (c) 110 direction.

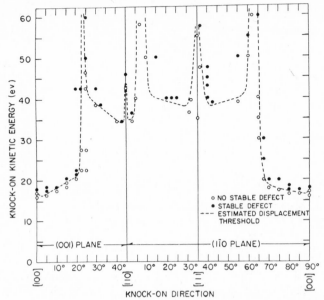

Fig. 3. Computer calculations for the directional dependence of the displacement threshold energy for α-Fe. (After Erginsoy et al., Ref 5)

ment threshold energy was highly dependent on the direction of motion of the knocked-on atom. Figure 3 shows the calculated dependence of the displacement threshold energy on the direction of motion of the struck atom. The lowest threshold was found to be 17 ev for knock-ons directed near ⟨100⟩ and about 34 and 38 ev for those directed near ⟨110⟩ and ⟨111⟩, respectively. For the last two directions, Fig. 3 shows that the minimum energies apply to directions slightly off the exact crystallographic directions. For the low-energy knock-ons treated in these calculations, the chief mechanism of displacement was a chain of correlated replacements, in which the knock-on atom itself does not go into an interstitial position, but strikes a neighboring atom and replaces it on its lattice site, and so on. Also, for these calculations the knock-on energies are sufficiently low so that only one or, at most, two displacements are produced, that is $\nu = 1$ or 2.

The simplest assumption concerning the shape of the displacement probability function, $p(T)$, is a sharp step-function threshold, such that $p(T) = 0$ for knock-on energies, T, below the threshold energy, T_d, and $p(T) = 1$ for $T > T_d$. However, it is realized that such a simple assumption is unrealistic. In fact, the computer calculations (4, 5) have indicated that for a given direction of motion the displacement probability increases

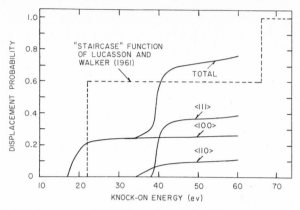

Fig. 4. Displacement probability versus knock-on energy for α-Fe. (After Erginsoy et al., Ref 5)

gradually with energy above T_d. Figure 4 shows the computed displacement probability curves for bcc Fe for the $\langle 100 \rangle$, $\langle 110 \rangle$ and $\langle 111 \rangle$ directions taken separately and the total displacement probability curve for a randomly directed knock-on (5). It is seen that although the lowest threshold energy (17 ev) occurs for the $\langle 100 \rangle$ direction, the displacement probability for the $\langle 111 \rangle$ direction rises more rapidly above 38 ev and exceeds that for the $\langle 100 \rangle$ direction above about 40 ev.

Measurements of the Displacement Production Rate and the Displacement Threshold Energy

In the experimental determination of the displacement production rate, the property most often measured is electrical resistivity. As has been pointed out most recently by Holmes (1), the observed values of K for Cu are found to be smaller than those predicted by expressions of the type given above. However, the agreement found for electron bombardment is better than that found for heavy-particle bombardment. The calculation of K for neutron irradiation leads to a particularly large overestimate of K, perhaps by a factor as large as 10.

A number of reasons for the overestimate have been suggested. First, because the neutron scattering is approximately isotropic, many of the energy transfers will be large enough to result in many displacements for each primary (neutron–atom) collision. This brings the multiplication factor, $\nu(T)$, into play. The simplest assumption is (1)

$$\nu(T) \cong \alpha T / T_d$$

for $T > T_d$ where $\alpha = 0.5$, but calculations indicate that smaller values of α may be more correct and that ν may be proportional to some fractional power of T less than unity. One reason for this is that some of the knock-on atoms become channeled (6, 7) into open cores between atom rows where energy is lost very gradually in subthreshold collisions. Because the channels depend on the detailed crystal structure, this factor may operate differently for fcc and bcc metals. Additional discussion of this point is given later.

A second factor to account for the overprediction of the displacement production rate for neutron irradiation is the loss of knock-on energy by ionization. Here it is assumed that the knock-on atom loses energy entirely by ionization until it slows down to some cutoff energy at which atom displacements begin. Also, for higher neutron energies (above about 1 mev), some forward scattering may take place, which favors low energy transfers to the lattice atoms. However, these last two factors should not depend strongly on crystal structure.

Because of the lower transferred energies and the simpler damage produced by electrons, the influence of crystal structure is probably best studied by means of electron irradiations. Figure 5 shows the increase in resistivity observed upon irradiation at 20.4 K with 1.5-mev electrons for Ag, Cu, Al, Ni and Fe (8). The higher damage rate for bcc Fe than for the fcc metals is thought to be due to a higher resistivity per Frenkel pair

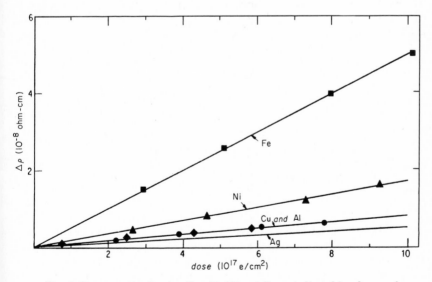

Fig. 5. Damage rates for Ag, Cu, Al, Ni and Fe as indicated by change of electrical resistivity upon irradiation at 20.4 K with 1.5-mev electrons. (After Walker, Ref 8)

Table 1. Effective Threshold Energies and Frenkel-Pair Resistivities for Various Metals(9)

Element	Crystal structure	T_d, ev	$\Delta\rho_f$, microhm-cm/at. %
Al...............	fcc	32	3.4
Ni...............	fcc	24	3.2
Cu...............	fcc	22	1.3
Ag...............	fcc	28	1.4
Au...............	fcc	>40	....
Fe...............	bcc	24	12.5
Mo...............	bcc	37	4.5
W...............	bcc	>35	....
Ti...............	Hexagonal	29	42.0

(see Table 1) rather than to a higher displacement production rate. Other irradiations at 20 K on Mo indicate a damage rate of about 10^{-26} ohm-cm per electron per cm^2 for 1.5-mev electrons (9), which would place the curve for Mo between those for Ni and Cu in Fig. 5.

Electron irradiations are well suited for the determination of displacement threshold energies because the damage rate may be measured easily as a function of electron energy. The damage rates at 20.4 K for Ag, Cu, Al, Ni, Fe and Mo as a function of electron energy are shown in Fig. 6. In order to determine the displacement threshold energy, we note from Eq 1 that the number of displacements or Frenkel pairs after a dose $\Phi = \phi t$, assuming no annealing during irradiation, is given by

$$n = \sigma_d \Phi$$

and if the resistivity per Frenkel pair is $\Delta\rho_f$,

$$\Delta\rho/\Phi = \Delta\rho_f \sigma_d$$

The displacement threshold energy is then chosen so that the shape of the $\sigma_d(E)$ curve fits the observed values of $\Delta\rho/\Phi$, and the $\Delta\rho_f$ value is chosen to give the absolute value predicted by theory. A plot of σ_d for Fe (10), normalized to its value for 1.35 mev, is shown in Fig. 7. For a sharp step-function displacement probability curve, the best value of T_d is 24 ev, but a better fit was found for a "staircase" function, as shown in the insert with $T_1 = 22$ ev and $T_2 = 66$ ev. The staircase function was also suggested by the results of the computer calculations of Erginsoy *et al.* (5), as shown in Fig. 4. In Table 1, the displacement threshold energies (assum-

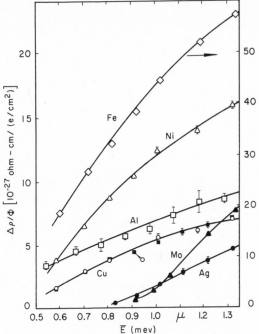

Fig. 6. Damage rates at 20.4 K as a function of electron energy for Ag, Cu, Al, Ni, Fe and Mo. (After Lucasson and Walker, Ref 9)

ing step-function displacement probabilities) and Frenkel-pair resistivities are given for various metals (9). It has been pointed out (11) that the threshold energies show a tendency to increase with increasing atomic number and decreasing atomic spacing, but no correlation with crystal structure alone is apparent in Table 1. However, Table 1 does suggest that the resistivity per Frenkel pair, $\Delta\rho_f$, is greater for the non-fcc metals. The value given for Cu, 1.3 microhm-cm per at. %, is somewhat lower than the lower limit of about 2 microhm-cm per at. % deduced from stored-energy (12), lattice-parameter (13) and length-change (14) measurements upon deuteron bombardment. This implies that the theory overestimates the damage rate in Cu upon electron irradiation by a factor greater than 1.5. Correspondingly larger values of $\Delta\rho_f$ for the other metals listed in Table 1 may also be appropriate.

The dependence of the displacement probability on the direction of the knock-on atom, as shown in Fig. 4, suggests the advisability of conducting beam-irradiation experiments on oriented single-crystal samples. No damage rates for such an experiment have been reported, although some

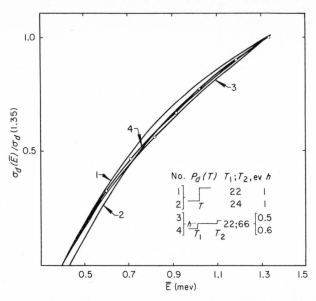

Fig. 7. Normalized calculated cross sections and observed damage rates for Fe. The best fit is with $T_1 = 22$ ev, $T_2 = 66$ ev and $h = 0.6$. (After Lucasson, Lucasson and Walker, Ref 10)

preliminary results are available for the isochronal annealing behavior after electron irradiation in oriented Cu and Fe whiskers (15).

Damage rates in bcc metals upon neutron irradiation have not been extensively studied, but some values are shown in Table 2 for certain fcc and bcc metals irradiated at about 4 K in the Oak Ridge Graphite Reactor (16). It is not known whether the apparently higher damage rates for the bcc metals are due to a greater displacement production rate, K, or to a higher resistivity per displacement, $\Delta\rho_f$. For Mo (17, 18), a comparison of the release of stored energy and the recovery of resistivity

Table 2. Damage Rates for Various fcc and bcc Metals Upon Neutron Irradiation at 4 K in the Oak Ridge Graphite Reactor (16)

Metal	Damage rate, $d\rho/dt$, (ohm-cm/hr) $\times 10^{11}$	Metal	Damage rate, $d\rho/dt$, (ohm-cm/hr) $\times 10^{11}$
Cu	2.5	Ni	13
Ag	5.2	Fe	16
Au	3.0	Cb	16
Pt	6.6	Mo	14
Al	8.4	W	17

after neutron irradiation at 30 C indicated that $\Delta\rho_f \cong 20$ microhm-cm per at. % displacements. The study of (n, γ) recoil damage (19) may facilitate the determination of $\Delta\rho_f$, but the appropriate experiments have not been performed on bcc metals. For W (20) irradiated at -196 C, the curve of change in resistivity versus neutron dose is not necessarily linear, but may show upward or downward curvature depending on the prior treatment, thus suggesting a dependence on impurity content. Measurements have also been made of the changes in lattice parameter and length in Mo (21) upon neutron irradiation at 30 C. The fractional increase in length was larger than that for lattice parameter, which indicates a preponderance of vacancies over interstitials upon irradiation at this temperature. This has a bearing on the important question of the nature of the defects annealing in various temperature ranges, which is discussed in the next section.

Annealing of Radiation Damage

Isochronal annealing after irradiation has been most widely studied for Cu (1). When the temperature is raised after irradiation at low temperature (4 to 25 K), the radiation-produced increase in resistivity is observed to anneal out in more or less distinct stages. For Cu, the annealing stages and temperatures are designated very roughly as follows: Stage I (below 70 K), II (70 to 220 K), III (220 to 300 K), IV (300 to 450 K) and V (above 450 K). For other metals, a similar pattern is used, although the temperatures are different. For example, the annealing stages in Mo (22) have been estimated to be as follows: I (below 120 K), II (120 to 350 K), III (350 to 600 K), IV (600 to 900 K) and V (above 900 K). A similar division of the annealing spectrum into stages has been suggested for W (20).

Because the sample is in the as-irradiated state only for Stage I annealing, considerable emphasis has been placed on this stage in recent years. Also, Stage I is generally larger than the other stages. This is especially true for electron irradiation. As is seen in Fig. 8, the Stage I annealing in Cu (15) is responsible for about 85% of the recovery. Another feature of Stage I annealing in Cu is the presence of substages (note the discontinuities in the annealing curves in Fig. 8). Originally, five substages were identified (23), but more recently the number of substages has grown to nine (24, 25). Figure 8 shows that substages in Stage I are also exhibited for Fe. The interpretation of Stage I and its substages is not settled (1), but at least for the lower-temperature substages it is likely that interstitials move to the vacant lattice sites from which they originated (close-pair recovery). The distinct substages are then associated with the motion of interstitials at various distances from the vacancies. This should depend

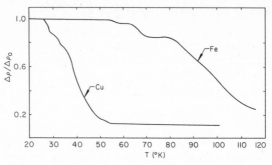

Fig. 8. Isochronal recovery in Stage I for polycrystalline Cu and Fe after electron irradiation at 20 K. Discontinuities in curves indicate substages.
(After Cusson, Lucasson and Walker, Ref 15)

on the crystal structure, and thus one might expect a characteristically different pattern of substages for fcc and bcc metals. However, factors other than crystal structure must play a part in the substage pattern. This is seen in the fact that differences exist even among the noble metals; Au, for example, shows a weak Stage I with no substructure, in contrast to Cu and Ag (Fig. 9).

In Fig. 9, the annealing curves for electron irradiation are plotted so that 50% recovery for each metal occurs at the point on the abscissa for 50% recovery for Cu (11). No striking differences in the shapes of the curves are discernible for the two bcc metals, Fe and Mo, as compared with the curves for the fcc metals. Also, as is seen in Table 3, although the temperatures for 50% recovery are somewhat higher for the two bcc metals, no clear correlation is seen with Debye temperature or melting point. A somewhat better correlation, discussed in Ref 11, is obtained with the Grüneisen constant times the atomic volume.

Table 3. Comparison of Stage I Recovery Temperatures With Various Parameters (11)

Element	Crystal structure	Temp for 50% recovery, °K	Debye temp, °K	Melting point, °C	Grüneisen constant times at. vol
Au	fcc	<30 ?	165	1063	31
Ag	fcc	30	225	961	25
Al	fcc	37.8	418	660	22
Cu	fcc	38.3	340	1083	14
Ni	fcc	57.1	456	1455	13
Mo	bcc	42.9	425	2625	15
Fe	bcc	99.8	467	1540	11

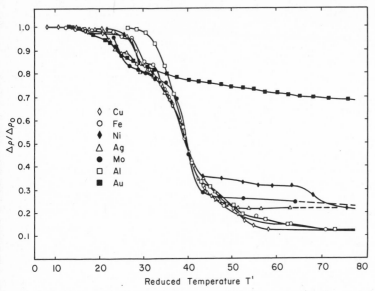

Fig. 9. Normalized plot of Stage I recovery in different metals after electron irradiation at 20 K. The experimental temperatures for all metals except Au were multiplied by a constant in order to place the 50% recovery at the abscissa value for Cu. (After Lucasson and Walker, Ref 11)

After low-temperature neutron irradiation, the substructure in Stage I annealing is greatly reduced or absent. This is true for both fcc and bcc metals. The annealing curves for Fe, Mo and W are shown in Fig. 10; the curve for Cu is included for comparison (26, 27). The absence of the substages upon neutron irradiation is probably a consequence of a more complicated defect structure. Upon electron irradiation, simple isolated interstitial-vacancy pairs are produced, whereas clusters of defects in various states of aggregation result from neutron irradiation. This has the effect of widening the effective range of activation energies of the annealing processes operating at a given temperature, thus causing the annealing to be less discrete. The annealing for Fe seems to take place at higher temperatures than that for Mo or W, a result similar to that for electron irradiation (Table 3). Substitutional impurities in the fcc metals, for example, Be in Cu (28) are known to suppress the annealing in Stage I, presumably because of trapping of interstitials at impurity atoms.

Stage II and Stage III annealing have been studied in Mo (17, 18, 21, 22) and W (17, 18, 20, 29, 30) after neutron irradiation at −196 C and at ambient temperature. Broad annealing peaks are observed. The lower-temperature annealing (Stage II) is considered to be due to free or

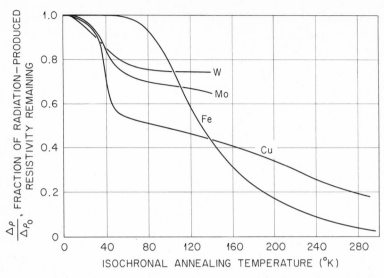

Fig. 10. Isochronal annealing curves for Cu, Fe, Mo and W. Annealing of Cu, Mo and W followed neutron irradiation at 4.2 K; annealing of Fe followed neutron irradiation at 14 K. Dose—4 × 10^17 neutrons/cm². (Coltman et al., Ref 26 and 27)

clustered interstitial motion (22) or to the release of interstitials from impurity traps (29), but opinions differ as to whether vacancy motion is to be assigned to Stage III or to Stage IV (17, 22). Measurements of the annealing temperature and activation energy for the annealing of vacancies in quenched bcc metals may help to resolve this question, but thus far results are available only for Mo (22). In this instance, the annealing temperature of quenched vacancies was observed to be somewhat greater than that for Stage III annealing after irradiation. This supports the assignment of vacancy motion to Stage IV, but the evidence is still quite preliminary. When the data for fcc and bcc metals are examined, Stage III annealing after irradiation seems to occur at about 0.2 T_m, whereas quench-annealing takes place at about 0.3 T_m (20, 22), where T_m is the melting point.

Observations of defect clusters produced by neutron irradiation have been made by transmission electron microscopy (see, for example, Ref 31), but again most of the work has been done on fcc metals. However, black spots 50 to 75 A in diameter have been seen (32) in Fe neutron-irradiated at 60 C to 10^{19} neutrons/cm² ($E > 1$ mev). Similar black spots have also been observed (33) in Mo irradiated under similar conditions. Furthermore, the spots were eliminated in straight bands by mobile dislocations.

Large dislocation loops in Mo result from irradiation at 600 C to a total fast neutron dose of 10^{18} neutrons/cm^2. The loops were found to be interstitial in character (34), but it was not established whether the interstitial loops were due to point defect clusters or to fine precipitates of interstitial impurities. In the instance of Fe irradiated at 100 C to low doses, the diffraction contrast observed in the microscope was attributed to the precipitation of C atoms (35).

Because of their technological importance, low-C pressure-vessel steels have been studied upon irradiation, chiefly from the point of view of radiation hardening and embrittlement (36). It is of interest to note that the annealing of the radiation-produced increase in yield stress was observed (37) to occur with an activation energy of 73 kcal/mole, which agrees well with the values of 73.2 kcal/mole (38) or 67.2 kcal/mole (39) determined for the diffusion of Fe in α-Fe. This result suggests that the recovery of the yield stress is governed by the motion of vacancies, which is perhaps reasonable if the hardening were due to immobile interstitial clusters. However, one difficulty that must be resolved is the extremely low number of vacancy jumps that seems to be required for the recovery process (36, 37).

Channeling and Focusing

Two effects that depend strongly on the lattice arrangement of the atoms in a crystal are channeling and focusing. As we have mentioned, channeling occurs when a knock-on atom is deflected into an open channel between atom rows. In the course of its motion down the channel, the atom experiences only glancing collisions with the atoms that constrain it in the channel. Hence, channeling provides a mechanism for long-range motion of energetic atoms. Furthermore, because only small amounts of energy are transferred in the glancing collisions of the channeled atom, its energy is expended in subthreshold collisions and, therefore, channeling reduces the number of displacements to be produced by the radiation.

The calculations of Robinson and Oen (7) predict that the ranges of channeled atoms should depend on how open the direction of motion is. Therefore, the ranges, R, for given directions should decrease in the order $R[011] > R[001] > R[111]$ for fcc crystals and $R[111] > R[001] > R[011]$ for bcc crystals. Experimental evidence for channeling has been obtained at Chalk River (40). In measurements of the penetration of 40-kev Kr ions bombarded upon single crystals of Al, a highly penetrating component is observed that depends on orientation in the way predicted by theory (7) for fcc crystals. These experiments have been extended recently to W (41). The results indicate even larger crystallographic effects than those for Al and agree qualitatively with theory, except that the curves for the $\langle 111 \rangle$ and $\langle 100 \rangle$ directions are reversed. Also, there is a still more penetrating tail on the distribution that was not predicted by the theory. The tail persists for ion bombardments at energies as low as 1 kev and is unaffected by raising the bombardment temperature to 1200 K. It will be interesting to see in future experiments whether this feature is characteristic of the bcc structure.

Unlike channeling, focusing occurs at low energies. It is a process, first pointed out by Silsbee (42), by which energy and momentum may be transmitted down a row of atoms by a series of correlated collisions (Fig. 11). Based on a simple billiard-ball model, it was shown that focusing will take place provided

$$\cos \beta > d/2r_0$$

where β is the angle between the direction of motion of the moving atom and the direction of the close-packed row, r_0 is the effective atomic diameter, and d is the distance between centers. As the energy of the moving atom decreases, its effective size increases, thus increasing the likelihood of a focusing collision and decreasing that for a channeling event. An experimental demonstration of focusing lies in sputtering experiments, in which atoms are ejected from metals along low-index crystal directions upon ion bombardment (43). The direction for maximum ejection is the close-packed direction, that is, $\langle 110 \rangle$ for fcc metals (44) and $\langle 111 \rangle$ for bcc metals (45). An ejection pattern from a W crystal having its $\{110\}$ plane in the surface of the crystal and bombarded by 50-kev A ions is shown in Fig. 12 (45, 46). Ejection spots arising from focused collisions along $\langle 111 \rangle$ and $\langle 100 \rangle$ directions are seen. The $\langle 111 \rangle$ spots are thought to arise from simple focused collisions of the type illustrated in Fig. 11, whereas the

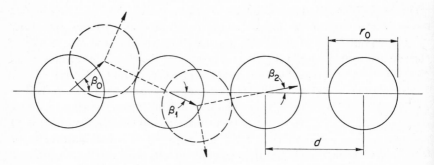

Fig. 11. Schematic diagram of a focused collision sequence. (After Silsbee, Ref 42)

Fig. 12. Ejection pattern from {110} face of a W crystal bombarded by 50-kev A ions, showing ⟨111⟩ and ⟨110⟩ ejection spots. (After Nelson, Ref 45, and Thompson, Ref 46)

focusing for the ⟨100⟩ spots is believed to be assisted by the rings of atoms shown in Fig. 2(b) that surround the ⟨100⟩ direction. This latter type of focusing, "assisted focusing," also operates for ⟨110⟩ collision sequences in bcc metals. In this instance, the ejection spots are oval-shaped (45), as would be expected from the diamond-shaped ring of barrier atoms shown in Fig. 2(c).

Radiation-Enhanced Diffusion

The motion of the point defects produced by radiation may give rise to an additional contribution to the diffusivity. However, such radiation enhancement of diffusion will be observed only in a critical temperature range, because at high temperatures the vacancies in thermal equilibrium will dominate, whereas at low temperatures the radiation-produced defects will not be mobile. In the latter instance, diffusion will occur when the temperature is raised after the low-temperature irradiation. But the effectiveness of each defect in enhancing diffusion may be reduced in this instance, because of the greater tendency toward mutual annihilation when the radiation-produced defects in higher concentration become mobile.

Unfortunately, relatively few attempts have been made to determine directly the effect of radiation on self-diffusion in pure metals. Radioactive tracer diffusion measurements by use of lathe-sectioning techniques were attempted for Ag bombarded by protons over a range of temperatures and fluxes, but the results were negative (47). Upon irradiation with α-particles, enhanced self-diffusion in Pb was measured by use of a special surface counting technique (48). Alpha-particle bombardment was also found to cause a decrease in the surface roughness of Cu, which was attributed to enhanced diffusion (49). In semiconductor materials, enhanced diffusion has been detected by the motion of p-n junctions due to diffusion of As in Ge under high-energy x-ray bombardment (50) and Ga in Si under proton bombardment (51). Finally, the production of high-energy He particles upon thermal neutron absorption has been observed to increase the diffusion of Ag in Li (52).

The reason for the difficulty in measuring the radiation enhancement of macroscopic diffusion is that at the high temperatures required for diffusion over macroscopic distances, the vacancies in thermal equilibrium are likely to over-ride the defects produced by the radiation. The relative likelihood of this for the fcc and bcc metals may be estimated: Let J be the number of atom jumps per atom necessary to observe macroscopic diffusion. For a diffusion anneal of duration t at temperature T

$$J = \Gamma t$$
$$= \nu_v v_0 t$$

where Γ is the atomic jump rate, ν_v is the vacancy jump rate, and v_0 is the vacancy concentration in thermal equilibrium. For ν_v and v_0, we let

$$\nu_v = A_M \nu_0 \exp(-M/RT)$$

and

$$v_0 = A_F \exp(-F/RT)$$

where the A's are entropy factors, F and M are activation energies for vacancy formation and motion, respectively, and ν_0 is the Debye frequency. Then

$$J = t A \nu_0 \exp(-Q/RT)$$

where $Q = F + M$ and $A = A_F A_M$, and the lowest temperature at which macroscopic diffusion can be observed is given by

$$RT = Q/\ln(A\nu_0 t/J) \qquad (3)$$

At this temperature, the concentration of vacancies in thermal equilibrium is

$$v_0 = A_F \exp[-(F/Q)\ln(A\nu_0 t/J)] \qquad (4)$$

We may estimate the minimum number of jumps for a macroscopic diffusion experiment as follows. The diffusion coefficient is given by (53)

$$D = d^2 \Gamma/6$$

where d is the nearest-neighbor jump distance, or

$$Dt = d^2J/6$$

The penetration distance, x, is given roughly by

$$x^2 = 4Dt$$

so that

$$J = 1.5(x/d)^2$$

For standard serial-sectioning or grinding techniques, the minimum penetration distance for a determination of D is several microns, and, because $d \cong 2$ Å, the necessary number of jumps is about $J = 10^8$. Also, for substitution into Eq 4, we may let (53–55) $A = 10$ ($A_F = 1$, $A_M = 10$), $\nu_0 = 10^{13}$ sec^{-1}, and for an upper limit to the diffusion time $t = 10^7$ sec. Then the minimum vacancy concentration for a macroscopic diffusion experiment is given by

$$\nu_0 \cong \exp\left(-30F/Q\right) \tag{5}$$

from Eq 4.

The vacancy formation and motion energies, F and M, have been determined by quenching and equilibrium experiments for several fcc metals, and their sum agrees rather well with the measured Q values (56). The ratio F/Q is found to be about 0.55. For the bcc metals, it is more difficult to quench-in vacancies, which indicates that F/Q is higher than that for fcc metals (57). Resistivity quenching experiments (58) on W have yielded a formation energy of 75 kcal/mole in agreement with the value of 73 kcal/mole determined by equilibrium specific-heat measurements (59). The diffusion activation energy for W has been measured as 120.5 kcal/mole (60) and 135.8 kcal/mole (61). However, the latter value had an exceedingly large pre-exponential factor associated with it. Choosing the value $Q = 120.5$ kcal/mole on these grounds, we obtain $F/Q = 0.61$ for W. For bcc Fe, a semi-empirical rule relating F to the enthalpy of fusion gives $F = 49$ kcal/mole (62) and, because $Q = 67.2$ kcal/mole (39), we obtain $F/Q = 0.72$. Thus, based on very limited information, it appears that $F/Q \cong 0.7$ for the bcc metals, as compared with 0.55 for the fcc metals. By substitution into Eq 4, we find tentatively that the vacancy concentration required to observe macroscopic diffusion in bcc metals is 10 to 100 times less than that required to observe macroscopic diffusion in fcc metals, and the magnitude of these vacancy concentrations is in the range of 10^{-7} to 10^{-9}.

The likelihood of achieving these concentrations by radiation depends on the mechanism of the annihilation of the defects, as well as the instantaneous defect production rate. Assuming that the annihilation of vacancies is governed by annealing to fixed sinks and by interstitial-vacancy recombination, Dienes and Damask (63) have shown that the steady-state excess concentration of radiation-produced vacancies is given by

$$\bar{v} = -\tfrac{1}{2}(\beta + v_0) + \tfrac{1}{2}[(\beta + v_0)^2 + (4K/\nu_v)]^{\frac{1}{2}} \qquad (6)$$

where K, ν_v and v_0 are quantities described previously and β is the concentration of sinks. By setting $\bar{v} = v_0$, we find that the K necessary for the establishment of an excess concentration of vacancies equal to the thermodynamic equilibrium concentration is

$$K = \nu_v v_0(\beta + 2v_0)$$
$$= \Gamma(\beta + 2v_0)$$

and, by use of Eq 4, the minimum K for observing radiation-enhanced macroscopic diffusion is found to be

$$K = (J/t)\{\beta + 2A_F \exp\left[-(F/Q)\ln\left(tA\nu_0/J\right)\right]\} \qquad (7)$$

or, by use of values given above

$$K = 10[\beta + 2\exp\left(-30F/Q\right)]\ \text{sec}^{-1}$$

Substituting further the ratios $F/Q = 0.55$ for fcc metals and $F/Q = 0.67$ for bcc metals, we obtain very roughly for the minimum K's

$$\text{fcc}: K = 10[\beta + (1 \times 10^{-7})]\ \text{sec}^{-1}$$
$$\text{bcc}: K = 10[\beta + (4 \times 10^{-9})]\ \text{sec}^{-1}$$

A practical upper limit of K for neutron irradiation is probably about 10^{-8} sec^{-1}. Therefore, the above equations show that enhanced macroscopic diffusion is unlikely for the fcc metals, but may be possible for the bcc metals provided β is reduced to values below about 10^{-9} and provided, of course, that the above estimates of F/Q are approximately correct. Because $\beta = \alpha d^2$, where α is the dislocation density and d is the nearest neighbor distance, $\beta = 10^{-9}$ corresponds to $\alpha \cong 10^6$ dislocations per square centimeter.

Radiation-enhanced macroscopic diffusion should be even more difficult to observe for those bcc metals such as Zr, Ti and U that exhibit anomalous diffusion of the type discussed in several papers in this volume (see, for example, Ref 64 and 65). If the anomalous diffusion is due to an extrinsic vacancy concentration of about 0.01 or 0.1 at. %, as has been suggested by Kidson (66, 67), then these vacancies would tend to swamp out the much lower concentration produced by the radiation. Furthermore, if the anomalous diffusion is associated with dislocations generated during martensitic phase transformations, the sink concentration, β, would likely rise to the point where the required displacement production rate K in Eq 7 would be unattainable.

Radiation-enhanced diffusion by the interstitialcy mechanism may take place by virtue of the motion of radiation-produced interstitials. The steady-state concentrations of vacancies, $\bar{v}$, and interstitials, $\bar{\imath}$, are related by the expression (63)

$$\nu_i \bar{\imath} = \nu_v \bar{v}$$

where ν_v and ν_i are the vacancy and interstitial jump rates, and thus the number of atom jumps due to interstitialcy migration will equal that due to vacancy migration.

For diffusion-controlled processes in alloys, such as ordering, clustering or precipitation, the number of atom jumps to establish the atomic rearrangement is only about one jump per atom, as compared with 10^8 jumps for macroscopic diffusion. As a result, it is possible to observe radiation-enhanced diffusion at substantially lower temperatures. It has been pointed out (68) that at these temperatures, the dynamic equilibrium giving rise to Eq 6 may not be achieved in the times over which the experiments are performed. As is indicated in several reviews (53, 69, 70), experiments on radiation-enhanced ordering and segregation have been limited largely to the fcc alloys. The effect of irradiation on precipitation reactions has been studied in fcc and bcc alloys (71), and the reader is referred to several other papers (72, 73) in this volume dealing with radiation effects associated with the precipitation of interstitial solutes in α-Fe.

Acknowledgment. This research was sponsored by the U. S. Atomic Energy Commission under contract with the Union Carbide Corporation.

References

1 D. K. Holmes, Radiation Damage in Non-Fissionable Metals, in The Interaction of Radiation with Solids, edited by R. Strumane, J. Nihoul, R. Gevers and S. Amelinckx, North Holland Publishing Co., Amsterdam, 1964

2 A. Sosin, Mechanisms of Atomic Displacements Induced by Radiation, in Radiation Effects on Metals and Neutron Dosimetry, ASTM-STP-341, American Society for Testing and Materials, Philadelphia, 1963, p 3

3 W. A. McKinley and H. Feshbach, Coulomb Scattering of Relativistic Electrons by Nuclei, Phys Rev, **74**, 1759 (1948)

4 J. B. Gibson, A. N. Goland, M. Milgram and G. H. Vineyard, Dynamics of Radiation Damage, Phys Rev, **120**, 1229 (1960)

5   C. Erginsoy, G. H. Vineyard and A. Englert, Dynamics of Radiation Damage in a Body-Centered Cubic Lattice, Phys Rev, **133**, A595 (1964)

6   O. S. Oen and M. T. Robinson, The Effect of Channeling on Displacement Cascade Theory, Appl Phys Letters, **2**, 83 (1963)

7   M. T. Robinson and O. S. Oen, Computer Studies of the Slowing Down of Energetic Atoms in Crystals, Phys Rev, **132**, 2385 (1963)

8   R. M. Walker, Electron-Induced Radiation Damage in Pure Metals, in Radiation Damage in Solids, Academic Press, New York, 1962, p 594

9   P. G. Lucasson and R. M. Walker, Production and Recovery of Electron-Induced Radiation Damage in a Number of Metals, Phys Rev, **127**, 485 (1962)

10 A. Lucasson, P. Lucasson and R. M. Walker, The Production of Atomic Displacements Near Threshold in Fe and Cu, in Properties of Reactor Materials and the Effects of Radiation Damage, Butterworths, London, 1962, p 83

11 P. G. Lucasson and R. M. Walker, Variation of Radiation Damage Parameters in Metals, Phys Rev, **127**, 1130 (1962)

12 T. G. Nilan and A. V. Granato, Stored Energy Release Below 80°K in Deuteron-Irradiated Copper, Phys Rev Letters, **6**, 171 (1961)

13 R. O. Simmons and R. W. Balluffi, X-Ray Study of Deuteron-Irradiated Copper Near 10°K, Phys Rev, **109**, 1142 (1958)

14 R. Vook and C. Wert, Expansion of Copper Upon Low-Temperature Deuteron Irradiation, Phys Rev, **109**, 1529 (1958)

15 Y. Cusson, P. Lucasson and R. M. Walker, The Production of Atomic Displacements Near Threshold in Fe and Cu, Part 2, Preliminary Results on Monocrystals Irradiation, in Properties of Reactor Materials and the Effects of Radiation Damage, Butterworths, London, 1962, p 92

16 R. R. Coltman, T. H. Blewitt and C. E. Klabunde, Irradiation Annealing Studies of Various Metals, in ORNL-2829, December 1959, p 72; private communication

17 G. H. Kinchin and M. W. Thompson, Irradiation Damage and Recovery in Molybdenum and Tungsten, J Nucl Energy, **6**, 275 (1958)

18 M. W. Thompson, Radiation Damage in Body-Centered Metals, in Radiation Damage in Solids, Academic Press, 1962, p 753

19 R. R. Coltman, C. E. Klabunde, D. L. McDonald and J. K. Redman, Reactor Damage in Pure Metals, J Appl Phys, **33**, 3509 (1962)

20 M. W. Thompson, The Damage and Recovery of Neutron Irradiated Tungsten, Phil Mag, **5**, 278 (1960)

21 J. Adam and D. G. Martin, Measurements of Unit Cell and Physical Dimension Changes of Molybdenum after Neutron Irradiation, Phil Mag, **3**, 1329 (1958)

22 J. Nihoul, The Recovery of Radiation Damage in Molybdenum, in Radiation Damage in Solids, Vol I, International Atomic Energy Agency, Vienna, 1962, p 309

23 J. W. Corbett, R. B. Smith and R. M. Walker, Recovery of Electron-Irradiated Copper, I. Close Pair Recovery, Phys Rev, **114**, 1452 (1959)

24 J. A. Tesk, E. C. Jones, Jr., and J. W. Kauffman, Stage I Recovery Spectrum of Pure Copper Irradiated with Electrons over the Range 1.25–3.25 Mev, Phys Rev, **133**, A288 (1964)

25 A. Sosin and W. Bauer, Recovery Spectrum of Copper from 14° to 65°K, Following Electron Irradiation, Bull Am Phys Soc, **9**, 283 (1964)

26 R. R. Coltman, T. H. Blewitt, C. E. Klabunde, J. K. Redman and D. L. McDonald, Annealing Studies of Various Neutron-Irradiated Metals, in ORNL-3213, 1961, p 15

27 R. R. Coltman, private communication

28 T. H. Blewitt, Low Temperature Irradiation Studies, in Radiation Damage in Solids, Academic Press, Inc., New York, 1962, p 630

29 M. W. Thompson, Evidence for Trapping of Interstitial Atoms in Irradiated Tungsten, Phil Mag, **3,** 421 (1958)

30 J. Moteff and J. P. Smith, Recovery of Defects in Neutron-Irradiated Tungsten, ASTM Symposium on Flow and Fracture Behavior of Metals and Alloys in Nuclear Environments, American Society for Testing and Materials, Philadelphia, 1964

31 Proceedings of the Fifth International Congress on Electron Microscopy, Academic Press, Inc., New York, 1962, p F-1 to G-14

32 B. L. Eyre, Direct Observation of Neutron Irradiation Damage in Alpha Iron, Phil Mag, **7,** 2107 (1962)

33 B. Mastel, H. E. Kissinger, J. J. Laidler and T. K. Bierlein, Dislocation Channeling in Neutron-Irradiated Molybdenum, J Appl Phys, **34,** 3637 (1963)

34 J. D. Meakin, Interstitial Loops in Neutron-Irradiated Molybdenum, Nature, **201,** 915 (1964)

35 D. Hull and I. L. Mogford, Precipitation and Irradiation Hardening in Iron, Phil Mag, **6,** 535 (1961)

36 M. S. Wechsler, The Radiation-Embrittlement of Metals and Alloys, in The Interaction of Radiation with Solids, edited by R. Strumane, J. Nihoul, R. Gevers and S. Amelinckx, North Holland Publishing Co., Amsterdam, 1964

37 R. W. Nichols and D. R. Harries, Brittle Fracture and Irradiation Effects in Ferritic Pressure Vessel Steels, in Radiation Effects on Metals and Neutron Dosimetry, ASTM-STP-341, American Society for Testing and Materials, Philadelphia, 1963, p 162

38 C. E. Birchenall and R. F. Mehl, Self-Diffusion in Alpha and Gamma Iron, Trans AIME, **188,** 144 (1950)

39 R. J. Borg and C. E. Birchenall, Self-Diffusion in Alpha Iron, Trans AIME, **218,** 980 (1960)

40 G. R. Piercy, F. Brown, J. A. Davies and M. McCargo, Experimental Evidence for the Increase of Heavy Ion Ranges by Channeling in Crystalline Structure, Phys Rev Letters, **10,** 399 (1963)

41 B. Domeij, F. Brown, J. A. Davies, G. R. Piercy and E. V. Kornelsen, Anomalous Penetration of Heavy Ions of kev Energies in Monocrystalline Tungsten, Phys Rev Letters, **12,** 363 (1964)

42 R. H. Silsbee, Focusing in Collision Problems in Solids, J Appl Phys, **28,** 1246 (1957)

43 G. K. Wehner, Controlled Sputtering of Metals by Low-Energy Hg Ions, Phys Rev, **102,** 690 (1956)

44 R. S. Nelson and M. W. Thompson, Atomic Collision Sequences in Crystals of Copper, Silver, and Gold Revealed by Sputtering in Energetic Ion Beams, Proc Roy Soc, **A259,** 458 (1961)

45 R. S. Nelson, Focused Collision Sequences in Tungsten and Molybdenum, Phil Mag, **8,** 693 (1963)

46 M. W. Thompson, Focused Collision Sequences and Replacements in the Collision Cascade, in The Interaction of Radiation with Solids, edited by R. Strumane, J. Nihoul, R. Gevers and S. Amelinckx, North Holland Publishing Co., Amsterdam, 1964

47 R. D. Johnson and A. B. Martin, The Effect of Cyclotron Bombardment on Self-Diffusion in Silver, J Appl Phys, **23,** 1245 (1952)

48   W. Biermann and D. Heitkamp, Selbstdiffusion in Blei unter Bestrahlung mit α-Teilchen, Z Physik Chem Neue Folge, **34,** 265 (1962)

49   R. Sizmann and U. Däunert, Radiation-Induced Diffusion in Metals, in Radiation Damage in Solids, Vol I, International Atomic Energy Agency, Vienna, 1962, p 351

50   N. L. Peterson and R. E. Ogilvie, The Effect of Radiation on the Rate of Diffusion of Arsenic into Germanium, Trans AIME, **215,** 873 (1959)

51   P. Baruch, C. Constantin, J. C. Pfister and R. Saintesprit, Vacancy Enhanced Diffusion in Silicon, Faraday Soc Disc, No. 31, Faraday Society, 1961, p 76–85

52   V. K. Zavoisky and B. V. Ershler, Results of the Influence of Irradiation on the Diffusion of Silver in Lithium, in Conference of the Academy of Sciences of the USSR on the Peaceful Uses of Atomic Energy, Vol III, USAEC, 1956, p 251

53   M. S. Wechsler, Fundamental Aspects of Radiation Effects on Diffusion-Controlled Reactions in Alloys, in Radiation Effects on Metals and Neutron Dosimetry, ASTM-STP-341, American Society for Testing and Materials, Philadelphia, 1963, p 86

54   A. C. Damask and G. J. Dienes, Point Defects in Metals, Gordon and Breach, New York, 1963

55   W. M. Lomer, Defects in Pure Metals, Progr Metal Phys, **8,** 255 (1959)

56   R. O. Simmons, J. S. Koehler and R. W. Balluffi, Present Knowledge of Point Defects in Irradiated fcc Metals, in Radiation Damage in Solids, International Atomic Energy Agency, Vienna, 1962, p 155

57   D. P. Gregory, Quenching Lattice Vacancies in bcc Metals, Acta Met, **11,** 623 (1963)

58   H. Schultz, Abschreckversuche an Wolfram mit Hilfe von Helium II, Acta Met, **12,** 761 (1964)

59   Y. A. Kraftmakher and P. G. Strelkov, Energy of Formation and Concentration of Vacancies in Tungsten, Soviet Phys Solid State, **4,** 1662 (1963)

60   W. Danneberg, "Selbstdiffusionsuntersuchungen an Wolfram," Metall, **15,** 977 (1961)

61   V. P. Vasil'ev and S. G. Chernomorchenko, On Methods of Studying Autodiffusion in Tungsten, Zavodsk Lab, **22,** 688 (1956)

62   R. F. Mehl, M. Swanson and G. M. Pound, Estimation of Equilibrium Vacancy Concentration in Solid Metals, Acta Met, **9,** 256 (1961)

63   G. J. Dienes and A. C. Damask, Radiation Enhanced Diffusion in Solids, J Appl Phys, **29,** 1713 (1958)

64   A. D. Le Claire, Chapter 1 in this volume

65   D. Lazarus, Chapter 10 in this volume

66   G. V. Kidson, On the Anomalous Self-Diffusion in Body-Centered Cubic Zirconium, Can J Phys, **41,** 1563 (1963)

67   G. V. Kidson, Chapter 25 in this volume

68   J. H. Barrett, Theory of Radiation-Enhanced Diffusion, Bull Am Phys Soc, **9,** 284 (1964)

69   S. F. Pugh, Radiation Damage in Alloys, Radiation Damage in Non-Fissionable Metals, in The Interaction of Radiation with Solids, edited by R. Strumane, J. Nihoul, R. Gevers and S. Amelinckx, North Holland Publishing Co., Amsterdam, 1964

70   D. E. Thomas, Irradiation Effect on Physical Metallurgical Processes, in Nuclear Metallurgy, Vol 3, American Institute of Mining, Metallurgical, and Petroleum Engineers, New York, 1956, p 13

71 C. R. Cupp, Effects of Neutron Irradiation on Precipitation-Hardening Alloys, in Radiation Effects on Metals and Neutron Dosimetry, ASTM-STP-341, American Society for Testing and Materials, Philadelphia, 1963, p 67
72 A. C. Damask, Chapter 24 in this volume
73 J. T. Stanley, Chapter 26 in this volume

Chapter 24

Effect of Neutron Irradiation on Precipitation of Carbon in Alpha Iron

A. C. Damask

C can be dissolved in α-Fe at high temperatures, up to a maximum of 0.019 wt % at 723 C, and quenched into a supersaturated solid solution. When the temperature of the quenched solution is raised, the C atoms will migrate interstitially with a migration energy of 0.86 ev and precipitate as an Fe carbide. The precipitate formed in the range of 50 to 200 C is called ϵ-carbide, has an approximate formula of $Fe_{2.4}C$ and is hexagonal in structure. This precipitate also forms heterogeneously on dislocations as well as homogeneously within the matrix. At higher temperatures, 200 to 300 C, the ϵ-carbide dissolves or transforms (the precise mechanism is not known) into a more stable carbide called cementite, which has the formula Fe_3C and is orthorhombic in structure.

Irradiation with neutrons of an alloy in which the solute is in interstitial positions can be expected to produce two major effects: (a) The severe local damage can create sites for heterogeneous nucleation of the precipitates, and (b) the lattice vacancies can serve as traps for the diffusing interstitial solute atoms and thereby retard precipitation of the solute. These two effects were studied in the Fe-C system with a variety of experimental techniques: internal friction, electrical resistivity, electron microscopy and calorimetry. Both effects were observed and are reported in this chapter.

Specimens

The starting material for all specimens in these experiments was $\frac{1}{4}$-in. diameter, 99.9% pure "Ferrovac E" Fe rod. After cleaning, the specimens were annealed for 1 hr at 804 C in an evacuated quartz capsule and allowed to air cool. The carburization was done by holding the specimens

The author is with the Brookhaven National Laboratory, Upton, N.Y., and the Pitman-Dunn Research Institute, Frankford Arsenal, Philadelphia, Pa.

in a flowing methane–dry-hydrogen mixture at 712 C for 68 hr and then quenching into brine at 0 C. The chemically determined C content was 0.0115 wt % for the specimens. The amount of C quenched into solid solution depends on the rate of quenching, and slight variations between specimens are to be expected. A portion of the material was cold rolled to 0.0035-in. sheet from which strips were cut for electron-microscopy specimens. The remaining stock was cold swaged to 0.115-in. diameter for calorimetry specimens and then cold drawn to 0.032-in. diameter for internal-friction specimens and finally to 0.013-in. diameter for electrical-resistivity specimens. Potential leads were spot-welded on the specimens for resistivity measurements, which were about 4 in. long and were bent in a hairpin shape, before carburization or quenching. The wire for internal-friction specimens was cut into lengths of 5 in. The 0.115-in.-diameter rod for calorimetry specimens was cut into lengths of 0.8 in., each specimen thus having a mass of about 0.75 g.

Measurements and Results

Internal-friction measurements of the Snoek peak can show directly the changes in the amount of C in solution because the peak arises from the motion of C atoms from their interstitial sites to adjacent ones (1). Quenched wires were irradiated for different times at 57 C in the Brookhaven reactor. The wires were then removed, and the decay of the peak at 57 C outside of the reactor was measured (2). This provided a continuity of temperature, with irradiation as the only variable. In general, the decay of the peak for all instances of irradiation is about ten times faster than that for instances of no irradiation, and, regardless of the irradiation time after 4 hr, the rate of decay is about the same for all instances. These results are shown in Fig. 1 (middle curve), where the aging times plus irradiation times are plotted. For comparison, a curve of thermal aging obtained by Doremus (3) is also shown (right-hand curve). This acceleration of time of disappearance of C from solution indicates that the mean free path of C migration for precipitation is one tenth of that in the unirradiated sample and therefore ten times the number of precipitation sites must be present.

An independent study of this system with electron-microscope techniques has been made by Hull and Mogford (4). They measured the density and size of precipitate particles in quenched specimens of 0.004 wt % C in Fe after both thermal and irradiation treatment. After several days of aging at 60 C, the precipitate-particle density was about $3 \times 10^{13}/cm^3$. When quenched Fe-C was irradiated at 60 C in a neutron flux of similar magnitude to the present work for 5 hr, the precipitate-particle

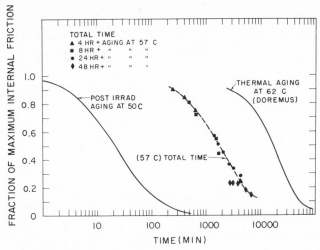

Fig. 1. Normalized plot of the height of the internal-friction peak for various irradiation and annealing conditions. The left curve is for a low-temperature irradiation; the center curve is for ambient-temperature irradiation; the right curve is for thermal aging and was obtained by Doremus.

density was $2 \times 10^{14}/cm^3$, or about an order of magnitude greater, in agreement with the interpretation of the data of Fig. 1. Subsequent irradiations up to 144 hr showed essentially no change in the density of precipitate particles although the precipitate size increased. This is also in agreement with the internal-friction results reported here, which show that after 4-hr irradiation in a similar flux, no change by further irradiation is evident. An estimate was made in the original paper that sufficient primary knock-ons were created in 2 hr at these fluxes to account for the extra precipitate nuclei. Therefore, a saturation effect clearly is occurring. The mechanism of this saturation is not known.

The change in height of the Snoek internal-friction peak as a function of time was also measured on specimens irradiated at low temperatures. The low-temperature irradiations were performed in the Brookhaven reactor at about 175 K for several days. After a 12-day irradiation, the internal-friction peak at 50 C was found to decrease about 1000 times faster than that in the unirradiated specimens. An example is shown by the left curve in Fig. 1. This process was studied in considerable detail, first with measurements of internal friction. The normalized results of a series of these internal-friction decay data following low-temperature irradiation are shown in Fig. 2. The activation energy determined from these curves is 0.86 ev, which is in close agreement with other measurements of the energy of diffusion of C in Fe. The kinetics of the decay rate

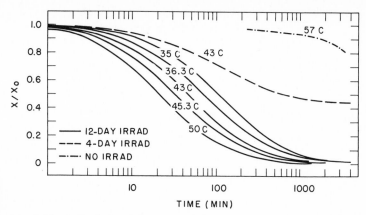

Fig. 2. Normalized plot of the internal-friction peak height as a function of time for various annealing temperatures. All of the irradiations were done at low temperature.

can also be determined from the normalized curves of Fig. 2, and they were found to be bimolecular. The kinetics of the incomplete decay of the 4-day irradiation (dashed line) are also bimolecular. A portion of the decay curve of an unirradiated specimen is shown labeled as 57 C. As seen in Fig. 2, the decay of the short irradiation did not go to completion. The evidence available from these internal-friction measurements suggests that after a low-temperature irradiation, C is trapped during its migration by a point defect in a one-to-one ratio.

Because measurements of internal friction could not show further effects of the C after it was trapped, the investigation was continued with measurements of electrical resistivity. The resistivity measurements clearly separate each of the steps that occur in the migration and precipitation process, and the curves of irradiated specimens show five stages of electrical-resistivity changes compared with two stages in the unirradiated specimens.

Quenched Fe-C was annealed isochronally, and the electrical resistivity was measured at liquid-nitrogen temperature after each annealing step (5). Typical results are shown in Fig. 3 by the solid circles. The quenched condition is taken as the zero value. The resistivity decreases in two very distinct steps, one around 170 C and the other around 250 C for the 5-min isochronal annealing curve. These two steps in the unirradiated specimens will be referred to by these characteristic temperatures. It is known from other studies that the 170 C step corresponds to the initial precipitation of the C into the metastable ϵ-carbide phase. The step at 250 C corresponds to the formation of the Fe_3C cementite phase.

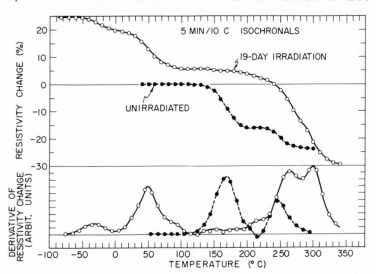

Fig. 3. Resistivity change for Fe-C alloys irradiated at low temperature for 19 days. Shown for comparison is the resistivity change for an unirradiated specimen. The lower curves are derivatives taken from the data points of the upper curves.

When a specimen irradiated for 19 days at 175 K is annealed isochronally, a decay spectrum containing several steps is obtained. This is illustrated in Fig. 3 by the open circles. The lower part is the derivative curve and shows four of the steps quite clearly. The first peak is around −30 C, the second at 50 C, a third (not clear) at 150 C, a fourth at 260 C, and a fifth at 300 C. By 350 C all of the resistivity increase has annealed, and the resistivity has also dropped to about 30% below that of the quenched state, a decrease similar to that exhibited by the unirradiated specimen. Figure 4 shows an isochronal annealing curve of a specimen irradiated for two days; the curve in Fig. 3 for unirradiated specimens is included for comparison. Although the decrease of resistivity below the quenched condition is still about 25%, the increase caused by the irradiation is only about 3%. It can be said that the increase in resistivity caused by the irradiation is roughly proportional to the radiation dose. One should also note that the height of the −30 C step is proportionately smaller, the step at 50 C has decreased, and the step at 150 C has grown. Also, a peak is present at 250 C and a small one is developing at 295 C. The characteristics of these five steps will now be summarized.

1. −30 C Step. Figures 3 and 4 show that this step depends on irradiation dose. Because of this characteristic, this step is believed to arise from the annealing of a point defect, possibly the Fe interstitial

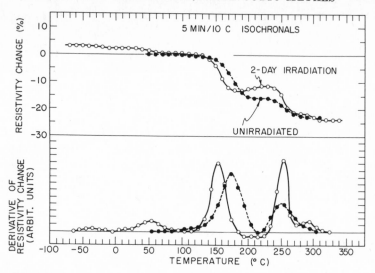

Fig. 4. Resistivity change for alloy irradiated at low temperature for two days. The derivative curves for these curves also are shown.

because calculations have shown the interstitial to be the faster moving defect (6). The Fe interstitial should give rise to an internal-friction resonance, which was looked for with the torsion-pendulum internal-friction technique above 140 K but was not observed (7). This is consistent with the low-temperature irradiation studies of Fe by Lucasson and Walker (8), which suggest that the Fe interstitial is freely mobile at 100 K and can migrate out of the crystal. However, calculations indicate that the Fe interstitial can be trapped by the C interstitial and bound with an energy of about 0.5 ev (9). This decay step at −30 C is therefore believed to arise from the dissociation of the C-Fe interstitial complex and the subsequent annealing of the Fe interstitial from the crystal.

2. 50 C Step. This is the temperature region in which the Snoek peak was observed to decay after low-temperature irradiation. Because the C disappears from solid solution in this temperature region with bimolecular kinetics and an activation energy of C migration, it is believed to be trapped by a point defect. The trapping defect is assumed to be the vacancy.

3. 150 to 170 C Step. If the 50 C step arises from the trapping of C atoms by vacancies in a bimolecular manner, then, one would expect the excess C to precipitate in a nearly normal manner when there are insufficient vacancies. The fact that this 150 to 170 C step continues to be present and is roughly inversely proportional to the size of the 50 C step conforms to this model. The 170 C step has shifted to 150 C after irradiation. This is also to be expected from the internal-friction study in which it was shown that irradiation does create some excess precipitation nuclei, which accelerate the precipitation of the C. It is to be noted that this step has been shifted to 150 C in both the 2-day and the 19-day irradiation curves. An analysis of the kinetics of this step after a 2-day irradiation showed that it has the same characteristics as that of the unirradiated specimen.

4. 265 and 300 C Steps. These steps are related and will be summarized together. The unirradiated specimen has one high-temperature decay step, 250 C. A 2-day irradiation appears to sharpen and to increase the height of the decay step, Fig. 4, although it is still centered at 250 C (the appearance of the peak in the derivative curve may be distorted by the increase in resistivity just prior to it), and a small decay is seen to be developing at 295 C. After 19 days the 250 C peak has shifted to 265 C, and the one at 295 has grown to equal height and has broadened considerably.

On the assumption that the 50 C decay step, which is observed with both internal-friction and electrical-resistivity techniques, arises from the trapping of C atoms by irradiation-produced vacancies, it was of interest to measure this trapping energy. This was done by measuring the enthalpy change associated with this step by means of a microcalorimeter (10). If the entropy change is assumed to be small, then the binding energy of the C atom to the vacancy is 0.41 ev. The enthalpy change associated with C precipitating in the metastable ϵ carbide was also measured and found to be 0.27 ev. Measurements by others of the enthalpy change associated with the cementite or Fe_3C precipitate are 0.52 ev (11) and 0.89 ev (12). Thus, if a sample with C trapped in vacancies is heated to a temperature high enough to cause the C atoms to boil out of the traps, they will have too much energy to fall into a trap of less energy, namely the 0.27 ev of the metastable carbide, but will go into the next deeper trap, the Fe_3C phase. This hypothesis was proved by electron-microscope observations.

Foils of Fe-C 0.0035 in. thick were prepared and quenched in the manner previously described. They were irradiated at about -100 C in the Brookhaven reactor for 19 days in the capsule used for the resistivity specimens. The annealings were also made in the manner used for the resistivity specimens. The entire group of specimens was in a wax bath for 5 min in steps of 10 C until one of the temperatures for study was reached. Some specimens were then set aside for study, and the isochronal annealing was continued until the second desired temperature was reached.

Figures 5 and 6 show electron micrographs of the alloy specimens after various annealing steps (13). Superposed on these micrographs are the

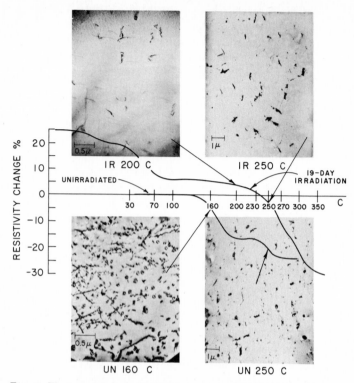

Fig. 5. Electron micrographs of specimens annealed isochronally (5 min/ 10 C). IR and UN mean irradiated and unirradiated, respectively. The temperatures after IR or UN are the final annealing temperatures. The irradiated specimens were irradiated for 19 days at −100 C. Superposed are the resistivity changes for the same isochronal anneal.

isochronal electrical resistivity curves of Fig. 3 to facilitate identification. The unirradiated specimen at 160 C shows a large amount of metastable carbide precipitated both in the matrix and on dislocations. In contrast, the irradiated specimen annealed as high as 200 C shows no such precipitation of the metastable carbide. Although there is no evidence of precipitation in the matrix, there is some precipitate on dislocations. This could be formed by the precipitation of a few free C atoms not bound to defects and would then correspond to the very slight resistivity decay at 150 C. After annealing at 230 C (not shown), the irradiated specimen still shows no definite matrix precipitation. The unirradiated specimen (not shown) loses metastable precipitates from the matrix with a corresponding coarsening of the same phase on dislocations. In the specimen irradiated and annealed to 250 C, precipitate particles are visible in the matrix for

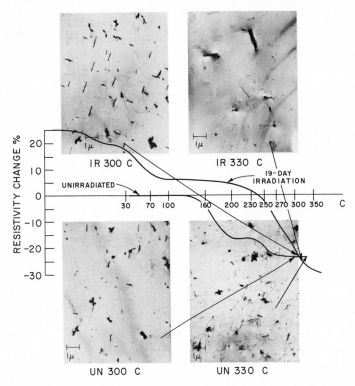

Fig. 6. Electron micrographs obtained from specimens treated similarly to those of Fig. 5 except for the final annealing temperature

the first time, and they have all been identified as Fe_3C, as indicated by their morphology, with no evidence of the metastable phase. Further annealing to 270 C (not shown) causes formation of Fe_3C in the unirradiated specimen with only a few particles of the metastable carbide. The irradiated specimen (not shown) shows some growth of the Fe_3C particles. In the specimen irradiated and annealed to 300 C, there has been no significant change from the 270 C state, and very little change from the 250 C state. The appearance of the unirradiated specimen annealed to 300 C has also changed very little from that after the 270 C annealing. In the specimen irradiated and annealed to 330 C, very large Fe_3C particles are visible with a corresponding decrease in number. The particles are generally much larger than those in an unirradiated specimen annealed at the same temperature. These large particles do not appear in the unirradiated specimens.

Because no precipitation is observable in the temperature region in which the indirect measurements indicate that the C disappears from

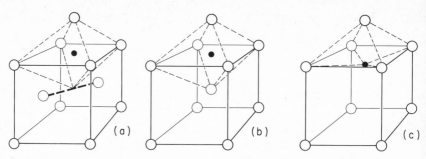

Fig. 7. Schematics of the most stable positions of a C atom (black circle) in an α-Fe cell with and without defects. (a) C position adjacent to a split Fe interstitial. Split interstitial is represented by heavy dashed line lying in ⟨110⟩ direction. (b) Normal C position without an Fe defect. (c) C position with an Fe vacancy. C atom has moved slightly toward the vacant lattice site at the center of the cell.

solution, it is concluded that the C has been trapped by a point defect, presumably the vacancy. The possibility that the C is in the form of precipitates too small to be visible is rejected by the one-to-one correspondence between C atoms and point defects that is required by the kinetics of the electrical-resistivity and internal-friction changes and the incompletion of the 50 C internal-friction decay after a 4-day irradiation. The trapping of the C and the relative energy of the trap compared with that of the metastable carbide are also confirmed because the metastable carbide does not appear in the alloy irradiated to a dosage sufficient to trap all of the C atoms. It is also suggested that the large Fe_3C particles that grow in the irradiated specimen above 300 C attain their size because of strain relief. This relief of strain can be caused by vacancies migrating to the precipitates. The vacancies are either the single ones that have trapped the C atoms, or clusters of vacancies that dissociate at these temperatures.

Calculations of defect configurations in crystallites by computer techniques are now rather well established (6, 14). Usually the energy of an array of about 500 atoms is minimized by successive iterations of the force equations between the atoms, these force equations having been constructed classically with interatomic potentials that match the elastic constants. There exist no such data for the Fe-C system, but an interaction potential was constructed by successive approximations of the constants of a cubic equation until a migrating C atom in an Fe lattice matched three experimentally determined numbers: the activation energy of C migration, the activation volume of C migration and the 0.41 ev binding energy of a C atom bound to a vacancy (15). This potential was then used with the Fe lattice to calculate the binding energy of the C atom to an Fe interstitial. This was found to be 0.5 ev. The configuration of this complex is illustrated in Fig. 7(a). The position of the carbon atom in the Fe vacancy was also calculated by this method and is illustrated in Fig. 7(c). The normal C position in the absence of a lattice defect is shown by Fig. 7(b).

Summary

The sequence of defect migrations following low-temperature irradiation and their effect on the precipitation of C are believed to be:

1. The Fe interstitial migrates freely above 80 K.
2. The migrating Fe interstitials can be trapped at immobile C atoms quenched into solution. They also can escape to surfaces, cluster, or annihilate vacancies. An excess concentration of vacancies remains.
3. The interstitial-C complex has a binding energy of about 0.5 ev and could be stable up to about -30 C. The decrease in resistivity observed at this temperature would then be caused by the escape of the Fe interstitials after dissociation.
4. Above room temperature, the C atom begins to migrate with a motion energy of 0.86 ev.
5. When a migrating C atom encounters a vacancy, it is trapped with a binding energy of 0.41 ev, with only one C atom trapped by each vacancy. This trapping phenomenon is not apparent after ambient-temperature irradiation because all of the C atoms have migrated to the precipitation sites before sufficient vacancies have been produced to trap a significant number.
6. C atoms in excess of the vacancies precipitate into a metastable carbide but at a rate faster than normal because of the extra precipitate nuclei caused by the primary knock-on damage.
7. At sufficiently high temperatures, above 230 C, the C atoms boil out of the vacancies and precipitate in the Fe_3C phase.
8. At 330 C either the vacancies or voids created by the irradiation anneal, some going to the Fe_3C precipitates. Vacancies arriving at these precipitates relieve the strains around the particles and allow them to grow, as illustrated in Fig. 6 by the irradiated 330 C specimens.

Acknowledgment. This work was supported in part by the U. S. Atomic Energy Commission.

References

1   A. S. Nowick, Progress in Metal Physics, Vol 1, Pergamon Press, Inc., Oxford, 1953, p 1
2   H. Wagenblast and A. C. Damask, J Phys Chem Solids, **23,** 221 (1962)
3   R. H. Doremus, Trans AIME **218,** 596 (1960)
4   D. Hull and I. L. Mogford, Phil Mag, **6,** 535 (1961)
5   F. E. Fujita and A. C. Damask, Acta Met, **12,** 331 (1964)
6   R. A. Johnson, Phys Rev, **134,** A1329 (1964)
7   H. Wagenblast and A. C. Damask, Acta Met, **10,** 333 (1962)
8   P. G. Lucasson and R. M. Walker, Phys Rev, **127,** 485, 1130 (1962)
9   R. A. Johnson and A. C. Damask, Acta Met, **12,** 443 (1964)
10 R. A. Arndt and A. C. Damask, Acta Met, **12,** 341 (1964)
11 G. Borelius and S. Berglund, Arkiv Fysik, **4,** 173 (1951)
12 R. Smith, Trans AIME, **224,** 105 (1963)
13 H. Wagenblast, F. E. Fujita and A. C. Damask, Acta Met, **12,** 347 (1964)
14 L. Tewordt, Phys Rev, **109,** 61 (1958); J. B. Gibson, A. N. Goland, M. Milgram and G. H. Vineyard, Phys Rev, **120,** 1229 (1960); A. Seeger, E. Mann and R. v. Jan, J Phys Chem Solids, **23,** 639 (1962); R. A. Johnson and E. Brown, Phys Rev, **127,** 446 (1962)
15 R. A. Johnson, G. J. Dienes and A. C. Damask, Acta Met, **12,** 1215 (1964)

Chapter 25

The Mechanism of Diffusion in Beta Zirconium, Beta Titanium and Gamma Uranium

G. V. Kidson

During the past ten years fundamental studies of self-diffusion and dilute solute diffusion in pure metals have been largely concerned with fcc systems. Reasons for this include the availability of high-purity single crystals and suitable radioactive tracer isotopes and the comparatively strong theoretical basis for the interpretation of the results in terms of a simple vacancy mechanism (1).

More recently, however, considerable interest has shifted toward the diffusion behavior of bcc metals. This is due largely to a combination of the growing technological importance of the refractory metals, to their increasing purity and to a natural extension of fundamental interest in these systems.

From the experimental evidence available, it would appear that the bcc metals can be classified into two fairly distinct groups with regard to their diffusion behavior. That is, there are those that behave normally in the sense that they conform to expectations based on previous experience, and there are those that behave abnormally in the sense that they depart from this behavior.

To be more specific, one criterion of normalcy has been the adherence of the diffusion coefficients to a simple Arrhenius-type temperature dependence of the form

$$D(T) = D_0 \exp\left(-Q/RT\right) \tag{1}$$

where D_0 is a temperature-independent frequency factor and Q is the activation energy for diffusion. In the past a strict linear dependence of log D on $1/T$ has been observed, implying that Q also is a temperature-independent constant.

Further criteria of normalcy are that the magnitude of D_0 has a lower

The author is with the Chalk River Nuclear Laboratories, Atomic Energy of Canada Limited, Chalk River, Ontario, Canada.

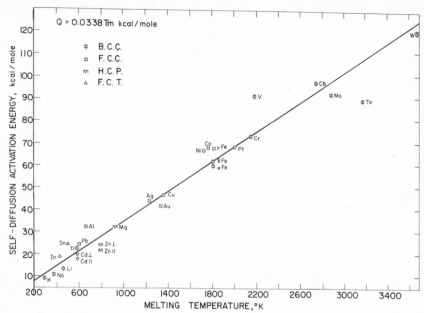

Fig. 1. Correlation of activation energy with the melting temperature for self-diffusion in metals. The anomalous bcc metals are not known.

limit of about 10^{-2} cm²/sec and that the Q's are related to the melting point of the metal by $Q \simeq 34T_m$ cal/mole. An indication of the strength of this correlation is given in Fig. 1, where Q has been plotted versus T_m for metals with various crystal structures.

The purpose of this paper is to review and discuss results of studies on the systems β-Zr, β-Ti and γ-U, which comprise the abnormal group.

Experimental Observations

The first suggestion of unusual behavior in bcc metals came during 1958 and 1959, when studies of solute diffusion in β-Ti and of self-diffusion

Table 1. Self-Diffusion in bcc Metals

System	D_0, cm²/sec	Q_d, kcal/mole	Reference
γ-U.....................	1.81×10^{-3}	27.5	2
γ-U.....................	1.17×10^{-3}	26.6	3
γ-U.....................	2.33×10^{-3}	28.5	4
Cr^{51} in β-Ti..............	5×10^{-3}	35.3	5
Cr.....................	1×10^{-4}	52.0	6

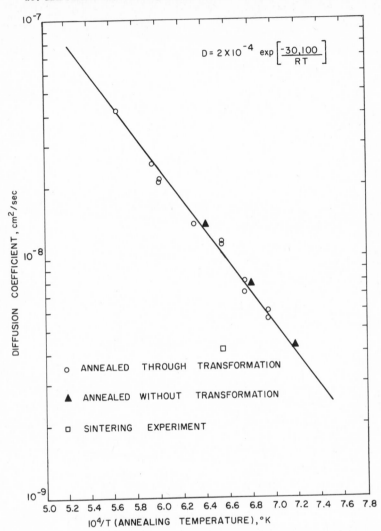

$$D = 2 \times 10^{-4} \exp\left[\frac{-30,100}{RT}\right]$$

Fig. 2. All diffusion measurements by Kidson and McGurn, plotted as log D versus 1/T

in Cr and γ-U indicated that the values of the diffusion parameters D_0 and Q were anomalously small, as shown in Table 1.

In view of the many similarities between Ti and Zr, a study of self-diffusion in bcc β-Zr was undertaken in 1959 at the Chalk River Nuclear Laboratories. The aim of this work was to establish whether or not the diffusion behavior of β-Zr was similar to that of the metals listed in Table 1, and if so, to attempt to clarify the mechanism responsible for it.

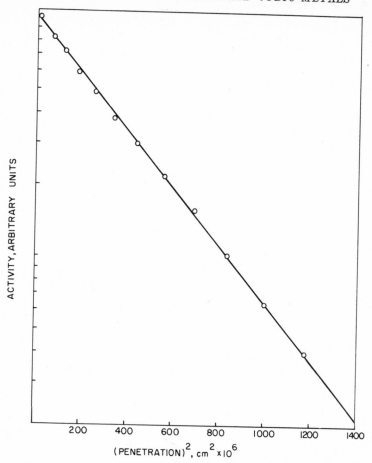

Fig. 3. A typical plot of log (activity) versus (penetration)², indicating no evidence of grain-boundary diffusion

A detailed report of the results of this investigation has been published elsewhere (7). In summary, the following points emerged:

1. The temperature dependence of the diffusion coefficients determined over the range of 1100 to 1500 C could be represented reasonably well by

$$D = 2.4 \times 10^{-4} \exp\left(-30{,}100/RT\right) \text{ cm}^2/\text{sec}$$

Figure 2 shows the Arrhenius plot of log D versus $1/T$.

2. The concentration-penetration profiles were typical of bulk diffusion, as indicated in Fig. 3. It was concluded that grain-boundary diffusion,

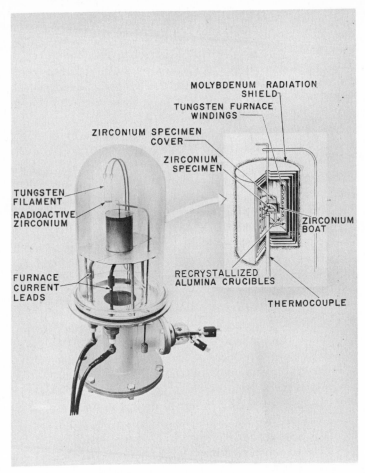

Fig. 4. The apparatus used for the pre-annealing diffusion experiments

which would have produced curvature in the plots of log (concentration) versus (penetration)², did not make any significant contribution to the observed diffusion coefficients.

3. In most of the runs, the radioactive tracer layer was evaporated onto a cold specimen that was then heated through the $\alpha \rightarrow \beta$ phase transformation to the annealing temperature. In some, however, the specimens were pre-annealed at the diffusion temperature, by use of the specially designed apparatus shown in Fig. 4, before the tracer layer was deposited. Although this appeared to promote the growth of large β grains

in the specimens prior to the diffusion anneal, it did not produce any significant difference in the measured diffusion coefficients.

4. It was observed that rapid sintering occurred in a bundle of 0.010-in.-diam Zr wires when annealed in the β phase. A diffusion coefficient, calculated from the rate of sintering on the basis of a vacancy mechanism for diffusion (8), was in order-of-magnitude agreement with the previous results.

5. By use of techniques similar to those developed by Barnes (9) for Cu and by Ells and Evans (10) for Al, Zr specimens were bombarded with monoenergetic He ions and subsequently annealed in the β phase. This treatment resulted in the formation of microscopic pores, which have been attributed to the clustering of the injected He ions, and a subsequent migration of vacancies to these clusters, which produced observable pores. The pore formation in β-Zr was very rapid.

It was concluded that these results, together with an observed Kirkendall shift in the bcc phase of U-Zr couples, as reported by Adda *et al.* (11), lent strong support to a vacancy diffusion mechanism. However, it was not possible to account for the unusually low values of D_0 and Q_d.

Subsequent to the work described above, further studies have been reported on self-diffusion in β-Zr (13), β-Ti (14), V (15) and Cb (15, 16) as well as on solute diffusion in β-Ti (17), β-Zr (15) and γ-U (18). Hagel (12), using 99.997% pure Cr, measured self-diffusion over a considerably extended temperature range. He found values of D_0 and Q_d that conformed with the more usual expectations. Lundy and Federer (13) remeasured self-diffusion in β-Zr by use of crystal bar material of a purity comparable to that used by Kidson and McGurn (7), but again extended the temperature range. When their results were plotted as log D versus $1/T$, they showed good agreement with those of Kidson and McGurn over the range covered by the latter, but indicated a marked departure from linearity when considered over the complete temperature range. Similar effects have been reported for solute diffusion and self-diffusion in β-Ti when the temperature range is extended (14, 17). Both D_0 and Q_d are anomalously low for self-diffusion in γ-U. Although the Arrhenius curves have been reported as linear (2–4), there may be some indication of curvature (18). Self-diffusion in V appears normal over the high-temperature range, but the log D versus $1/T$ plot shows a definite departure from linearity in the low-temperature region. Finally, self-diffusion in Cb is reported to behave normally in all respects over a large range of temperature (15).

There are several interpretations of these results. Some of them will be examined below, particularly with regard to the measurements of self-diffusion in β-Zr.

Discussion

The most direct interpretation of the nonlinear Arrhenius curves is that they simply reflect a single temperature-dependent activation energy. This, however, ignores the problem of accounting for the extraordinarily rapid diffusion in β-Zr, β-Ti and γ-U and also fails to explain the lack of observable curvature in most other metal systems studied.

An alternative point of view is that the observed diffusion coefficient, D, is in fact, made up of two components, D_1 and D_2, both having the simple form of Eq 1. Thus we may write

$$D = D_1{}^0 \exp\left(-Q_1/RT\right) + D_2{}^0 \exp\left(-Q_2/RT\right) \qquad (2)$$

The problem then is to decompose the measured curve into these separate contributions and to account for each in a rational way.

It is not possible, of course, to obtain a unique resolution of the two components in a purely analytical way. Because any interpretation of the diffusion mechanism will depend to a large extent on the particular values of the parameters extracted from the data, it is apparent that the method of decomposition of the measured Arrhenius curve must be considered rather carefully. The approach used here, which was adopted previously by the author, was based on two points. First, the supplementary observations described in the previous section of this paper strongly suggest that vacancies not only occur in β-Zr but also play a role in the diffusion process. Second, if the contribution of a simple vacancy mechanism can be represented by $D_1 = D_1{}^0 \exp\left(-Q_1/RT\right)$, as assumed in Eq 2, then the parameters $D_1{}^0$ and Q_1 will be of the order predicted for normal behavior. This leads to the conclusion that the contribution of D_1 to the measured diffusion coefficient becomes negligibly small at the lower temperatures. The curves may be decomposed, therefore, by assuming that the observed diffusion at the lower temperatures is due entirely to the mechanism represented by D_2.

In the specific instance of self-diffusion in β-Zr, the results of Kidson and McGurn and of Lundy and Federer were considered together. For temperatures below about 1400 C, the curve can be fitted quite well by $D_2 = 8.5 \times 10^{-5} \exp\left(-27{,}700/RT\right)$ cm²/sec.

Values of D_1 were obtained as $D_1 = D - D_2$ from the higher-temperature data. Plotted separately as log D_1 versus $1/T$, these results can be represented by

$$D_1 = 1.34 \exp\left(-65{,}200/RT\right) \text{ cm}^2/\text{sec}$$

Thus one possible representation of the experimental results is given by
$$D = 1.34 \exp\left(-65,200/RT\right) + (8.5 \times 10^{-5}) \exp\left(-27,700/RT\right) \text{ cm}^2/\text{sec}$$
This expression is represented by the solid curve in Fig. 5.

The values of D_1^0 and Q_1 obtained in this way are certainly of the magnitude expected for normal behavior and lend support to the assumptions made concerning a simple vacancy mechanism for D_1.

It remains, then, to account for D_2. Clearly, any model proposed must be consistent with the following facts: (a) the shape of the concentration profiles are characteristic of volume diffusion over the whole temperature range; (b) the deduced activation energy Q_2 is slightly less than half of Q_1 and (c) the pre-exponential D_2^0 is extremely small. One would hope, of course, that a model applicable to β-Zr would hold also for the other anomalous systems.

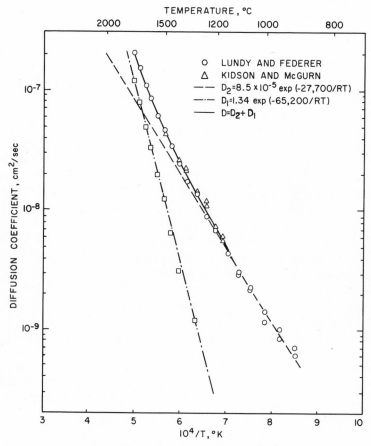

Fig. 5. D versus 1/T for β-Zr

Two mechanisms that appear to satisfy the above criteria have been proposed. The first of these, which attributed D_2 to enhanced diffusion along a dense dislocation network, was previously rejected by the author in favor of an alternative model that assumed D_2 was due to extra vacancies introduced into the lattice by impurities.

Both of these will be re-examined in the light of recent data.

Extrinsic Vacancy Model

It will be shown in the subsequent section of this paper that the dislocation model requires the assumption of a very large dislocation density in order to account quantitatively for D_2. Moreover, it predicts that the enhancement of diffusion, represented by D_2, is directly proportional to this dislocation density. The experimental observation that was particularly difficult to understand, on the basis of this model, was the apparent lack of effect of the pre-annealing experiments on the observed diffusion coefficient, as described previously in the section titled Experimental Observations. These experiments were specifically designed, of course, to see if a reduction in the number of dislocations that may have been introduced by the $\alpha \rightarrow \beta$ phase change produced a corresponding reduction in the observed diffusion coefficient. The apparent lack of any such effect was a major cause of the rejection of the model by the author. A further consideration was that it almost certainly could not account for the nonlinear Arrhenius curve observed in the self-diffusion measurements in V (15) because single crystals were used in these studies and no known phase change was involved.

These various difficulties led to the suggestion (19) that the anomalous self-diffusion behavior in β-Zr could be due to effects analogous to those that produce rapid diffusion and nonlinear Arrhenius curves in ionic crystals. It has long been known that diffusion coefficients in these materials can frequently be expressed in the form

$$D = D_1 + D_2 \tag{3}$$

if aliovalent impurities are present. In such instances D_1 has been associated with the diffusion coefficient arising from the normal thermal, or "intrinsic," vacancy concentration, and D_2 has been attributed to that arising from a temperature-independent concentration of "extrinsic" vacancies that are associated with the impurities. In ionic crystals, these extrinsic vacancies occur in order that charge neutrality be maintained.

It is well known, of course, that dissolved impurities can alter the total vacancy concentration in metals as well if there is an interaction energy between the two. When this interaction is such that the formation energy of a vacancy in the region of an impurity is less than that in the pure metal, there will be a tendency to form vacancy-impurity pairs as well as free vacancies in the crystal. As a result the total vacancy concentration will be increased. That such an increase results in an enhancement of the solvent diffusion coefficient has been demonstrated experimentally (20, 21) and discussed theoretically by a number of authors (22, 23) for the instance of substitutionally dissolved impurities in fcc lattices.

In applying such a model to the diffusion results observed in what was nominally high-purity Zr, the author suggested that the impurity responsible was interstitially dissolved O. This was based on the following considerations. Both Zr and Ti absorb up to about 30 at. % O in the low-temperature hcp phase. This large solubility can probably be attributed in part to an unusually strong chemical binding and in part to the fact that the O ions are accommodated in the octahedral interstitial sites with very little lattice strain. As the material transforms to the bcc structure, however, the space available in the octahedral sites is considerably less, so much so, in fact, that a rather large lattice strain can be expected. It was proposed that this strain would be reduced if a vacancy occupied a substitutional site in the coordination shell of the impurity. It was assumed that the vacancy-interstitial pair would retain their separate identities in much the way recently described for C in bcc Fe (24). Partly for simplicity and partly to account for the large effects observed, it was further postulated that each O ion in the lattice had a vacancy associated with it. As a result, the total vacancy concentration

$$c_v = c^i + c^e$$

where c^i is the concentration of "intrinsic" vacancies arising from normal thermal effects, and c^e the concentration of "extrinsic" vacancies in association with impurities. Writing

$$D = b^2 f \bar{\Gamma}/m$$

where b is the lattice parameter, m is a geometrical constant, f is the correlation factor and $\bar{\Gamma}$ is the average jump frequency of the solvent atoms, and assuming $\bar{\Gamma} = \Gamma_v c_v$ where Γ_v is the jump frequency of both free and associated vacancies, one obtains

$$\begin{aligned}
D &= (b^2 \nu f/8)\Gamma_v c^i + (b^2 \nu f/8)\Gamma_v c^e \\
&= (b^2 \nu f/8) \exp\left[(S_m + S_f)/R\right] \exp\left[-(Q_m + Q_f)/RT\right] \\
&\quad + c^e(b^2 \nu f/8) \exp\left[S_m/R\right] \exp\left[-Q_m/RT\right]
\end{aligned} \tag{4}$$

where S_m and S_f are the activation entropies for vacancy movement and formation, Q_m and Q_f are the enthalpies for vacancy movement and formation and ν is the Debye frequency. On this basis, then, $D_2{}^0 = (b^2\nu f/8)c^e \exp (S_m/R)$ and $Q_2 = Q_m$, and $D_1{}^0$ and Q_1 are associated with the normal diffusion coefficient for the vacancy mechanism.

A value of c^e was estimated by setting $D_2{}^0/D_1{}^0 = c^e \exp (S_f/R)$ and taking (S_f/R) to be about 1.8 e.u. From this one obtains $c^e \simeq 0.038$ at. %.

The fact that the value deduced for c^e appeared physically reasonable and that the activation energy $Q_2 = 27{,}700$ cal/mole could be associated with vacancy movement alone lent some support to the proposed interpretation.

The model can be improved in a number of ways. In particular, the method used by Lidiard (23) in his analysis of the effect of substitutionally dissolved impurities on the solvent diffusion coefficient in fcc lattices can be adapted to the present model in a fairly straightforward way. Lidiard calculated the total vacancy concentration in a lattice containing N_a solvent atoms, $N_b{}^f$ free impurity atoms, $N_v{}^f$ free vacancies and N_p vacancy-impurity pairs from the expression for the total Gibbs free energy of the system. He then calculated the average solvent-atom jump frequency $\bar{\Gamma}$, taking into account the fact that the jump frequencies of associated and free vacancies may be different.

Although the entire procedure will not be followed through, it will be indicated below that the total vacancy concentration c_v can be more rigorously derived for the specific model proposed here and that it has a form similar to that previously given.

In the Appendix the expression for G, the Gibbs free energy, is determined for the specific model proposed. Setting $(\partial G/\partial N_p)_{N_a,N_b,N_v} = 0$ one obtains

$$N_p N_i/N_b{}^f N_v{}^f = \exp [-(\Delta g - kT \ln z)/kT] \tag{5}$$

where N_i is the number of octahedral interstitial sites, Δg is the difference in the partial Gibbs free energy less the configurational entropy, for the formation of vacancy-impurity pairs and for separated vacancies and impurities, z is the number of octahedral interstitial sites neighboring a substitutional site ($z = 6$ for bcc lattices) and kT has its usual meaning. The term $k \ln z$ arises from the contribution of the z possible orientations of pairs to the configurational entropy. Defining

$$c_p = N_p/N_s$$
$$c_v{}^f = N_v{}^f/N_s$$
$$(c_b{}^f)' = N_b{}^f/N_i$$

where N_s is the total number of substitutional sites, we can write from Eq 5

$$c_p/[c_v{}^f(c_b{}^f)'] = \exp\left[-(\Delta g - kT \ln z)/kT\right] \qquad (6)$$

This is the form given by the law of mass action when it is assumed that the reaction [free vacancies + free impurities $\rightleftharpoons$ pairs] is at equilibrium. For convenience, we define $c_b{}^f = N_b{}^f/N_s = \alpha(c_b{}^f)'$, where $\alpha = N_i/N_s$. Whence

$$c_p = c_v{}^f c_b{}^f(z/\alpha) \exp\left(-\Delta g/kT\right) \qquad (7)$$

The total vacancy concentration can be written as

$$\begin{aligned} c_v &= c_v{}^f + c_p \\ &= c_v{}^f[1 + (z/\alpha)c_b{}^f \exp\left(-\Delta g/kT\right)] \end{aligned} \qquad (8)$$

By setting $(\partial G/\partial N_v)_{N_a, N_b, N_p} = 0$ (see Appendix), we obtain

$$c_v{}^f = (1 - z'\alpha c_b{}^f) \exp\left(-g_v/kT\right) \qquad (9)$$

where z' is the number of substitutional sites surrounding a free interstitial impurity and g_v is the partial Gibbs free energy of formation less the configurational entropy for free vacancies. ($z' = 2$ for this model.)

If we write $c_b{}^f = c_b - c_p$ and neglect second-order terms in concentration, c_v becomes

$$\begin{aligned} c_v \simeq (1 - z'c_b) \exp\left(-g_v/kT\right) &+ (z/\alpha)c_b \exp\left[-(g_v + \Delta g)/kT\right] \\ &+ c_p[z' - (z/\alpha)] \exp\left(-g_v/kT\right) \end{aligned} \qquad (10)$$

Finally, noting that $z/\alpha = z' = 2$ for the bcc lattice, we obtain

$$c_v \simeq (1 - z'c_b) \exp\left(-g_v/kT\right) + z'c_b \exp\left[-(g_v - |\Delta g|)/kT\right] \qquad (11)$$

where the absolute value of Δg is taken because the model assumes a binding energy to occur. Equation 11 is of the form obtained by Lidiard (23) for substitutional solutes in fcc lattices.

Lidiard went on to consider $\bar{\Gamma}$ by calculating the total number of solvent-atom jumps/sec in the crystal, taking into account the difference in jump frequencies between solvent atoms in the region of the impurities and those away from them. Although this procedure provides a more satisfying theoretical description of the proposed model, its application to the experimental results is hampered by a lack of knowledge of the various atom jump frequencies invoked. The end result, however, does indicate that the measured diffusion coefficient can be written as a sum of two components, one (D_1) being the diffusion coefficient of the solvent in the pure metal and the other (D_2) representing the influence of the impurities. Moreover, D_2 is proportional to the impurity content and its associated activation energy is roughly equal to that of D_1 reduced by the solute-vacancy binding energy.

It appears, therefore, that if we are seriously to consider the unusual self-diffusion behavior of β-Zr in terms of the impurity model, we must assume a large vacancy-impurity binding energy. It is interesting to note that recent work of Johnson (24) and of Damask *et al.* (25–27) suggests the occurrence of interstitial C-vacancy pairs in bcc Fe that have a binding energy of 9200 cal/mole. The Zr studies require a binding energy of about 30,000 cal/mole.

The nonlinear Arrhenius curves reported for solute diffusion in β-Ti, can, of course, be considered in the same way. Here, however, we must account also for the rather large differences between the coefficients of the various solutes. Gibbs *et al.* (17) have compiled a summary of all the work done by the Reading University group, which indicates that the diffusion coefficients occur in the order

$$D_{\mathrm{Ni}} \simeq D_{\mathrm{Co}} > D_{\mathrm{Fe}} > D_{\mathrm{Mn}} > D_{\mathrm{Cr}} > D_{\mathrm{Cb}} \simeq D_{\mathrm{Ti}} > D_{\mathrm{Mo}}$$

Values of the activation energies Q_1 extracted from the data in the ambiguous manner described in the previous section of this paper fall in the reverse order of the diffusion coefficients. Apart from Mo, this is the order one might expect, if the Lazarus-Le Claire (28, 29) theory for solute diffusion in the noble metals can be applied, by assuming that the valence differences between the solvent and the various solutes are taken simply on the basis of their positions in the periodic table. Le Claire has discussed the pitfalls in this procedure, particularly for the transition-element solutes. Peterson and Rothman (18) have considered the interpretation of their results for solute diffusion in bcc γ-U on this basis, and again emphasize the serious difficulties raised.

In summary, then, we see that although the simple interpretation of the results for self-diffusion in β-Zr previously proposed by the author can be treated in a somewhat more rigorous manner to yield a diffusion coefficient of the form given by Eq 3, it implicitly assumes a binding energy for the interstitial O vacancy complex that is disturbingly large. The model also predicts that the degree of enhancement should depend directly on the O content of the solvent. This has been challenged by

Graham (30), who reported little if any effect on the solute diffusion rates in β-Ti when specimens of markedly differing purity were used.

In view of the foregoing, and because of certain recent observations to be described below, it seems worthwhile to reconsider the dislocation model in more detail.

Dislocation-Enhanced Diffusion

As mentioned earlier, Hart (31) pointed out that provided the total diffusion distances are large compared with the dislocation spacing, the shape of the concentration-penetration profiles in a diffusion experiment will be characteristic of true volume diffusion, even though the diffusing atoms spend a significant portion of their time in the region of dislocations. He showed that the measured diffusion coefficient D can be expressed as

$$D = (1 - g)D_b + gD_d \tag{12}$$

where g is the fraction of time spent by the atoms in the vicinity of the dislocations, D_b is the true bulk or lattice diffusion coefficient and D_d is the coefficient for diffusion along dislocations.

For self-diffusion, g is simply the fraction of sites in the region of the dislocations and can be written as $g = \rho\alpha/d$ where ρ is the density of dislocations, α the number of sites associated with the cross section of a dislocation and d the total site density. Thus if we identify $(1 - g)D_b$ with D_1 and gD_d with D_2, we have

$$D_2{}^0 = 8.5 \times 10^{-5} \text{ cm}^2/\text{sec} = (\rho\alpha/d)D_d{}^0$$

and

$$Q_2 = 27{,}700 \text{ cal/mole} = Q_d$$

for self-diffusion in β-Zr.

Although it appears quite reasonable to associate Q_2 with the activation energy for diffusion along dislocations, $D_2{}^0$ is more difficult to account for. Setting $d = 10^{15}/\text{cm}^2$ and $\alpha = 10$, we have

$$\rho D_d{}^0 = 8.5 \times 10^9 \simeq 10^{10}$$

Experiments (32, 33) suggest that $D_d{}^0$ should lie between 10^{-2} and $10 \text{ cm}^2/\text{sec}$. Thus the dislocation density required would lie between 10^{12} to 10^9 lines/cm^2 for β-Zr.

If the resolution of the Arrhenius curve for self-diffusion in β-Ti as reported recently by Murdock *et al.* (14) is accepted, one finds the required dislocation density, ρ, to lie between 4×10^{12} and 4×10^9 lines per square centimeter.

As mentioned in the previous section of this paper these large values of ρ plus the apparent lack of influence of pre-annealing on the measured diffusion coefficient previously led the author to reject this interpretation. A recent report by Fisher and Renken (34), however, appears to call for a careful reappraisal. Fisher noted that a single crystal of α-Zr that was being used for elastic-moduli measurements could be cycled over the $\alpha \rightarrow \beta \rightarrow \alpha$ transformations with no change in the α orientation. Some specimens were thermally cycled as many as ten times and in each instance the single crystal structure of the α phase was retained. This almost certainly indicates that the $\alpha \rightarrow \beta$ transformation, as well as the $\beta \rightarrow \alpha$, is martensitic in character. Even more pertinent to the present discussion was their observation that the acoustical waves used to measure the elastic moduli could not penetrate the crystals in the β phase. Perhaps the most direct inference from this is that large dislocation densities were generated during the transformation. This is known to occur during martensitic transformations in steels for example (35). Fisher reported similar effects for Ti crystals, and recent unpublished results by L. M. Howe (36), who used thin-film electron microscopy for direct observation of the effect of the $\alpha \rightarrow \beta$ phase change in pure Zr, confirm that typical martensitic needles and copious dislocation tangles are produced as a result of the transformation in Zr.

The significance of these results is twofold. First, it provides a rational account for the production of the high dislocation densities required by the dislocation model. Second, it may indicate why no reduction in D was noted in the pre-annealing experiments described by McGurn and the author (7), even though large β grains were observed prior to the diffusion experiment. That is to say, the β grains could have been a reflection of grains existing in the material during its prior history. Le Claire (37) has suggested that it may be necessary to pre-anneal at temperatures near the melting point for prolonged periods in order to lower the dislocation content appreciably.

The most compelling argument in favor of the dislocation model, however, arises when we consider the solute diffusion results in β-Ti. In such instances, the fraction of time the diffusing solute atoms spend in the region of the dislocation will depend not only on the fraction of sites in dislocations, as for the instance of self-diffusion, but also on the degree to which atoms tend to segregate along the dislocations. Mortlock (38) has considered this point and suggests g should be written as $g = (\rho a/d)\sigma$, where $\sigma = c_d/c_b = A \exp (Q_s/RT)$ is the segregation ratio and Q_s the binding energy of the solute to the dislocation. c_d and c_b are the solute concentrations near the dislocations and in the bulk, respectively.

Clearly, therefore, the degree of enhancement of diffusion by dislocations will depend upon σ. Although the effect could be looked for in the values Q_2 and $D_2{}^0$, these are subject to the uncertainties described previously. The most direct way is to examine the measured diffusion coefficients themselves, and as already pointed out in the previous section of this paper, these can be arranged in the following sequence:

$$D_{Ni} \simeq D_{Co} > D_{Fe} > D_{Mn} > D_{Cr} > D_{Cb} > D_{Mo}$$

One useful guide to the degree of segregation that might be expected for each solute is the range of solid solubility of the solute in the β-Ti lattice. That is to say, the smaller the range of solubility, the greater the value of σ expected, and hence the larger the degree of enhancement. A survey of the pertinent binary phase diagrams (39) indicates that

$$\sigma_{Ni} \approx \sigma_{Co} < \sigma_{Fe} < \sigma_{Mn} < \sigma_{Cr} < \sigma_{Cb} \simeq \sigma_{Mo}$$

in essentially complete agreement with the dislocation model. Applying the same criterion to the results of Peterson and Rothman for solute diffusion in γ-U, we find

$$D_{Co} \simeq D_{Fe} > D_{Ni} > D_{Mn} > D_{Cr} > D_{Cu} > D_{Au} > D_{Cb}$$
and
$$\sigma_{Co} < \sigma_{Fe} \simeq \sigma_{Ni} < \sigma_{Mn} < \sigma_{Cr} \simeq \sigma_{Au} < \sigma_{Cb}$$

again, in qualitative agreement with the hypothesis, with the exception of Cu and possibly Au.

Conclusions

On the assumption that the nonlinear Arrhenius curves in β-Zr, β-Ti and γ-U can be resolved into two components, one of which, D_1, represents the contribution of normal vacancy diffusion, two alternative models for the second component, D_2, have been examined. Although one of these models, based on the postulate of an enhanced vacancy concentration due to interstitially dissolved O, yields an expression for the measured diffusion coefficient that has the proposed form and can account for the low values of D_2 and Q_2 in a physically reasonable way, it requires the assumption of a binding energy for the interstitial-vacancy complexes of about 30,000 cal/mole.

The second model, that of enhanced diffusion along dislocations, appears more reasonable in the light of recent reports indicating large dislocation densities generated by the martensitic-type $\alpha \to \beta$ transformation for Zr and Ti, and possibly also for γ-U. It has the added feature of giving a more acceptable rationale for the very large differences in the diffusion coefficients of solutes in both β-Ti and γ-U, in terms of solute segregation effects.

There remains a need for an experiment in which a high-purity specimen is pre-annealed in a very high vacuum near the melting point for a prolonged period to see if the removal of dislocations will decrease the observed diffusion coefficient. Until such time, no definitive conclusions can be drawn about the diffusion behavior of these materials.

Acknowledgment. I am grateful to the Conference Organizers, in particular Dr. F. R. Winslow, for the opportunity to revise the manuscript. Permission to use Fig. 2, 3, 4 and 5 from the Canadian Journal of Physics is acknowledged.

Appendix

We aim to calculate the total vacancy concentration in a bcc lattice by use of the assumption that O is dissolved in octahedral interstitial sites and that interstitial-vacancy pairs are formed. The procedure follows that adopted by Howard and Lidiard (40).

Let the number of solvent atoms be N_a, the total number of interstitial solutes be N_b, the total number of vacancies be N_v and the number of interstitial-vacancy pairs be N_p. Then, the total number of substitutional lattice sites is $N_s = N_a + N_v$. The number of octahedral interstitial sites is $N_i = \alpha N_s$, where $\alpha = 3$ for the bcc lattice. The number of unpaired vacancies $N_v{}^f$ is $N_v - N_p$, and the number of unpaired solutes $N_b{}^f$ is $N_b - N_p$.

Let G_0 be the Gibbs free energy of a perfect crystal containing N_a solvent atoms only and g_v, g_b and $(g_v + g_b + \Delta g)$ be the Gibbs free energy, exclusive of the configurational entropy, of formation of unpaired vacancies, unpaired solutes and solute-vacancy pairs, respectively. We can write the total Gibbs free energy of the alloy as

$$G = G_0 + (N_b - N_p)g_b + (N_v - N_p)g_v + N_p(g_v + g_b + \Delta g) - kT \ln \Omega$$
$$= G_0 + N_b g_b + N_v g_v + N_p \Delta g - kT \ln \Omega$$

where $k \ln \Omega$ represents the contribution of the vacancies, impurities and pairs to the configurational entropy. We define $\Omega = \Omega_p \cdot \Omega_b \cdot \Omega_v$ where Ω_p is the number of ways of arranging N_p pairs among the available sites,

Ω_b is the number of ways of arranging $N_b - N_p$ free solutes among the available sites and Ω_v is the number of ways of arranging $N_v - N_p$ free vacancies among the available sites, as described below. We can calculate Ω_p by assuming we distribute N_p vacancies among the N_s substitutional sites, each vacancy having an associated interstitial solute. Because there are z possible orientations of the interstitial around the vacancy, we have

$$\Omega_p = \frac{z^{N_p}[N_s]!}{(N_p)!(N_s - N_p)!}$$

where z is the number of octahedral interstitial sites around a substitutional site. Note that only one substitutional site is used for each pair. The remaining $(N_b - N_p)$ unpaired interstitial solutes may now be distributed among the $(\alpha N_s - N_p)$ interstitial sites, so that

$$\Omega_b = \frac{(\alpha N_s - N_p)!}{[N_b - N_p]![\alpha N_\circ - N_b]!}$$

Finally, we distribute the $(N_v - N_p)$ free vacancies among the available substitutional sites, taking into account that none of the sites neighboring a free solute may be used. If z' is the number of substitutional sites neighboring an interstitial solute, the number of available substitutional sites is $[N_s - z'(N_b - N_p) - N_p]$ so that

$$\Omega_v = \frac{[N_s - z'(N_b - N_p) - N_p]!}{[N_s - z'(N_b - N_p) - N_v]![N_v - N_p]!}$$

The equilibrium number of pairs is then obtained by setting $(\partial G/\partial N_p)_{N_a, N_v, N_b} = 0$; the equilibrium number of vacancies, by setting $(\partial G/\partial N_v)_{N_a, N_b, N_p} = 0$. The results are given in the text.

References

1 D. Lazarus, Solid State Phys, **10**, 71 (1960)
2 Y. Adda and A. Kirianenko, Compt Rend, **247**, 744 (1958)
3 A. A. Bochvar, V. G. Kuzenefsova and V. S. Sergeev, A/Conf. 15/P/2306 (1958)
4 S. Rothman, L. Lloyd and A. Harkness, Trans AIME, **218**, 605 (1960)
5 A. Mortlock and D. Tomlin, Phil Mag, **4**, 628 (1959)
6 H. Paxton and E. Gondolf, Arch Eisenhuettenw, **30**, 55 (1959)
7 G. V. Kidson and J. F. McGurn, Can J Phys, **39**, 1147 (1961)
8 G. C. Kuczynski, J Appl Phys, **21** (7), 632 (1950)
9 R. S. Barnes, AERE-R3162 (1959)
10 C. E. Ells and W. Evans, Trans AIME, **227**, 438 (1963)

11   Y. Adda, C. Mairy and J. L. Andreu, Comm. aux Journees D'Automme, CEA, 1959
12   W. Hagel, Trans AIME, **224,** 430 (1962)
13   T. S. Lundy and J. I. Federer, ORNL-3339 (1962)
14   J. F. Murdock, T. S. Lundy and E. E. Stansbury, Acta Met. **12** (9), 1033 (1964)
15   T. S. Lundy, ORNL-3617 (1964)
16   R. Resnick and L. S. Castleman, Trans AIME, **218,** 307 (1960)
17   G. B. Gibbs, D. Graham and D. H. Tomlin, Phil Mag, **8,** 1269 (1963)
18   N. L. Peterson and S. Rothman, Phys Rev, **136 (3A),** A842
1⁹   G. V. Kidson, Can J Phys, **41,** 1563 (1963)
20   R. E. Hoffman and D. Turnbull, J Appl Phys, **23,** 1409 (1952)
21   N. H. Nachtrieb, Petit and Wehrenberg, J Chem Phys, **26,** 106 (1957)
22   H. Reiss, Phys Rev, **113,** 1445 (1959)
23   A. B. Lidiard, Phil Mag, **5** (59), 1171 (1960)
24   R. A. Johnson and A. C. Damask, Acta Met, **12** (4), 443 (1964)
25   F. E. Fujita and A. C. Damask, Acta Met, **12** (4), 331 (1964)
26   R. A. Arndt and A. C. Damask, Acta Met, **12** (4), 341 (1964)
27   H. Wagenblast, F. E. Fujita and A. C. Damask, Acta Met, **12** (4), 347 (1964)
28   D. Lazarus, Phys Rev, **93** (5), 973 (1954)
29   A. D. Le Claire, Phil Mag, **7,** 141 (1962)
30   D. Graham, private communication, 1964
31   E. W. Hart, Acta Met, **5,** 597 (1957)
32   R. E. Hoffman and D. Turnbull, J Appl Phys, **22,** 634 (1951)
33   E. S. Wajda, Acta Met, **2,** 184 (1954)
34   E. S. Fisher and C. J. Renken, Phys Rev, **135 (2A),** A482 (1964)
35   G. Krauss, Acta Met, **11** (6), 499 (1963)
36   L. M. Howe, private communication, 1964
37   A. D. Le Claire, paper presented at the International Symposium on High Temperature Technology, Asilomar, Calif., 1963
38   A. Mortlock, Acta Met, **8,** 132 (1960)
39   M. Hansen, Constitution of Binary Alloys, McGraw-Hill Book Co., Inc., New York, 1958
40   R. Howard and A. B. Lidiard, AERE-TP/111 (1963), p 45

Chapter 26

The Effect of Irradiation on Precipitation
of Nitrides in Iron

J. T. Stanley

Wagenblast and Damask have shown that neutron irradiation increases the rate at which C is removed from supersaturated solid solution (1). According to their interpretation, two different reactions occur: (a) C atoms are trapped by individual point defects produced by the irradiation and (b) irradiation produces nucleation sites for precipitation of the metastable carbide. To observe the first effect, the concentration of point defects must be comparable to the concentration of C atoms in solution, which is about 10^{19}/cm^3. Wagenblast and Damask irradiated to high doses at low temperature and studied the trapping of C atoms at vacancies. They also made a few measurements that indicated that the second effect predominates when the number of primary knock-on events is comparable to the number of particles in the usual aging experiment, that is, 10^{14}/cm^3.

Our experiments on the effect of irradiation on precipitation of nitrides in Fe have been carried out at doses such that the number of point defects produced by the irradiation is much smaller than the number of N atoms. Thus only the enhanced nucleation of precipitates should be observed.

Experimental Procedure and Results

Specimens used in this investigation were cut from 0.005-in.-thick Ferrovac E foil that had been cold rolled from 1½-in.-diam bar. The specimens were decarburized by heating in moist H at 720 C for 72 hr. The decarburized specimens were then heated to 950 C for 1 hr in a dry H atmosphere and slow cooled (100 C per hr) to 590 C to obtain a large grain size. Nitriding was performed at 590 C by use of a mixture of ammonia and H gas that was adjusted, with the aid of data given by Darken and Gurry (2), to give a N content of about 0.015 wt %. The

The author is with the Solid State Division, Oak Ridge National Laboratory, Oak Ridge, Tenn.

nitrided specimens were quenched in water from 590 C to retain the N in solid solution.

The amount of N in solution was determined by measuring the height of the N internal-friction peak. We assumed the constant relating the N concentration in weight per cent to the height of the internal-friction peak to be unity. Internal friction was measured on 1½- by ³⁄₁₆- by 0.005-in. specimens vibrating in flexure at approximately 33 cps. The N peak occurs at 60 C for this vibration frequency.

The apparatus used for the neutron irradiations was designed to fit into the low-temperature irradiation facility in Hole 50 of the Oak Ridge Graphite Reactor. A drawing of the apparatus is shown in Fig. 1. With this apparatus the specimen could be cooled rapidly enough to retain N in solution after annealing at 400 C. This treatment will be referred to as a re-solution anneal because it restores the original N internal-friction peak after an aging treatment at some lower temperature. The re-solution anneal was carried out by heating the specimen to 400 C in a vacuum and then cooling rapidly by simultaneously turning off the heater current and admitting He gas into the chamber.

Out-of-reactor experiments in a mockup of the reactor facility showed that essentially all of the N could be retained in solution if the specimen

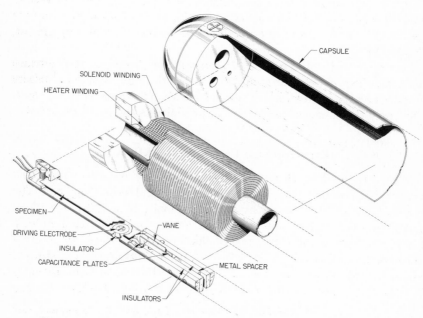

Fig. 1. Approximate scale drawing of in-reactor internal-friction apparatus

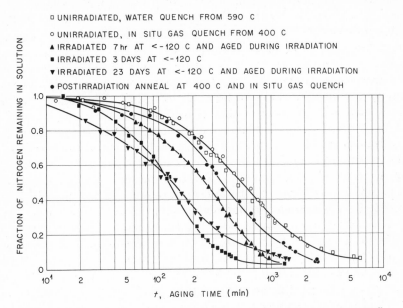

Fig. 2. Effect of various neutron irradiations on aging of the N peak at 65 C

was cooled from 400 to 50 C in about 6 min. To achieve this cooling rate in the mockup, it was necessary to cool the chamber walls with dry ice. In the low-temperature irradiation facility, the chamber walls were kept cool by the flow of cold He gas through the heat exchanger. Even though the specimen is cooled fast enough to retain all of the N in solution, as detected by the internal-friction peak, it is still possible for there to be differences in the number of nucleation sites for precipitation for different cooling rates. However, studies of the aging of the N peak at 65 C showed little difference between the peak obtained after the specimen was water quenched from 590 C and the peak obtained after the specimen was gas quenched from 400 C as described above. These two sets of data are shown in Fig. 2 along with the data for this specimen after various amounts of irradiation at low temperature.

The results presented in Fig. 2 represent measurements made on two specimens, A and B, of about the same N content. Specimen A was used for the aging run after the 23-day irradiation; Specimen B was used for the rest of the aging runs. The measurements for Specimen B were made in the order listed in the caption, and, except for the initial water quench, each aging run was preceded by a 400 C re-solution anneal as described above. The results presented in Fig. 2 show that irradiation does increase the rate of N precipitation, and that the 400 C re-solution anneal removes most of the effect of the irradiation.

A comparison of the aging runs made after the 23-day irradiation and the 3-day irradiation shows that the time for half completion of the reaction is about the same in both instances. Thus there is a saturation of the enhanced precipitation effect after a relatively low dose. This saturation occurs, we believe, after a 1-day low-temperature irradiation, which corresponds to a fast neutron dose of 3×10^{15} neutrons/cm². This conclusion is based on results obtained on Specimen A and shown in Fig. 3. In this instance internal friction was measured at a series of temperatures upon warming after a 1-day irradiation at low temperature. It was noted that considerable precipitation of N occurs during the time required to warm up and cool down in the temperature range of the N peak. It is possible to construct an effective isothermal aging curve from these data by use of the known shape of the N internal-friction peak, the known activation energy for N diffusion and the time-versus-temperature curve for the experiment. This was done and the results are shown in Fig. 4. Thus it seems that a 1-day irradiation is just as effective as a 23-day irradiation in increasing the rate of nitride precipitation.

In addition to the above neutron irradiations, the aging of a specimen was studied after irradiation with 2-mev electrons. In this instance the specimen was irradiated at about 0 C for 30 min at a current density of 2 micro-amp/cm² and then placed in a flexure pendulum apparatus for

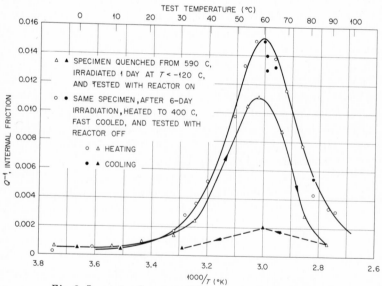

Fig. 3. In-reactor flexure pendulum measurements at 33 cps

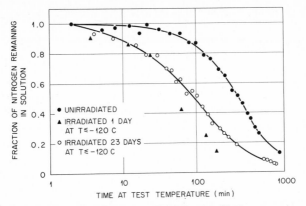

Fig. 4. Comparison of the effect of 1- and 23-day irradiations on aging of the N peak at 65 C

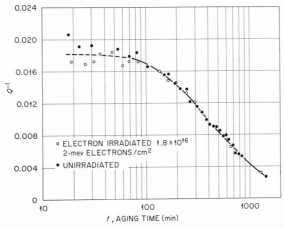

Fig. 5. Effect of electron irradiation on the aging of the N peak at 65 C

measurement. The aging of the N internal-friction peak for this sample before and after irradiation is shown in Fig. 5. We see that the electron irradiation did not change the aging kinetics. The calculated number of point defects produced by this irradiation would give a concentration of 1.3×10^{-6} atomic fraction. This is approximately the same concentration of defects that would be produced by the 1-day neutron irradiation.

Discussion

Transmission electron microscope observations by Keh and Wreidt (3) have shown that nitrides precipitate preferentially on dislocations, but for high supersaturations, nitride particles also precipitated uniformly in the matrix. It is not known if the nitride particles that precipitated in the matrix did so on some lattice defect that was not visible in the electron microscope, but Leslie (4), who found similar effects for precipitation of carbides in Fe, suggested that individual lattice vacancies might act as nucleation sites for carbide precipitation. Various impurity atoms in the Fe matrix might also act as nucleation sites for nitride precipitation because it has been shown that certain elements added to Fe in small amounts can greatly change the rate of nitride and carbide precipitation (5, 6). The irons used for the precipitation studies typically contain about 10 ppm of various impurities. This amount of impurity would be sufficient to account for the particle density usually observed in the precipitation experiment.

The point of the preceding discussion is just to show that carbide and nitride particles require some sort of defect for nucleation. Thus, it is not surprising to find that the defects produced by irradiation can form structures that act as nucleation sites. The surprising feature of our data is that the enhanced nucleation saturates after a very low irradiation dose of about 10^{15} neutrons/cm². This is far below the dose at which radiation damage, as measured by other properties, shows saturation effects.

The lack of enhanced nucleation after electron irradiation is a very significant fact because it immediately narrows down the field of possible radiation-produced nucleation sites. As we know from the present theories of radiation damage, neutron irradiation produces highly damaged regions in the lattice with clusters of many vacancies and interstitials, whereas electron irradiation produces only isolated interstitial-vacancy pairs. It is known that the fraction of interstitials and vacancies that recombine is higher for electron irradiation as compared with neutron irradiation, but even so, a significant number of vacancies and interstitials are left to migrate to other traps. Because we did not observe enhanced nucleation after electron irradiation, we must conclude that the irradiation-produced nucleation sites are clusters of vacancies or interstitials.

The electron-irradiation experiment eliminated from consideration as nucleation sites several possibilities that seemed capable of explaining the saturation at low doses. These potential nucleation sites would be produced by the combination of an existing lattice defect with a radiation-produced defect. Some examples of these possibilities are jogs on dislocations and the combination of vacancies with substitutional impurity atoms. Because the experiments indicate that the nucleation sites are clusters of vacancies or interstitials, we must conclude that the saturation effect is related to some property of the solid solution and the precipitate that prevents finer division of the precipitate.

J. W. Cahn (7) assumed a model for nucleation on a dislocation in which the free energy of the nucleus consisted of the sum of three terms, a strain-energy term, a surface-energy term and a volume-energy term. According to this model, growth of a particle on the dislocation lowers the strain energy of the dislocation so that for small particle diameters the free energy decreases rapidly with increasing diameter. As the particle grows, the surface energy of the particle increases and may cause the total free energy to rise again. Finally, at very large diameters, the volume-energy term predominates and the free energy decreases again. Whether or not there is a minimum in the curve for free energy versus particle diameter depends on the relative magnitudes of the three energy terms. Now we can imagine that in a system with a large number of nucleation sites, particles at first start growing on all of the sites because of the rapid decrease in the strain energy. It may be that because of the large number of such sites, the solution becomes depleted of solute atoms to such an extent that the volume free-energy term is substantially reduced. In this instance the curve for free energy versus particle diameter will have a bump, whereas for a smaller initial number of particles it would not have a bump. At this time we have not been able to carry the model to the point of making calculations to determine if it could account for our results. Thus, it is offered just as a suggestion to explain the peculiar saturation effect.

Conclusion

Neutron irradiation of supersaturated Fe-N solutions causes an enhancement in the rate of precipitation of nitrides from solution. The enhanced rate of precipitation is caused by nucleation sites produced by the irradiation. Lack of an enhanced rate of precipitation after electron irradiation shows that individual lattice defects cannot produce the nucleation sites for precipitation.

Acknowledgments. It is a pleasure to acknowledge the help of W. E. Brundage in making some of the internal-friction measurements and in building parts of the apparatus. Much thanks is due Monroe Wechsler for many suggestions and discussion relating to this work.

This research was sponsored by the U. S. Atomic Energy Commission under contract with the Union Carbide Corporation.

References

1 H. Wagenblast and A. C. Damask, Kinetics of Carbon Precipitation in Irradiated Iron, J Phys Chem Solids, **23,** 221 (1962)
2 L. S. Darken and R. W. Gurry, Physical Chemistry of Metals, McGraw-Hill Book Co., Inc., New York, 1953, p 377

3   A. S. Keh and H. A. Wriedt, An Electron Transmission Study of Nitride Precipita-
    tion in Alpha Iron, Trans AIME, **224,** 560 (1962)
4   W. C. Leslie, The Quench-Aging of Low-Carbon Iron and Iron-Manganese Alloys:
    An Electron Transmission Study, Acta Met, **9,** 1004 (1961)
5   L. J. Dijkstra and R. J. Sladek, Effect of Alloying Elements on the Behavior of
    Nitrogen in Alpha Iron, J Metals, **5,** 69 (1953)
6   C. A. Wert, Diffusion and Precipitation of Carbon in Some Alloys of Iron, J Metals,
    4, 602 (1952)
7   J. W. Cahn, Nucleation on Dislocations, Acta Met, **5,** 169 (1957)

Chapter 27
Point-Defect Calculations in Alpha Iron

R. A. JOHNSON

Detailed calculations for defects in a crystal lattice in which the lattice atoms are treated as individual particles can be carried out at the present time by use of high-speed digital computers. A mathematical model of a perfect lattice must first be devised in such a way that it approximates various known physical properties of a real crystal. Defects are then introduced into the model, and the resulting energy change, volume change and relaxation of atoms near the defects are calculated. A variety of models simulating fcc metals (primarily Cu) has been used in such calculations (1), but there has been very little effort toward the study of bcc metals. Erginsoy et al. (2) at Brookhaven National Laboratory have investigated the dynamics of radiation-damage events near the threshold energy for damage by use of a model for α-Fe, and we have carried out static calculations for various defects in α-Fe, V and W. The results of these calculations, some of which have been published elsewhere (3), are summarized in the present paper.

Model

In the bcc model used in the present calculations, each atom within a spherical crystallite containing about 530 atoms was treated as an independent particle with three degrees of freedom. The lattice atoms interacted with one another by a central pairwise force between first and second nearest neighboring atoms. The crystallite was surrounded by an elastic continuum with the lattice atoms embedded in it. A radial displacement field $\mathbf{u}$ that decreased as $1/r^2$ was used to determine the displacement of the elastic continuum, and hence of all atoms in it

$$\mathbf{u} = C(1/r^2)\hat{\imath}_r$$

where C is the "strength" of the displacement field and $\hat{\imath}_r$ is a radial unit

The author is with the Brookhaven National Laboratory, Upton, N.Y.

vector. When such an elastic model is used, the volume expansion associated with a defect configuration is linear with C.

The energy of the crystallite is given by a sum of the energy in the bonds in the crystallite plus a term linear with C and a term quadratic with C. The linear term accounts for the work done in altering the volume of the crystallite, and the quadratic term accounts for the energy stored within the elastic field.

The process for finding energy minimums and saddle points was as follows. Initial vector positions of each atom within the crystallite were chosen to approximate the configuration of interest. Each coordinate of each atom within the crystallite was varied in turn until the corresponding force component became zero, and then the value of the elastic variable C was adjusted so that the generalized force on C (the partial derivative of the energy with respect to C) was zero. Usually 10 to 20 such iterations were required for the energy and the configuration to converge sufficiently.

Experimental elastic-constant data were used as a basis for obtaining the interatomic potentials for the bcc metals for the present calculations. The elastic constants of a metal may be thought of as arising primarily from two contributions: long-range electronic interactions and short-range ionic interactions. The short-range interactions predominate for transition metals, but corrections were included for the long-range terms.

The potential used for the Fe-Fe interaction is shown in Fig. 1 and is

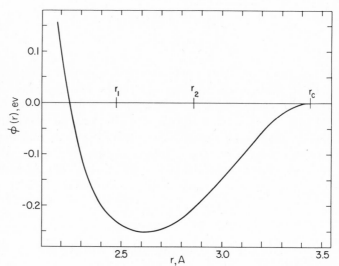

Fig. 1. The Fe-Fe interaction potential used in the present calculations

Table 1. Interatomic Potentials Used in the Present Calculations

Element	Range, A	Potential, ev
Fe............	<2.40	$-2.195976(r - 3.097910)^3 + 2.704060r - 7.436448$
	2.40–3.00	$-0.639230(r - 3.115829)^3 + 0.477871r - 1.581570$
	3.00–3.44	$-1.115035(r - 3.066403)^3 + 0.466892r - 1.547967$
V............	<2.53	$-1.496112(r - 2.731297)^3 - 0.599656r + 1.614190$
	2.53–3.17	$0.095514(r - 0.304042)^3 - 2.201314r + 4.625125$
	3.17–3.63	$-1.430039(r - 3.361421)^3 + 0.309466r - 1.095655$
W............	<2.65	$-4.198744(r - 3.017659) + 0.607270r - 2.519887$
	2.65–3.32	$-0.235362(r - 5.610045) + 5.091237r - 20.297978$
	3.32–3.80	$-4.254329(r - 3.446692) + 1.593157r - 5.866373$
C-Fe........	<2.523	$-3.365(2.236 - r)^3 + 0.886r - 2.156$
N-V.........	<2.611	$-5.705(2.305 - r)^3 + 1.596r - 4.005$

listed in Table 1. The analytic form is that of three smoothly joined cubic equations. At close distances this potential joins with matching value and slope the potential used for radiation-damage calculations (2). Furthermore, it was constructed so that it yields the short-range contribution to the elastic moduli, and goes to zero with zero slope at a cutoff distance midway between the second- and third-nearest-neighbor distances.

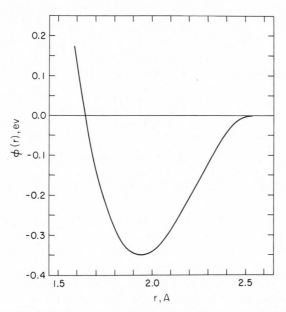

Fig. 2. The C-Fe interaction potential used in the present calculations

A V-V potential and a W-W potential have been constructed by use of the method used for the Fe-Fe potential, and they are also listed in Table 1. No potentials at close distances are available for V and W from radiation-damage studies, so the present potentials were simply made to rise rapidly and smoothly at close separations. The reported results are quite insensitive to this part of the potential, and so the fact that it is not as well determined as that for the Fe-Fe potential should not be troublesome.

A C-Fe and a N-V potential also have been constructed. The analytic form for these potentials is a single cubic equation. They are also listed in Table 1, and the C-Fe potential is shown in Fig. 2. The derivation of these potentials is associated with the results and will be discussed later.

Pure Metals

Vacancies in α-Fe. As might well be expected, the stable single-vacancy configuration consisted of one atom missing from a normal lattice site. The nearest neighboring atoms of the vacancy relaxed radially inward toward the vacancy by about 2.5% of a lattice constant. Some more-distant neighbors relax inward and some relax away from the vacancy, but the net effect is a small inward displacement. The vacancy migration process consisted of the jumping of the nearest neighboring atom of the vacancy from its relaxed position into the vacancy site, thus filling the old vacancy and leaving a new vacancy behind. This process may also be thought of as the vacancy migrating by jumping to a nearest neighboring lattice site. The migration energy was found to be 0.68 ev, and the activation volume for motion was negligible.

Divacancy configurations, in which two single vacancies are in close proximity to each other, also were investigated, and it was found that the most stable divacancy was that in which two vacancies were at second nearest neighboring lattice sites. The binding energy for this configuration was 0.20 ev. The binding energy for vacancies at nearest neighboring sites was 0.13 ev. Divacancy migration was by a stepping process in which one of the vacancies of a divacancy pair moved as a single vacancy in each step. In the first step the divacancies separated from second nearest neighboring lattice sites to fourth neighboring sites, and in the second step they closed up again to second neighboring sites. The migration energy of 0.66 ev is very similar to the single-vacancy migration energy.

Interstitials in α-Fe. The interstitial story is somewhat more complicated than the vacancy problem, because there are many more different possible interstitial configurations and migration paths. It turned out that the stable, or minimum-energy, configuration was that in which two

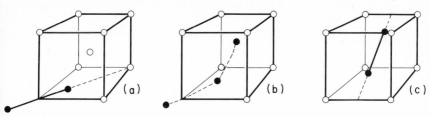

Fig. 3. The Fe interstitial migration process. (a) and (c) are stable configurations and (b) is the saddle-point configuration.

atoms are symmetrically split in a ⟨110⟩ direction at a distance of 0.37 lattice constant from a vacant normal lattice site. Some metastable configurations, that is configurations at which the energy is a local minimum, also were found. The migration process is rather awkward to describe because it does not have much symmetry. If the initial configuration is a [110] split interstitial centered at (000), then the next equilibrium configuration after one jump might be a [101] split interstitial centered at (½ ½ ½). This migration sequence is shown in Fig. 3. The activation energy for motion was found to be 0.33 ev, and the activation volume for motion was found to be 0.1 atomic volume. The activation energy for rotation of a split interstitial keeping its center fixed, that is, reorientation without migration, was also 0.33 ev, the same as the motion energy. Migration along a close-packed direction, that is, the so-called crowdion migration, was found to have a very small activation energy, 0.04 ev. The crowdion configuration was just on the borderline of being metastable.

There are also many possible di-interstitial configurations, and the calculations showed that many of them are metastable. Di-interstitial configurations consist of two split single interstitials in reasonably close proximity to each other: no instances that resulted in more complex configurations were found. The most stable di-interstitial is shown in Fig. 4(a). It consists of two split interstitials parallel to each other at nearest neighboring lattice sites, with their axes perpendicular to the line joining their centers. The binding energy of this configuration relative to two separated interstitials was 1.08 ev. The migration of di-interstitials is by a stepping process in which the two split interstitials partially dissociate. This migration process is shown in Fig. 4, and it should be noted that the interstitial moving in each step roughly follows a single interstitial migration path. The di-interstitial motion energy was 0.18 ev, and the activation volume for motion was 0.3 atomic volume.

Vacancies and Interstitials in W. Calculations similar to those made for vacancies and interstitials in α-Fe also have been made for W. The stable configurations in W are the same as those in α-Fe, although the

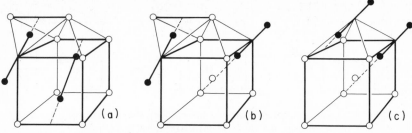

Fig. 4. The Fe di-interstitial migration process. (a) and (c) are stable configurations and (b) is the intermediate metastable configuration between (a) and (c). There are saddle-point configurations between (a) and (b) and between (b) and (c).

relaxation of the atoms around the defects is somewhat altered: the nearest neighboring atoms of the vacancy relax inward by 2.0% of a lattice constant, and the atoms in the split-interstitial configuration are 0.36 lattice constant from the center of the split. The migration paths for W are the same as those for α-Fe, and the migration energies were found to be 2.00 ev for vacancies and 1.07 ev for interstitials. The activation energy for rotation of a split interstitial keeping its center fixed, that is, reorientation without migration, was 1.36 ev, which is considerably higher than the motion energy. Migration along a tight-packed row, that is, so-called crowdion migration, was found to have a very low activation energy, about 0.05 ev, but such configurations were very unstable and decayed rapidly to the split configuration.

C Interstitials in α-Fe

The C-Fe Potential.   The basic bcc model used earlier was retained for the impurity-interstitial calculations, and only minor modifications to the computer program were required to allow for the insertion of impurity defects. The development of the C-Fe interaction potential was an intricate process, though. First it was found that no purely repulsive interaction with a reasonable interatomic distance could yield the C migration energy of 0.86 ev in α-Fe (4). For example, in the instance of a hard-sphere interaction, the tetrahedral configuration (Fig. 5b) was most stable for small impurities with a radius less than about 0.5 A, the octahedral configuration (Fig. 5a) was most stable for larger impurities with a radius between about 0.5 A and 0.9 A, and the tetrahedral configuration was again the most stable for still larger impurities with a radius greater than

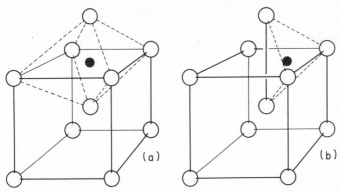

Fig. 5. The stable and the saddle-point configurations for C in Fe. (a) has octahedral symmetry and (b) has tetrahedral symmetry. The Fe lattice displacements are not shown.

about 0.9 A. This pattern was found to exist for all the repulsive interactions, and for a radius of about 0.7 A the migration energy was greatest, but was only about 0.5 ev.

A cubic equation was then tried for the C-Fe interaction. This potential was chosen to be similar in form to that for the Fe-Fe interaction, that is, strongly repulsive at close separations, having a minimum (which implies strong chemical binding between the C and Fe atoms), and then going to zero value with zero slope. A cubic equation has four coefficients, but the last condition, zero value and slope at the same point, reduces this to three independent coefficients. The three experimental conditions that were matched to uniquely determine the potential were a C motion energy of 0.86 ev (4), a zero activation volume for motion (5) and a C binding energy to a lattice vacancy of 0.41 ev (6). These conditions were matched by a trial-and-error process of running the motion and vacancy binding calculations on the computer for a variety of potentials until one that fit the conditions was found. The resulting potential is given in Table 1 and is shown in Fig. 2. The location of the minimum, the depth of the minimum and the cutoff distance might be considered as three critical parameters associated with the potential. Variation in the shape of the potential without altering these parameters is expected to have very little effect upon the calculation; that is, only the general shape of the potential is important and a cubic function is not unique in the reproduction of the experimental values. The minimum in the Fe-C potential occurs at a separation distance of 1.94 A, and the Pauling theory of atomic radii for metals (7) predicts that the C-Fe distance for a C atom surrounded by four Fe atoms is 1.936 A. Thus the position of the minimum obtained for this potential seems to be quite reasonable.

The C-Fe Results.   The experimental values of the motion energy and activation volume for motion of C in α-Fe were used as inputs in arriving at a C-Fe interaction. In matching these conditions it was found that the octahedral configuration (Fig. 5a) was stable and that the migration path was a straight line from octahedral to tetrahedral to octahedral.

In an octahedral configuration the C atom has its two closest neighbors in the [± 1, 0, 0] directions, and the lattice shows a tendency toward expansion in these directions. The four second nearest neighbors of the C atom are in the [0, ± 1, ± 1] directions and are pulled in slightly toward the C atom. The lattice shows a tendency toward contraction in these directions. This general displacement pattern, expansion in the [± 1, 0, 0] directions and contraction in the [0, ± 1, ± 1] directions, is maintained for the atoms near the defect. This displacement field will tend to alter a sphere to a prolate spheroid with its axis of rotation in the [1, 0, 0] direction and will give rise to stress-induced ordering. Powers and Doyle (8) report the relaxation strength of C in Fe as 0.57 per at. % C at one tenth the melting temperature. A comparison of the present calculations with this experimental result may be made by use of the treatment of Huntington and Johnson (9). The "strength" factor C used in the spheroidal displacement field given by Huntington and Johnson should be 0.140 to give the experimental relaxation strength. A value of C was found from the calculated displacements by taking an average of the values of C required to reproduce the displacements for the closest 108 Fe atoms to the C impurity. This procedure gave a value of 0.128 for C, which is in excellent agreement with experiment.

Volume-expansion results are not so encouraging, however. The calculated value of the volume expansion per C atom (equivalent to the partial molar volume for very small concentrations) is 0.33 Fe atomic volume, whereas the experimental value is roughly 0.8 $\pm$ 0.2 Fe atomic volume (10). Thus the calculated value is small by a factor of about two or three.

The activation volume can be defined as (11)

$$V_m = \frac{\partial G}{\partial P}\bigg|_T = \frac{\partial H}{\partial P}\bigg|_T - T\frac{\partial S}{\partial P}\bigg|_T$$

Neglecting the entropy factor and taking the activation energy calculated in the model as the enthalpy, one can then write

$$V_m \cong \Delta E_m/\Delta P$$

The activation volume for C migration was forced to be zero in deriving the C-Fe potential. An excellent check on the consistency of the model may be made by calculating the activation volume by use of this thermodynamic definition. This was done by applying a pressure on the crystallite and recalculating the motion energy. The activation volume calculated by this procedure was $V_m = -0.004$ Fe atomic volume, which is well within the experimental limits. There is no obvious analytic link between the activation volume calculated by these thermodynamic considerations and that obtained by comparing the formation volumes of the stable and saddle-point configurations. Thus the agreement here indicates excellent internal consistency within the model.

A number of calculations have been carried out for the interaction of C interstitials in α-Fe with Fe interstitials and vacancies. It was found that a C interstitial and an Fe interstitial (split configuration) form a stable complex with a binding energy of 0.5 ev. Because the Fe-interstitial migration energy was found to be about 0.3 ev, this complex can be formed by a migrating Fe interstitial becoming trapped by a C interstitial and should require an energy of about 0.8 ev for the Fe interstitial to escape from the trap. No internal friction should be observed with this complex. This C-interstitial–Fe-interstitial complex can trap a second Fe interstitial with a binding energy of about 1.0 ev. This complex also would probably not show any internal friction.

The C-Fe interaction potential was chosen so as to give a C-interstitial–Fe-vacancy binding energy of 0.41 ev. The C atom did not stay at the center of the vacancy, but moved over to any one of six equivalent sides of the vacancy. The resulting configuration can be seen by removing the body-centered Fe atom in Fig. 5 (a) and moving the C atom downward toward the vacancy by about 14% of a lattice constant. The strains in this configuration are very small, and at first it was thought that any resulting internal-friction peak would be negligibly small. Wagenblast and Swartz have evidence (12) that this configuration does yield a damping peak, though, and so a relaxation-strength calculation similar to that for the octahedral configuration for C in α-Fe was carried out. The experiments of Wagenblast and Swartz indicate that a relaxation strength of about 3% of that for interstitial C is associated with the C-vacancy complex, and the calculation yields about half of this value. When the small values in both the experiment and the calculation are considered, this is excellent agreement. The calculated reorientation energy was 0.78 ev.

Some calculations in which two C atoms are in close proximity within the Fe lattice also have been carried out. No C-C interaction was used, so the results primarily reflect the interaction of the local strains near the two

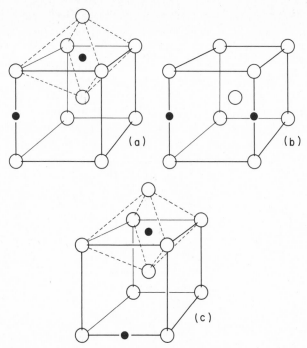

Fig. 6. The three bound di-C configurations. The binding energies for (a), (b) and (c) are 0.13, 0.11 and 0.08 ev, respectively. The Fe lattice displacements are not shown.

C atoms. Three di-C complexes were found to have an appreciable binding energy. They are shown in Fig. 6 (a), (b) and (c), and have binding energies of 0.13, 0.11 and 0.08 ev, respectively. Fisher's calculations (13) indicated that two configurations have significant binding; the configuration in Fig. 6 (a), which is bound by 0.07 ev, and that in Fig. 6 (c), which is bound by 0.11 ev. The configurations in Fig. 6 (a) and Fig. 6 (b) have strain fields that should give rise to internal damping. The energy calculated for reorientation was 0.91 ev and 0.94 ev, respectively. This is between the single-C migration energy, 0.86 ev, and the di-C dissociation energies, 0.99 ev and 0.97 ev, respectively. Keefer and Wert (14) have studied the clustering of C and N in α-Fe by use of anelastic techniques. Their data for N confirm the existence of di-N, for which they report a binding energy of 0.07 ev and a reorientation energy of 0.06 ev above that for single-N migration. The results for C are not as definitive, but indicate that the corresponding di-C values are quite comparable: a small di-C binding energy and a di-C motion energy slightly above single-C motion energy. The calculations are in excellent agreement with these experimental results.

The potentials used in these calculations are intended to describe the Fe-Fe and the C-Fe interaction in α-Fe. It is difficult to tell how much they would have to be modified to describe the corresponding interactions for the various phases of C in Fe, but some rough calculations indicate that these potentials can be applied in other situations to a fair approximation. Of great interest is Fe_3C, or cementite, which is the stable precipitate of C in α-Fe. A calculation was made in which the Lipson and Petch (15) values for the Fe_3C lattice constant were used, but the 12 Fe atoms and the four C atoms were allowed to relax to minimize the Fe_3C energy. The resulting changes in the cementite structure have been reported elsewhere (3), and are noticeably different than the Lipson and Petch values, especially in the placement of the C atoms. The energy of the Fe_3C configuration, that is, the average energy of three Fe atoms in Fe_3C plus the total C-Fe interactions in Fe_3C per C atom, can be compared with the corresponding energy for inserting a C atom in α-Fe, that is, the average energy of three Fe atoms in α-Fe plus the energy required to insert one C atom. The energy of solution of C in α-Fe relative to Fe_3C is the difference between these energies, and was found to be 0.38 ev. The corresponding experimental value is not too well known, but ranges from about 0.4 to 0.9 ev, with the higher values probably being more reliable. The experimental data are discussed elsewhere by Smith (16). When it is considered that the result is the difference between two moderately large numbers, which in turn are the sum of many small numbers (energy per bond) that depend critically upon the potentials, the agreement is satisfactory.

N Interstitials in V

The C-Fe model gives a zero activation volume when determined by either of two independent methods of calculation. It was felt that the possibility existed that the zero activation-volume result was implicitly built into the model. The calculation for N in V was carried out to study the activation-volume problem, and also to find out whether or not the model can be extended to other metals.

A N-V interaction potential was developed by scaling the Fe-C potential and matching the N motion energy in V. The Pauling V-N distance for a N atom surrounded by four V atoms is 2.00 A (7). From this it was decided to scale the distance axis for the Fe-C potential by a factor of 2.00 to 1.94. The energy axis was scaled to yield the experimental migration energy for N in V of 1.5 ev (8). The resulting potential is given in

Table 1. The V-V potential discussed above was used between the lattice atoms.

The resulting migration path of N in V also is from octahedral to tetrahedral to octahedral. The calculations gave 0.185 V atomic volume for the activation volume for motion whereas the experimental value is 0.135 V atomic volume (17). Clearly the model can yield large activation volumes and appears to be capable of satisfactory extension to other metals.

The relaxation strength of N in V was determined by use of the procedure used for C in Fe. Powers and Doyle (8) report this relaxation strength as 0.33 per at. % N at one tenth the melting temperature. To match this result the spheroidal "strength" factor should be 0.101, and the calculation yields 0.084. Here again only an order-of-magnitude agreement was required, and the results are entirely satisfactory.

Discussion

Very little experimental data pertaining to interstitials and vacancies in α-Fe are available. Experiments on the isochronal annealing of resistivity after irradiation with electrons at energies slightly above the threshold for damage by Lucasson and Walker (18) indicate that there is a defect that freely migrates with an energy of about 0.30 ev. The calculated value for single interstitials was 0.33 ev, which is in very good agreement. The defect that Lucasson and Walker are observing anneals out of Fe in 10 min at 120 K. In an internal-friction experiment by Wagenblast and Damask (19) that searched for a relaxation associated with the interstitial in irradiated Fe, the irradiation was performed at 140 K and the relaxation was looked for at higher temperatures, with negative results. These findings are consistent with the interpretation that the defect seen by Lucasson and Walker is the α-Fe interstitial.

In a series of experiments measuring resistivity, magnetic aftereffect and stored energy in α-Fe after neutron irradiation (20), workers at the Centre d'Etudes Nucléaires de Grenoble have concluded that interstitials in α-Fe migrate with an energy of 0.25 ev, and have a stress field with a [100] orientation. The energy is in excellent agreement with the present calculations, but the orientation is in disagreement. The cause for this discrepancy has not yet been resolved. Furthermore, they conclude that di-interstitials migrate at several different energy values, 0.22, 0.28 and 0.34 ev, and do not have [100] symmetry. Different migration channels were not looked for in the calculation, but for the lowest-energy path, the calculated results are considered to be in excellent agreement with the experiments.

No direct experimental evidence is available for the motion energy of

Table 2. Summary of Results for Pure Metals

Defect	α-Fe energies, ev			W energies, ev	
	Motion	Reorientation	Binding	Motion	Reorientation
Interstitial..........	0.33	0.33	....	1.07	1.36
Crowdion...........	0.04	....	....	0.05	....
Di-interstitial........	0.18	0.18	1.08	....	....
Vacancy............	0.68	....	....	2.00	....
Divacancy..........	0.66	0.78	0.20	....	....

Table 3. Summary of Results for Impurity Interstitials

Property	C in Fe		N in V	
	Calculated	Experimental	Calculated	Experimental
Migration energy, ev.........	0.86(a)	0.86	1.5(a)	1.5
Activation volume, ev........	0.00(a)	0.00	0.185	0.135
C-vacancy binding........... energy, ev	0.41(a)	0.41	....	....
Impurity–metal-atom......... distance, A	1.94	1.936	2.00(a)	2.00
Coefficient for relaxation...... strength	0.128	0.140	0.084	0.101
Formation volume, Ω.........	0.33	$\overset{\sim}{<}1$	0.08	....
Activation volume ($\Delta E_m/\Delta P$),. Ω	0.00	0.00	....	....
C–Fe-interstitial............. binding energy, ev	0.5	....	....	....
C-vacancy relaxation......... strength	0.002	0.004	....	....
Di-C binding energy, ev......	0.13	0.08	....	....
Di-C motion energy above.... E_m, ev	0.05	....	....	....
Heat of solution relative...... to Fe_3C	0.38	0.4–0.9	....	....

(a) Agreement with experiment insured by the model.

vacancies in Fe. Damask *et al.* (21) in an extensive study of C in α-Fe did not find a vacancy annealing stage at temperatures that would correspond to a motion energy of 0.68 ev, and the model that they proposed to explain their results assumes that vacancies move at a temperature corresponding to a motion energy greater than about 1.0 ev.

There are also no definitive experiments for W. Thompson (22) has found an annealing stage after neutron irradiation between 350 and 450 C with an activation energy of 1.7 ev. Schultz has quenched W and reports a vacancy migration energy of 1.93 ev and has measured the resistivity annealing of cold-worked W. In the latter work he reports an activation energy of 1.47 ev in the range of 200 to 250 K and a spread of activation energies of 1.70 to 1.95 ev in the range of 300 to 500 K. The calculations and the experiments do not yield full agreement or severe disagreement, and thus no firm conclusions may be drawn regarding W.

The basic numerical results from these calculations are summarized in Table 2 for the pure metals and in Table 3 for the impurity defects. As is easily seen from these tables, there is still a great deal of experimental and theoretical work to be done. Calculations such as those described in this paper are at a rather elementary level, but do show promise of being very helpful for the understanding of many properties of metals.

Acknowledgments. It is a pleasure to acknowledge stimulating discussions with Dr. A. C. Damask and Dr. G. J. Dienes and to thank them for many useful suggestions during the course of this work.

This work was performed under the auspices of the U. S. Atomic Energy Commission.

References

1   H. B. Huntington, Phys Rev, **91,** 1092 (1953); L. Tewordt, Phys Rev, **109, 61** (1958); J. B. Gibson, A. N. Goland, M. Milgram and G. H. Vineyard, Phys Rev, **120,** 1229 (1960); A. Seeger, E. Mann and R. v. Jan, J Phys Chem Solids, **23,** 639 (1962); R. A. Johnson and E. Brown, Phys Rev, **127,** 446 (1962)

2   C. Erginsoy, G. H. Vineyard and A. Englert, Phys Rev, **133,** A595 (1964)

3   R. A. Johnson and A. C. Damask, Acta Met, **12,** 443 (1964); R. A. Johnson, Phys Rev, **134,** A1329 (1964); R. A. Johnson, G. J. Dienes and A. C. Damask, Acta Met, **12,** 1215 (1964)

4   C. A. Wert, Phys Rev, **79,** 601 (1950); R. H. Doremus, Trans AIME, **218,** 596 (1960); H. Wagenblast and A. C. Damask, J Phys Chem Solids, **23,** 221 (1962); F. E. Fujita and A. C. Damask, Acta Met, **12,** 331 (1964)

5   A. J. Bosman, P. E. Brommer and G. W. Rathman, Physica, **23,** 1001 (1957); J. Bass and D. Lazarus, J Phys Chem Solids, **23,** 1820 (1962)

6   R. A. Arndt and A. C. Damask, Acta Met, **12,** 341 (1964)

7   L. Pauling, Proc Roy Soc London, **A196,** 343 (1949)

8   R. W. Powers and M. V. Doyle, J Appl Phys, **30,** 514 (1959)

9   H. B. Huntington and R. A. Johnson, Acta Met, **10,** 281 (1962)

10   W. B. Pearson, Lattice Spacings and Structures of Metals and Alloys, Pergamon Press, London, 1958, p 919

11   N. H. Nachtrieb, J. A. Weil, E. Catalano and A. W. Lawson, J Chem Phys, **20,** 1189 (1952)

12   H. Wagenblast and J. C. Swartz, Acta Met, **13,** 42 (1965)

13   J. C. Fisher, Acta Met, **6,** 13 (1958)

14   D. Keefer and C. Wert, J Phys Soc Japan, **18,** Suppl III, 110 (1963); Acta Met, **11,** 489 (1963)

15   H. Lipson and N. J. Petch, J Iron Steel Inst, **142,** 95 (1940)

16 R. P. Smith, Trans AIME, **224,** 105 (1962)
17 G. W. Tichelaar, R. V. Coleman and D. Lazarus, Phys Rev, **121,** 748 (1961)
18 P. G. Lucasson and R. M. Walker, Phys Rev, **127,** 485 (1962)
19 H. Wagenblast and A. C. Damask, Acta Met, **10,** 333 (1962)
20 C. Minier-Cassayre and D. Dautreppe, Compt Rend, **256,** 2368 (1963); P. Moser and D. Dautreppe, J Phys, **24,** 516 (1963); E. Bonjour and P. Moser, Compt Rend, **257,** 1256 (1963); C. Minier-Cassayre, Compt Rend, **258,** 541 (1964); D. Dautreppe, V. Hivert, P. Moser and A. Salvi, Compt Rend, **258,** 4539 (1964)
21 H. Wagenblast and A. C. Damask, J Phys Chem Solids, **23,** 221 (1962); F. E. Fujita and A. C. Damask, Acta Met, **12,** 331 (1964); R. A. Arndt and A. C. Damask, Acta Met, **12,** 341 (1964); H. Wagenblast, F. E. Fujita and A. C. Damask, Acta Met, **12,** 347 (1964)
22 M. W. Thompson, Phil Mag, **5,** 278 (1960)
23 H. Schultz, Acta Met, **12,** 761 (1964)
24 H. Schultz, Acta Met, **12,** 649 (1964)

PART 6
Discussion

Introduction and Survey of Experimental Work

Discussion of Chapter 1 (p 3)
by A. D. Le Claire

D. LAZARUS (University of Illinois, Urbana, Ill.): I believe there is an error in your analysis relating to the impurity concentration required for a given vacancy-impurity binding energy. The important term that must remain constant is the total diffusion coefficient, not the slopes or pre-exponential factors. Accordingly, if the binding energy of a vacancy and impurity is decreased, there must be more, not fewer, impurities present, to explain the observed enhanced diffusivity. Your expression indicates the opposite conclusion.

A. D. LE CLAIRE (AERE, Harwell, England): No. I think everything is all right. If instead of taking $B \sim E_f$ in Eq 10, as Kidson did, we put $B < E_f$, then the term $\{1 + (1/z) \exp [(E_f - B)/RT]\}^{-1}$ becomes $z \exp [-(E_f - B)/RT]$, which is usually less than unity. But at the same time we must decrease the activation energy $H_m^{(1)}$ in the w_1 term of Eq 10 because we have to account for the same observed value of Q_2 as well as of A_2, and $Q_2 = H_m^{(1)} + E_f - B$. Thus, in going from the $B \sim E_f$ model to the one in which $B < E_f$ the $\{1 + (1/z) \exp [(E_f - B)/RT]\}^{-1}$ term contributes $z \exp [-(E_f - B)/RT]$ in place of unity as before, and the w_1 term contributes an additional $\exp [+(E_f - B)/RT]$. The net effect is to bring a z into the expression for A_2 that was not there before, so the value of c required to account for the observed A_2 must be *decreased* by a factor z. Other effects contribute to the change in c too, as shown in Eq 16.

M. S. WECHSLER (Oak Ridge National Laboratory, Oak Ridge, Tenn.): I wonder if we could have some comment on the possibility of another mechanism for the nonlinear $\ln D$ versus $1/T$ behavior that has been observed for some of the bcc metals. I have in mind that next-nearest-neighbor [100] vacancy jumps, as well as nearest-neighbor [111] jumps, may contribute to the diffusion. The activation energies for the two types of jumps would be different, and the result would be a non-Arrhenius temperature dependence for D. It would appear that a competition between nearest-neighbor and next-nearest-neighbor jumping would be more likely for bcc metals than for fcc metals. For the nearest-neighbor jump in bcc metals, the jumping atom must go through *two* barrier rings (equilateral triangles at one third and two thirds of the nearest-neighbor distance), whereas for the next-nearest jump only one square barrier ring is involved. On the other hand, there is only one barrier ring for both nearest-neighbor and next-nearest-neighbor jumps for fcc metals.

A. D. Le Claire: What you say is certainly possible. Competing [111] and [100] jumps could lead to a non-Arrhenius behavior, just as competing cation vacancy and interstitialcy jumps do in AgBr. But I do not think this will account for the results on Ti, Zr etc. because there is no reason why either one of these jumps should have the abnormally low A value required in the second term of Eq 8.

The double-humped potential barrier for [111] jumps will be of no great importance if the central minimum is shallow, and what calculations there are on this suggest it is very shallow, for example, 0.04 ev in Fe, so that it is much less than kT at diffusion temperatures (Johnson, Phys Rev, June, 1964).

As for distinguishing between the two types of jumps, the most likely possibility is by measurement of the correlation factor. This will be 0.65 for the 6-coordination [100] jumps but 0.72 for the 8-coordination [111] jumps, so in principle the difference could be observed but it would be a difficult experiment.

H. B. Huntington (Rensselaer Polytechnic Institute, Troy, N.Y.): In connection with the hypothesis of nearest-neighbor jumping, it occurs to me that there may be a problem here in explaining the high rate of impurity diffusion on the basis of impurity-vacancy complexes. The geometry is different from the fcc lattice in that two sites neighboring an atom in a bcc metal are not mutual neighbors. There is bound to be a certain probability for dissolution of the impurity-vacancy complex whenever the vacancy jumps about the impurity atom.

A. D. Le Claire: Yes, this is true.

Discussion of Chapter 2 (p 27)
by D. Graham

P. G. Shewmon (Carnegie Institute of Technology, Pittsburgh, Pa.): One of the hypotheses for this break in ln D versus $1/T$ is that there is a marked association between vacancies and some magical but unspecified impurity or impurities. To make things simple, let's say that one impurity accounts for the break in all of your plots of ln D versus $1/T$. Out of the hypothesis that one impurity is doing the binding with the vacancies in every instance, would you really expect to get as much variation as you do?

D. GRAHAM (NASA, Westlake, Ohio): The exact nature of the defect is required if we are to predict the position of the maximum curvature in the Arrhenius plots for the various solutes. If it is assumed that the process occurring at lower temperature is the same as that for normal single-vacancy motion except that a temperature-independent concentration of vacancies exists, then one might expect those solutes with high Q values to exhibit a break close to the melting temperature and those with lower Q values to show less curvature, with the break moving toward lower temperatures. Most of the solutes obey this trend but notable exceptions are P^{32} and Mo^{99}.

P. G. SHEWMON: Can you go the other way with the analysis and point out that the impurity-vacancy effect requires so many "magical" impurities that the hypothesis is useless?

D. GRAHAM: No, for we have only considered the position of the break in the most simple manner. It is unlikely that the vacancy-impurity-tracer complex can be regarded as a simple vacancy-tracer pair. A detailed knowledge of the configuration and relative exchange rates of the components would be necessary to estimate the temperatures at which thermal-equilibrium vacancies become more numerous than those associated with the impurity complex.

Discussion of Chapter 3 (p 35)
by T. S. Lundy *et al.*

G. J. DIENES (Brookhaven National Laboratory, Upton, N.Y.): I would like to make some comments on the temperature dependence of the free energy of activation. All the theories (1–3) of diffusion proposed so far lead to an exponential temperature dependence for the diffusion coefficient, D, given by

$$D = D_0 \exp\left(-G/RT\right) \qquad (1)$$

where G is the free energy of activation for the process and may be a function of temperature. If one assumes G to be a function of temperature, there is considerable restriction on the form of the effective activation energy, a point already made some years ago in a somewhat different connection (4). Specifically it can be shown that if Eq 1 is valid, then the effective activation energy, E_{eff}, defined by

$$E_{eff} = -d \ln D/d\beta; \; \beta = 1/RT \qquad (2)$$

does not contain a term linear in the temperature.

By differentiation of Eq 1

$$E_{\text{eff}} = G(T) - T \, dG(T)/dT \tag{3}$$

Let $G(T)$ be expressed as a power expansion in T around $T = 0$ (the same result is obtained if one expands around $T = T_0$)

$$G(T) = G_0 + G_1T + G_2T^2 + \cdots \tag{4}$$

where

$$G_1 = (\partial G/\partial T)_P, \ G_2 = (\partial^2 G/\partial T^2)_P/2, \ \cdots$$

From the standard thermodynamic relations, $G_1 = -S$ and $G_2 = -(\partial S/\partial T)_P$, where S is the entropy of activation. By differentiation of Eq 4 one obtains

$$dG/dT = G_1 + 2G_2T + 3G_3T^2 + \cdots \tag{5}$$

Upon substitution of Eq 4 and 5 in Eq 3 the terms linear in T *cancel* and E_{eff} is given by

$$E_{\text{eff}} = G_0 - G_2T^2 + \cdots \tag{6}$$

The argument given above is valid for any rate process, and the conclusion is that a linearly temperature-dependent component of the measured effective activation energy is not compatible with Eq 1. All the theories so far proposed for diffusion lead to an exponential temperature dependence described by Eq 1. Within this framework, then, a linear temperature dependence in E_{eff} is not acceptable.

Equation 6 can be fitted accurately to the diffusion data (5, 6) for C in Fe with a sensible value of G_2 (about -2.4×10^{-6} cal/°K²), and this may well be an example of a single process characterized by a temperature-dependent activation energy. Other diffusion processes in bcc metals are perhaps better described by the sum of two exponentials, as suggested by Kidson (7), indicating a change in mechanism as a function of temperature.

1   G. H. Vineyard, J Phys Chem Solids, **3**, 121 (1957)
2   S. A. Rice, Phys Rev, **112**, 804 (1958)
3   R. E. Howard and A. B. Lidiard, Reports on Progress in Physics, **XXVII**, p 161–240 (1964)
4   G. H. Vineyard and G. J. Dienes, Phys Rev, **93**, 265 (1954)
5   R. P. Smith, Trans AIME, **224**, 111 (1962)
6   C. G. Homan, Acta Met, **12**, 1071 (1964)
7   G. V. Kidson, Can J Phys, **61**, 1563 (1963)

C. T. Tomizuka (University of Arizona, Dept. of Physics, Tucson, Ariz.): David Styris and I found this near-surface effect in Cu. (A description of our work has been published elsewhere.) Also, we observed a similar effect in Bi. This near-surface effect appears in Bi self-diffusion even at high hydrostatic pressures (up to 9000 kbars). The first region of the penetration plot is the near-surface region and is almost linear; the second region, which also is linear in the square of the distance, looks like the conventional volume diffusion; the tail region is somewhat irregular. The general picture agrees very well with Lundy's work and with his explanation.

P. G. Shewmon: Do you mean that you have three regions in a penetration plot instead of two, as reported here, and that your second region agrees with volume diffusion?

C. T. Tomizuka: It is a matter of classification and interpretation. Many people including Seith have been misled by the near-surface effect, interpreting it as the volume diffusion. Sometimes one observes the near-surface region and the volume-diffusion region. The third region is occasionally observed but it is not very reproducible. All three regions could exist within a micron from the surface. Cu and Bi, of course, are not pertinent subjects of the bcc conference, but I thought I would mention them as examples of the generality of Lundy's observation.

T. S. Lundy (Oak Ridge National Laboratory, Oak Ridge, Tenn.): For a particular set of experimental conditions, the probability that one or more of the different regions of diffusion will be missed entirely is large. We believe, however, that in the general case there are three regions—near-surface, volume and short-circuiting. The near-surface region was not evident for diffusion in Cb and Ta. It is possible, of course, that under certain circumstances the short-circuiting region might be subdivided into grain-boundary and dislocation parts as suggested by Dr. James.

D. W. James (Westinghouse Research and Development Center, Pittsburgh, Pa.): With further regard to the subdivision of penetration curves into two or more components, I would like to report the following observation made at Manchester University, England, during some recent grain-boundary diffusion studies. Penetration curves for grain-boundary self-diffusion (Fe[59]) in α-Fe, obtained by normal sectioning techniques, showed definite "diffusion tails" similar to those indicated previously in this discussion. This effect was noticed in all specimens although the magnitude was not entirely reproducible. It therefore appears that in addition to the surface-penetration, bulk-diffusion, and grain-boundary or dislocation sections of the penetration curve, there is a fourth section of, as yet, undetermined origin.

G. V. Kidson (Chalk River Nuclear Laboratory, Chalk River, Ont., Canada): We at Chalk River suspected that the unusual penetration curves reported by Lundy and his group in their study of diffusion in Ta could be due to surface effects. We have carried out similar experiments by use of the anodizing-stripping technique on single crystals of Au, because we felt there would be no problem of surface contamination in this case. We found penetration profiles having the two-stage shape that was characteristic of those reported by Lundy for Ta. Diffusion coefficients deduced from the initial portion of these curves agreed well with values extrapolated from high-temperature measurements. We tentatively attributed the more deeply penetrating tail to diffusion along dislocations. In order to check this assumption, Ni powder was sprinkled onto the crystal with the aim of increasing the dislocation density near the surface. The diffusion experiment was then repeated. The total amount of tracer contained in the tail portion of the curve was found to be greatly increased. The single crystal was subsequently annealed at high temperature to decrease the dislocation content, and the diffusion measurements were again repeated. The shape of the penetration curve returned to that of the original experiment. We consider this to be strong evidence that the deeply penetrating section of the curve can be associated with short-circuit diffusion along dislocations.

G. J. Dienes: Could you comment on the type of diffusion penetration profiles obtained in Zr at low temperatures? It has already been mentioned that there is a possibility that volume diffusion is not being observed.

T. S. Lundy: All of the penetration profiles for diffusion in Zr, including those for the low temperatures, were linear when plotted as $\ln A$ versus x^2. This linearity is generally believed to indicate that volume diffusion dominates the transport process.

Discussion of Chapter 4 (p 51)
by C. S. Hartley *et al.*

D. Lazarus: I am somewhat confused about your use of the term "negative diffusivity." You surely do not imply a nonphysical case in which the concentration gradient increases with time. If you are referring only to the relative shift between the Matano interface and the markers, following the Darken equation, this is not particularly meaningful. Le Claire and Manning have shown that there is another extremely important term, the "drift" term, that must be included, particularly in instances of large concentration gradients.

C. S. Hartley (WPAFB-AF Materials Laboratory, Wright-Patterson

AFB, Ohio): The use of the term "negative intrinsic diffusivity" is explained in the text in connection with the simultaneous solutions to the Darken relations:

$$\tilde{D} = N_1 D_2 + N_2 D_1 \tag{1}$$

and

$$Xm/2t = (D_2 - D_1)(dN_1/dX) \tag{2}$$

where t is the diffusion time and N_i is the atom fraction of the ith species. All we mean is that in some instances of the observed marker shift (taken as the distance between the Matano interface and the markers, Xm), simultaneous solution of Eq 1 and 2 yields a negative value for the intrinsic D of the slower moving component. Equivalently we may say that the product $N_1 D_2$ for the faster moving component is greater than the observed $\tilde{D}$. Physically this does not mean that the concentration gradient increases with time; rather it implies that the net flux of the slower moving species is in the *same* direction as its concentration gradient rather than in the *opposite* direction as in the "normal" case.

The reason for this must certainly be ascribed to a drift force that is larger than the force caused by the chemical potential gradient due to the slower moving species and is opposite to this force. As Dr. Manning points out, such a drift force exists because there is a net flux of vacancies from one end of the couple to the other, and such a flux would exist even if vacancies were in thermal equilibrium throughout the diffusion zone, because of the variation in equilibrium vacancy concentration with composition.

The question, then, is whether the drift force produced by the equilibrium vacancies is sufficiently large to overcome the "chemical" force due to the chemical potential gradient of the slower moving component. Although we do not have sufficient data to apply rigorously Dr. Manning's treatment [J. R. Manning, Phys Rev, **124** (2), 470] to the systems studied, some approximate calculations on Cb-V and Cb-Zr alloys indicate that this correction alone would not be large enough to account for the anomalously large marker shift. However, if one postulates, as we have done, a nonequilibrium vacancy concentration due to dislocation climb or some other effect in the diffusion zone, an additional vacancy flux could result. This would produce a drift force that would add to that caused by the equilibrium vacancies. Conceivably the combination of the two drift forces could result in a net flux of the slower moving species that would require a negative apparent intrinsic diffusivity in order to satisfy the Darken relations (Eq 1 and 2). Viewed in this light, the physical meaning of a negative apparent intrinsic diffusivity is somewhat clearer. Certainly we must regard the description of diffusion behavior given by the Darken equations as incomplete; however, more detailed experiments than the ones reported here are necessary to treat the entire process of interdiffusion more rigorously.

Discussion of Chapter 5 (p 77)
by C. G. Homan

R. J. BORG (University of California, LRL, Livermore, Calif.): I do not believe that one can conclude from these arguments, or measurements, that there is no effect of magnetism upon the diffusion of C in Fe. I would suggest that the variation in the elastic properties of Fe, in the vicinity of the Curie temperature, is reflected in the non-Arrhenius behavior of the diffusion of C just as this variation appears to be reflected in the non-Arrhenius behavior of substitutional diffusion. The temperature dependence of substitutional diffusion in α-Fe is of the form shown in Fig. 1. Now the temperature variation in Young's modulus is complementary to the sigmoidal shape provided by the diffusion data. Furthermore, one can account for the unusual temperature dependence of the substitutional diffusion by combining these data with the measured values of Young's modulus by use of the Zener theory. There is no reason to suppose that variation of the elastic properties could not account for the unusual temperature dependence of the C diffusion as well.

C. G. HOMAN (Watervliet Arsenal, Watervliet, N.Y.): I agree with Dr. Borg that the abrupt magnetic transformation at about 770 C may have a small effect on the C diffusivity, but the data of this experiment and Smith's permeability data from 616 to 850 C appear to vary smoothly over this range. I also agree that the sigmoidal shape of the substitutional diffusion is complementary to the sigmoidal variation in Young's modulus. However the C diffusivity does not appear to be sigmoidal. Furthermore,

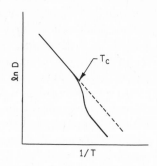

Fig. 1. Temperature dependence of substitutional diffusion in α-Fe

the recent measurements of Turkdogan, which extended the N diffusion to the δ-Fe region, have no deviation at all and thus seem incompatible with the model based on the variation in elastic properties.

A. C. DAMASK (Brookhaven Laboratory and Frankford Arsenal, Brookhaven, N.Y.): I would like to call your attention to the fact that on Friday morning Dr. Johnson and I will be discussing the radiation-damage work done at Brookhaven on the Fe-C alloys. Calculations showing that the C atom rests inside the Fe vacancy with the binding energy measured as 9 kcal/mole will be reported. I see offhand no way in our model to move the Fe vacancy with a C atom inside without shoving the C atom partially back into the Fe lattice with each step of its motion. This would increase the energy of migration of the vacancy, and therefore Homan's model requiring 10 kcal/mole energy of migration per C-vacancy pair forces the Fe vacancy to have an unreasonably low value. I don't think that these two experiments and calculations can be reconciled. Unless experiments eventually show the Fe vacancy to have a migration energy considerably below 10 kcal/mole, which I doubt, then on the basis of the Brookhaven work we must reject Homan's model.

D. LAZARUS: Is it possible that this effect is simply due to the operation of a new set of interstitial sites at sufficiently high temperature? The difference in energy between the two sites is presumably only a few tenths of an electron volt. If the high-temperature enhancement were simply the result of activation of the higher-energy configuration, it might be possible to explain the result without inventing any new mechanism for the process.

R. A. JOHNSON (Brookhaven National Laboratory, Upton, N.Y.): There are two sets of interstitial sites, octahedral and tetrahedral, but this does not necessarily imply that there are two different migration paths. In fact, I find it very difficult to explain the two-mechanism scheme when the atomic configurations are considered. For example, migration from an octahedral site to another octahedral site in all probability goes through a tetrahedral site, and thus both kinds of interstitial are involved in one migration channel.

H. B. HUNTINGTON: I agree with Dr. Johnson that the possibility of two different kinds of interstitial jumps appears remote, particularly if the tetrahedral sites are the equilibrium ones at all temperatures. The C could hardly emerge from one of these sites without passing through an octahedral site. If the octahedral site had lower energy, the reverse would not be true. Conceivably the C could move either through the tetrahedral site as its saddle point (along [100]) or directly to the neighboring octahedral site (along [110]).

Discussion of Chapter 6 (p 87)
by N. Engel

P. G. SHEWMON: Are you saying that you can plot your results in a manner similar to that used by Dr. Le Claire in his paper and get better agreement between ΔH and your parameter than he did with the more usual melting-point correlation?

N. ENGEL (Georgia Institute of Technology, Atlanta, Ga.): I would say so. I have worked on the idea to a certain extent and have developed it on a very broad basis to a qualitative agreement. It explains many things like this, things I have not known about before, which makes you a little confident. However, to make it quantitative, it is necessary to know a little more than I have presented here. To make it really quantitative I must be able to develop a formula that shows how fast the equilibrium changes with the temperature. I am sorry I have not licked that problem yet! But I think it is possible to do that. I am working on it.

A. D. LE CLAIRE: There is a very recent measurement of self-diffusion in Pd, by Dr. N. Peterson at Argonne, that does tie in very nicely with your predictions. You predict 66 kcal/mole for the activation energy for Pd self-diffusion; Peterson's measurements give 63.6.

N. ENGEL: I am glad to know that.

Diffusion by Stress Relaxation Methods

Discussion of Chapter 8 (p 131)
by R. Gibala and C. A. Wert

R. A. WOLFE (Westinghouse Electric Corp., Bettis Atomic Power Laboratory, Pittsburgh, Pa.): When there is relaxation of atoms around a vacancy in a bcc lattice, there is a possibility that you can get a collapsed vacancy, where, instead of eight nearest neighbors relaxing uniformly, four of them collapse to form a tetrahedron with close packing. Because the "big three" of anomalous diffusion—Zr, Ti, U—crystallize at room temperature in nearly close-packed structures, you might expect this type of vacancy in the bcc phase of these elements. This might account for the anomalous diffusion.

If the relaxation of the atoms around a vacancy in a bcc lattice had the tetragonal symmetry instead of cubic, would motion of that nonsymmetrical vacancy be observable by internal friction?

C A. WERT (University of Illinois, Champaign, Ill.): Whether an asymmetric vacancy could cause the anomalous diffusion observed in Zr, Ti or U, I do not know. Concerning the internal friction of such a collapsed vacancy, one can say this: (1) Such vacancies, having lower symmetry than the lattice itself, would indeed relax into preferred groups under stress and should produce anelastic behavior, including internal friction. Dr. Nowick and Dr. Heller are presently composing a long paper in which they point out specifically what types of point defects should or should not produce mechanical relaxation in all the crystal classes. This paper should be published soon. They do not, however, consider the specific strength of the relaxation, and so one will not be able to deduce from their paper how many defects one needs in a given material to see the effect by use of present techniques. (2) For alloys that already contain interstitials, say O in Ti, the O atoms could conceivably fall into this collapsed asymmetric vacancy and produce an entity that could also undergo mechanical relaxation.

P. S. RUDMAN (Battelle Memorial Institute, Columbus, Ohio): In your decomposition of the relaxation curves I gather you assume that when you change the stress all you do is rearrange the clusters, without any dissociation-association changes. How do you rule out that what you are measuring is not this change in the relative populations of each type of cluster?

C. A. WERT: One cannot rule this out, of course. We simply do these things in interpreting the data: (1) We decompose the raw data into a sum of n exponentials, in fact into the smallest number that the data fit reasonably well. (2) This analysis gives (with no further assumptions) $2n$ constants, n strengths and n relaxation times. (3) We attempt to relate these to physically interpretable models by using temperature and composition as variables in the appropriate laws of the equilibrium thermodynamics of the models we devise.

The question that you ask is this—how do you know that the interpretation you describe is unique? We do not know, of course. As is true in many investigations, we have attempted an analysis that fits the data with no tremendous deviations. But we cannot prove that our interpretation is unique, and disassociation or association by the stress used in measurement may occur. Such changes in relative cluster concentration must be accompanied by preferred orientation of clusters, of course. If not, no anelastic strain would occur.

We did attempt to determine possible effects of stress by making several sets of measurements that were identical except for a variation in stress level. Measurements of both elastic aftereffect and internal friction were made. Unless the specimens suffered plastic deformation (we went no higher than the microstrain range), no effects of stress could be ascertained within our limits of analysis.

L. S. DARKEN (U.S. Steel Fund. Res. Lab., Monroeville, Pa.): If migration of pairs and triplets of O occurs by dissociation and recombination, this would presumably be a very slow process. The question then arises as to whether the strain and hold brings the specimen to equilibrium. If not, one would expect the peak heights to be a function of prior history.

C. A. WERT: We have seen some effects of prior history on the quadruplet cluster. Early in the work the data showed a tail with a time constant longer than that which we associated with triplets. We didn't then anticipate the possibility of observing effects of clusters larger than triplets, so we tried to merge this tail into that component exponential we associated with triplets. This attempt produced an A_3 and a τ_3 that varied tremendously from run to run, depending on the over-all interstitial concentration, hold time, temperature and other details of the technique. Not until the hold time was increased to a time that was several times longer than a time constant we later described as τ_4 did these variations in A_3 and τ_3 disappear. After that no effects of specimen history were observed within the accuracy with which we could make measurements and decompose the data.

R. J. BORG: Can the existence of doublets and triplets be confirmed by observing the dependence of the magnitude of the internal-friction peaks upon the partial pressure? Just by inspection it would appear to be a fifth-power dependence; five halves for a triplet plus a doublet.

Would it not be possible to decide whether rotation of the cluster or a true translational diffusion jump gives rise to the observed relaxations by comparing the jump frequency obtained from tracer diffusion with that calculated from internal friction?

C. A. WERT: (1) The measurement or even detection of clusters of interstitials in metals by an experiment on gas-metal equilibrium is an intriguing one. Because of evaporation problems we have not found a way to attempt this measurement on a system of O and a refractory metal. We have attempted such measurements on the N-Cb system, which should be rather analogous as far as clustering is concerned. These measurements, reported by J. Cost in Acta Met, **11**, 231 (1963), have been well corroborated by Gebhardt, Fromm and Jakob in Z Metallk, **55**, 423 (1964). Even in this system we have been unable to unequivocally detect a power of pressure different from the two that one expects from dissolution of a diatomic gas into singly dissolved atoms.

(2) Correlating these internal-friction effects with bulk diffusion is possible, of course, but the accuracy demanded in both measurements is relatively high. Bulk-diffusion measurements must be carried out at a somewhat higher temperature (above 600 C) than the internal-friction measurements (about 100 C). This gives two problems; not only is a wide extrapolation required, but also the ratio of clusters of the various sizes is itself a function of temperature so that the two experiments are not made on directly comparable samples. One could, of course, take the internal-friction measurements to the high megacycle range and do the experiments at the same temperature. This adds the further complexity that such internal-friction measurement is not isothermal as one would like.

R. W. HENDRICKS (Oak Ridge National Laboratory, Oak Ridge, Tenn.): In the plots of the τ_i versus temperature, all lines seem to have the same slope, and all processes, the same activation energy, as a consequence. Is this true?

C. A. WERT: No. This is not true. The slopes actually increase slightly with increasing i so that the activation energy for the $(i + 1)$st cluster is always greater than that of the ith cluster.

Discussion of Chapter 9 (p 149)
by D. N. Beshers

H. I. AARONSON (Ford Motor Company, Metallurgy Department, Dearborn, Mich.): Wouldn't the size of an interstitial site, before an atom is inserted in it, enter into your calculations to some extent, in that the quantity of interest would be the size of the final site *minus* the size of the initial site?

D. N. BESHERS (Columbia University, New York, N.Y.): Yes, it does, but it is not the over-riding factor. The final radius of the site is generally more than twice the initial radius, but the difference between the initial radii of the two sites is generally less than a fourth of the final radius. The change in radius as the interstitial sites are opened to receive an impurity is so large that the important geometrical relations are altered. This effect is more pronounced for the octahedral site for which the number of atoms of the host lattice in contact with the impurity changes.

J. F. Cox (Watervliet Arsenal, Watervliet, N.Y.): I still think there is a question open on the determination of D_0. A recent paper by Maringer on magnetic relaxation gives a value of 19.9 kcal/mole to the slope of the anelastic data, up to around 200 degrees, and I think Lord gives about 19.2. It might be possible that Lord's point is a little high so that he is biasing all the low-temperature data. Then the D_0 might still be open to question.

D. N. BESHERS: The relevant measurements are those of the frequency of the pulsed oscillator and the temperature of the peak. The former is easily made. Calibrated thermocouples were used to measure temperature and care was taken to obtain thermal equilibrium, so that the largest source of error would be in determining the temperature of the peak from the graphs. This might be several degrees, but no more than that.

J. F. Cox: I wonder how good a background correction there was. It seems to me that the background correction is a pretty substantial part of this.

D. N. BESHERS: Yes, the background is appreciable, but for reasonable variations in background, the peak doesn't move more than two or three degrees. It is not a very large thing.

J. F. Cox: It just seems, from a re-examination of the data, that it would be possible that Lord's point would fall on an extrapolation from the high-temperature data.

D. N. BESHERS: The high-temperature data are so ragged at the lower end that I wouldn't know what to extrapolate. I think it is open.

N. ENGEL: A few remarks on your discussion about the N atoms. For several reasons we must assume that these are ionized. That means that they are much smaller. If so, N atoms placed in a vacancy of the metal lattice will be small enough to rattle. Considering the difference between a tetrahedral placement and an octahedral position first, one sees that there will be 24 arrangements in each unit cell of the bcc lattice. Which is right, I do not know. Secondly, considering the metal atoms as rigid balls allows atoms the size of $0.29d$ to go into the tetrahedral sites and atoms the size of $0.155d$ to occupy the octahedral positions, where d is the diameter of the metal atoms in the bcc lattice. If the N atoms are small enough to assume the octahedral positions, then they will rattle around in the tetrahedral sites.

D. N. BESHERS: The point you raise is one of the major unanswered questions in this field. Internal friction clearly shows that the deformation of the metallic lattice by the interstitial impurities is large. There is evidence from conductivity measurements that these impurities are highly ionized, which, as you say, would indicate much smaller radii. There is no resolution of this matter available. In a vacancy, there is some possibility that the interstitials will seek a site to one side. I find 12 tetrahedral sites for each body-centered cube.

R. J. BORG: Could you offer us some suggestions as to why N behaves differently than C? If the activation energy does not reflect in a large measure the energy necessary for a local deformation at the saddle point, what else would you propose?

D. N. BESHERS: I have no ideas as to why C and N behave differently. Heller has proposed in a different, but similar, situation that quantum mechanical tunneling may occur from activated vibrational states that are still below the top of the energy barrier, but little work has been done on the idea.

I would like to take the opportunity to say that Dr. Borg was responsible several years ago for a suggestion that led to my considering these tetrahedral sites, and I would like to thank him for introducing me to this problem.

L. S. DARKEN: Although this is a diffusion conference, I don't think that we should forget that if we are going to propose different types of sites and bindings for these interstitials, then these proposals will have implications as to the thermodynamic behavior. If we look at the solubilities (or activities at constant composition), we find just the reverse anomaly. That is, for N, the logarithmic plot versus reciprocal temperature is curved. For C, there is good evidence that there is no such curvature. One would hope to find a consistent interpretation to fit both the solubility and diffusion behavior of C and N. So far this has not been found.

D. N. BESHERS: Let me subscribe to your position by saying that ten years ago we thought that the field of relaxation methods was going to enable us to determine both diffusivities and solubilities. Anomalies have appeared on both sides, and, in addition to the problem you raise, we have not tracked down all the anomalies on either side.

C. HARTLEY: It seems to me that some years ago the people at Oak Ridge determined, from neutron-diffraction data on V-O alloys, that the O in these alloys occupy octahedral sites. Does this correspond with your calculations?

D. N. BESHERS: Yes.

C. A. WERT: In a recent paper that you submitted for publication (and that you showed to a number of persons as a report), you predicted that both C and N in Fe should occupy octahedral sites. Now in your discussion of diffusion of these atoms in Fe, you bring in a discussion of tetrahedral sites. Have you changed your thinking about octahedral sites in Fe?

D. N. BESHERS: No, all the evidence is still that C and N in Fe occupy the octahedral sites, but it is possible that diffusion is enhanced by the opening of additional paths among metastable tetrahedral sites at high temperatures.

Chemical and Tracer Diffusion

Discussion of Chapter 10 (p 155)
by D. Lazarus

R. J. Borg: Approximately how much O will dissolve in Ti before TiO_2 precipitates?

D. Lazarus: Approximately 10 at. % will go into solution in the β phase without formation of oxide at high temperatures.

K. G. Kreider (Watertown Arsenal, Watertown, Mass.): I am wondering how W fits into this picture. Very little has been mentioned and the information available is sketchy; but do you believe that W would show this anomalous behavior?

D. Lazarus: Because W is not nearly as good a getter as Ti or Zr, I would suppose it would not show this anomaly. However, the only published data I have seen were some very-low-temperature diffusion measurements at about half the melting temperature, and these gave a questionable value for D_0 of about 10^6 cm²/sec.

K. G. Kreider: Dr. Andelin of Los Alamos has published high-temperature tracer self-diffusion work on W and finds an activation energy of about 120 kcal/mole and a D_0 of about 1 cm²/sec.

D. Lazarus: Thank you. I had not seen this work. His result sounds completely in accord with expectations for "good" metals, so presumably W is not anomalous.

J. H. Frye (Oak Ridge National Laboratory, Oak Ridge, Tenn.): The probability of tunneling decreases very rapidly with mass, and I would have thought that it would be negligible for the atoms considered here.

D. Lazarus: The probability of tunneling for any atom much heavier than H, with a normally shaped barrier, is clearly negligible. I wished to raise the possibility that electronic transitions could conceivably arise involving the normally unfilled d-shells of these transition metal atoms when they are in an activated state near the saddle point, and so the shape of the barrier near the top might not be smooth and sinusoidal, as usually assumed. There might be the equivalent of narrow peaks at the top of the barrier.

J. H. Frye: In other words, what you are saying is that the tunneling is not through the entire barrier.

D. Lazarus: In such a model, tunneling could occur only through the tip of the barrier. It would correspond to a thermally activated tunneling process. Such an effect might introduce some important quantum considerations that are ordinarily ignored.

S. J. ROTHMAN (Argonne National Laboratory, Argonne, Ill.): Must it be the diffusing atom that undergoes this change, or does this idea of tunneling also apply to the saddle-point atoms? With this idea in mind, after finding anomalous results for self-diffusion in γ-U, I measured the diffusion of Au in γ-U. The results were almost the same as those for self-diffusion, indicating that an internal electronic change is not responsible for the anomalous self-diffusion in γ-U.

D. LAZARUS: Let me state first that I seriously doubt that consideration of an activated tunneling process is actually of great importance in explaining the current anomalous results; the discrepancies are much larger than one could hope to explain with relatively small quantum corrections. I feel that the effects are more likely associated with the presence of a considerable excess concentration of vacancies at the diffusion temperature. The tunneling effects, if important, should affect the neighboring saddle-point atoms as well as the diffusing atom, but to a lesser extent. However, for substitutional diffusion, the rate of motion of the tracer is intimately related to that of the solvent for a vacancy mechanism because of correlation effects, and so your results, although suggestive, cannot be taken as proof that some strange electronic interactions may not actually be of some significance.

S. J. ROTHMAN: Let me also remark that the equilibrium measurements of O solubility in solid γ-U have shown that it is very, very small—about 2 to 3 ppm at high temperature—although I do not know how the measurements were made. However, C is soluble in γ-U to several hundred ppm, and there was about 10 ppm by weight, or 200 at. ppm, in our samples.

R. F. PEART (International Business Machines Corp., Yorktown Heights, N.Y.): The diffusion coefficients for Co and Fe in Cb are approximately 500 times the self-diffusion value. How consistent is this with the ideas you have put forward?

D. LAZARUS: This result is difficult to reconcile with any simple model, unless there is a very high binding energy between the vacancy and impurity. Otherwise, the correlation effects should severely limit the rate of diffusion of the solute. However, the factors you mention are, as I recall, appropriate for diffusion at about half the melting temperature, where the diffusion rate in Cb is two or three orders of magnitude below that for Ti. This may make some sort of an impurity effect more plausible, but I have been unable to construct a quantitative model for this case that does not involve an excessive number of arbitrary and questionable assumptions.

C. T. TOMIZUKA: How does your model explain the negative activation volume found in these materials?

D. LAZARUS: What is actually found is an increase in diffusion with increasing pressure, at low pressures, as shown in Fig. 3 in my paper; the data do not fit Eq 15. Thus it is premature to assume that the true activation volume is negative. I would guess, however, that the effect observed may result from impurities in the A gas used in the high-pressure system—the gas is certainly no cleaner, in O and N content, than a vacuum of 10^{-5} mm Hg. If Ti and Zr can take on interstitial O and N in such vacuums, they can also extract such impurities from the A. Indeed, the initial rise in diffusivity might occur because the concentration of dissolved interstitials increases initially as the pressure is raised, increasing the concentration of extrinsic vacancies more rapidly than the mobility is decreased. Decreased mobility, found by Adda, might correspond to the "normal" pressure effect, that is, a depressing of the diffusion coefficient, which corresponds to a positive activation volume for the intrinsic diffusion process. The data are clearly not yet sufficiently complete to warrant any detailed analysis.

J. R. COST (Ford Scientific Laboratory, Dearborn, Mich.): First, is it possible that the silica encapsulated specimens are contaminated by O because of Zr reduction of the silica? Secondly, would it be possible to use Ti or Zr gettering to get rid of O?

D. LAZARUS: In the published work on these materials, specimens have been vacuum encapsulated to temperatures of only about 1200 C. A residual O or N concentration of a few parts per million is sufficient to explain the large enhancement of diffusion at these low temperatures even without considering reduction of the silica, but is quite inadequate to explain the enhancement at temperatures near the melting point. However, in all reported work, the specimens were actually held in standard dynamic vacuum systems at temperatures much above 1300 C, where Ti and Zr, in particular, should have been able to accumulate fairly large concentrations of interstitial gases by a self-gettering action. It would be good to repeat the measurements either by using a hypervacuum system at extremely high temperatures, or by vacuum sealing the diffusion specimens inside a thick-walled can of the same material, which might keep the pressure of O or N at the specimen extremely low. The sharp break in self-diffusion in V observed by Dr. Peart does not appear to have anything to do with uptake of atmospheric gases at high temperature. His low-temperature diffusion coefficients are quite normal, and the break at 1350 C is very sharp. It seems more likely that there may be a hitherto unreported phase transition in V at that temperature.

J. H. Westbrook (General Electric Research Laboratory, Schenectady, N.Y.): Although I don't know exactly how it relates to the diffusion anomalies that we have been talking about this morning, I think it is worthwhile recalling that for several of these "bad" systems, Ti, Zr, and I think also Hf, there has recently appeared some evidence that some ordered phases of the M_3O or M_6O type appear at low temperatures in the broad solid-solution fields of these metals. [Evidence for Zr_3O has been reported by Wallwork, Smeltzer and Rose, in Acta Met, **12,** 409 (1964), Holmberg and Magneli, in Acta Chem Scand, **12,** 1341 (1958), Holmberg and Dagerhamn, in Acta Chem Scand, **15,** 919 (1961), Ostberg, in Acta Met, and Pemsler, in J Electrochem Soc, **111,** 381 (1964). Evidence for Ti_3O has been reported by Holmberg, in Acta Chem Scand, **16,** 1245 (1962), and Kornilov and Glazova, in Dokl Akad Nauk SSSR, **150,** 313 (1963).] From the resistivity and hardness tests that have been made, this ordering, whatever it is, disappears at temperatures rather lower than the region for most of the diffusion anomalies. However, it is still suggestive that the metal-O interaction in these "bad" systems is quite complicated indeed.

P. G. Shewmon: I am not certain that I understand this mechanism that we are discussing. Are you saying that the O is trapped in a vacancy, that once there it stabilizes the vacancy, and that as a result a high O content will stabilize a high vacancy concentration?

D. Lazarus: Effectively, yes.

P. G. Shewmon: You further assume that these O-stabilized vacancies can easily exchange with substitutional atoms, that is, that the O can easily get out of the way when another atom wants to move in?

D. Lazarus: I would assume that the O traps a vacancy either by actually occupying the vacancy or by taking an interstitial position immediately adjacent to the vacancy. During motion of the O-vacancy complex, the O would presumably be in an interstitial site, and so the whole motion process could presumably not take place faster than the interstitial could move. If the binding energy between the O (or N) and the vacancy were quite large, there could be an enormous enhancement in the vacancy concentration at high interstitial concentrations and, as a result, an increase in diffusion rate for both self-diffusion and impurity diffusion. In this case, the interaction between a substitutional impurity and an O-vacancy complex might be quite complicated.

P. G. Shewmon: Does the O have any effect at high temperatures?

D. Lazarus: My guess is that these effects may be important over the whole temperature range for Ti, Zr and U, that we have never had specimens free of residual gaseous impurities, with the experimental conditions so far employed, and that the concentrations could increase at high temperatures. Thus the whole observed diffusion range could well be considered extrinsic.

Discussion of Chapter 11 (p 171)
by L. W. Barr and J. N. Mundy

D. LAZARUS: I believe that your conjecture about the relaxation around the vacancy in the bcc lattice is quite reasonable. In the case of an interstitial, the question of whether it would have a positive or negative activation volume always arises. The unrelaxed interstitial would clearly have a negative activation volume, because a lattice site has been eliminated in forming the defect. However, when relaxation is included, it is not at all clear whether or not the subsequent expansion of the remainder of the lattice would not more than compensate for the loss of the first lattice site, and so the total activation volume might be positive, as it would be for a vacancy. In your case, however, there are no strong closed-shell repulsion terms, and the relaxation might be presumed to be much smaller than that in a noble metal. In such a case, the net activation volume for an interstitial would be negative. Accordingly, the model of a highly relaxed vacancy, which is consistent with the positive activation volume determined by Nachtrieb's pressure measurements, seems much more reasonable.

L. W. BARR (AERE, Harwell, England): I agree with your comment. One possibility we are pursuing in connection with Nachtrieb's relaxed-vacancy model is an isotope-effect measurement in liquid Na. We feel that if the isotope effects in liquid and solid Na are identical, this will support the relaxed-vacancy model rather than the interstitial model.

S. J. ROTHMAN: One trouble, I think, with doing an isotope-effect experiment in bcc metals is that the presence of impurities is going to muddle it up. If the vacancy is bonded to an impurity, this could lower the correlation coefficient, as I think you have proved experimentally. I do not know how you can separate this particular lowering of the product ΔKf from the effects of the various mechanisms you have mentioned.

L. W. BARR: I agree. There is no way from a purely isotope-effect measurement to separate the terms on the right side of Eq 6. If diffusion in Na were by an impurity-vacancy pair, which we think is unlikely, f could have any value between naught and one. The actual value of f would be determined by the relative jump rates of the Na and the impurity.

D. LAZARUS: The work at Reading showed no isotope effect. However, this was for a fast diffusing impurity, and the isotope effect is expected to be cancelled by correlation effects. One needs a slow diffusing impurity for which f can be assumed to be about 1.

L. W. BARR: Again I must agree with the remark. To use Eq 6 to study the isotope effect, f must be known. That is, either self-diffusion by a known mechanism or, as you point out, impurity diffusion for which f is known from other evidence must be studied.

Discussion of Chapter 12 (p 183)
by S. J. Rothman

A. L. DAVIS: I want to call attention to remarks of Dr. Alvin Weinberg, director of the Oak Ridge National Laboratory, made in a keynote address on "Metallurgy and Information" at a meeting of the American Society for Metals in Cleveland. He observed that "many important advances in the metallurgical sciences have come from a clever marshalling of a variety of seemingly disconnected facts rather than by deduction using the mathematical methods of quantum theory of metals. . . . My main point is that for a science like metallurgy . . . *the inductive method must remain at least as important as the deductive (method)."*

The excellent data examined during this 3-day conference are invariably illustrated on ln D versus $1/T$ plots. This is from our inherited deduction that the diffusion coefficients obey the simple Arrhenius relation. However, the data points almost invariably repose in a concave-lens section traversed by a rectilinear least-squares derivation or are actually delineated with a distinct upward curvature.

The admonition of Dr. Weinberg is well taken. Now in about 1 min the results of induction as it relates to a re-examination of most of the data published over the last 20 years on the self-diffusion in solid elements can be presented.

The self-diffusion coefficients have a linear temperature dependence in any temperature range wherein the heat capacity of the solid has a substantially linear temperature dependence. This relation is well expressed by ln $D = a$ ln $T + b$ with $Q = aRT$. This is fully consistent with the second law of thermodynamics relating to the degradation and dissipation of energy in any thermal process. This relation has been found to apply for diffusion in more than 24 elements in 12 subgroups of the periodic table.

Such a phenomenological approach is generally considered less than dishonorable because it does not have as a prerequisite the knowledge or use of any fictional mechanism, model or theory. Consequently, one of my most competent advisors has estimated that at least 20 years may elapse before the relations stated will be recognized or admitted.

I thank you.

C. S. HARTLEY: If you find that the solubility of interstitial impurities in γ-U is low, that there is no evidence for their going in and out of solution reversibly and that there is no composition change after the diffusion experiment, would it not be difficult to accept the suggestion of an entirely extrinsic vacancy contribution to diffusion in γ-U?

S. J. ROTHMAN: I do not know about N. The solubility of C is several hundred parts per million, and we have about 10 ppm C in our diffusion samples. This is 10 ppm by weight or about 200 mol ppm, and if there is a vacancy attached to each C atom, there would be more than enough vacancies, especially at low temperatures, to show the enhancement. I am told by Dr. Blumenthal, who was responsible for the development of our U purification techniques, that the solubility of O in γ-U is quite small, a few parts per million by weight. There is also no evidence that C goes into and out of solution reversibly during the diffusion anneal.

I should like to comment on the possible reaction with the Vycor in which the sample is sealed. In the case of U it is dreadful if you are not careful. The U does not even have to be in contact with the silica; if it "sees" the silica at high temperature, it, on occasion, picks up enough Si to form the eutectic! We always put our sample into a Ta capsule so that it does not "see" any silica. Also we load the capsule with Zr chips.

Occasionally the samples have a little oxide film on the sides when we load the capsule. This comes from the sputtering process that the samples undergo before we evaporate on the isotope. Putting in the Zr actually cleans up the surface of the sample. In connection with this, Dr. Lazarus commented that encapsulation for a high-temperature anneal was impossible. Dr. Peterson has worked out a technique for this. He puts his samples, together with other things to cut down on the volume, into a Ta capsule, and this is electron-beam welded shut. The electron-beam welder operates at a vacuum of about 10^{-4} mm Hg, and so if gettering is good, very clean conditions are attained inside the capsule.

Discussion of Chapter 13 (p 197)
by W. C. Hagel and J. H. Westbrook

H. I. AARONSON: When the Ford data first became available and we compared them with those from the careful study of Hagel and Westbrook, we were afraid for a little while that, in addition to the other problems troubling students of bcc materials, there might be an effect of geography upon diffusion. We are now relieved to learn that this effect does not exist. With the exception of differences in opinions concerning the immediate vicinity of the stoichiometric composition, we now seem to agree that Q_{Ag} decreases with increasing deviation from the stoichiometric composition on the Ag-rich as well as on the Mg-rich side of this composition.

The only other point on which I would like to comment is the use of the Illinois data on diffusion in disordered β-CuZn to "scale-off" the diffusivities of Ag and of Mg in hypothetical disordered β-AgMg. You have remarked that Zn diffuses with anomalous rapidity in disordered β-CuZn. But there do not appear to be any diffusivity data in any other disordered bcc intermediate phase that transforms to a CsCl-type ordered phase at lower temperatures upon which such a statement can be based! A comparison with the diffusivity of Cd in β-AuCd, for example, is obviously not to the point, because this compound is ordered essentially to the solidus. As the β-CuZn work has shown, the imposition of CsCl-type long-range order markedly reduces the diffusivities of both species. Your criticism of our (admittedly approximate) scaling procedure accordingly appears to be without experimental foundation.

R. A. WOLFE: In regard to the vacancies with tetragonal symmetry that have been mentioned several times, Lomer (W. M. Lomer, Vacancies and Other Point Defects in Metals and Alloys, Institute of Metals, London, 1958, p 82) postulated that the β and γ brass structures have this type of vacancy. I think it is interesting to note that your data for diffusion in these compounds fall within the same high range as the three anomalous bcc elements. That may indicate that they have the same kind of vacancy structure.

W. C. HAGEL (General Electric Research Laboratory, Schenectady, N.Y.): Except for ordered β-CuZn, most CsCl-type intermetallic compounds become disordered only on heating quite close to their melting temperatures. Hence, we are left with a paucity of diffusion data for Aaronson's scaling procedure. Compared with self-diffusion in pure bcc metals (as a function of reciprocal reduced temperature), the diffusion coefficients of Cu and Zn in *both* ordered and disordered β-CuZn do appear to be about two orders of magnitude too high. In contrast, results from diffusion in other ordered CsCl-type compounds, for example, CoAl, AgMg and AuCd, tend to fall about an order of magnitude lower than the scatter band for pure bcc's. Disordering should not cause a shift in D values of three to four orders of magnitude. These general observations are the reasons for questioning reliance on data from β-CuZn in regard to AgMg. A direct experiment might be to measure Ag diffusion in AgPd. According to Savitskii and Pravoverov [J Inorg Chem, Acad Sci SSR, **6,**

499 (1961)], it becomes disordered a good 100 C below the liquidus. Dr. Wolfe's comment suggests a thought-provoking reason for why certain diffusion results are too high.

Discussion of Chapter 14 (p 209)
by H. Domian and H. I. Aaronson

S. J. ROTHMAN: The Arrhenius plots you show for the diffusion of Ag and of Mg seem to be very close together. I have two questions about them. (1) Did you apply any of the routine statistical tests for significance to see if the slopes were significantly different? (2) Your equation for Q shows that it should be somewhat temperature dependent. Did you find it to be so?

H. I. AARONSON: (1) Statistical tests show that the Arrhenius plots for D_{Ag} and D_{Mg} differ significantly. (2) The predicted variations of Q_{Ag} and Q_{Mg} with temperature fall within the experimental limits of error.

J. H. WESTBROOK: Any suggestion as to why, experimentally, the Q you found in a single crystal is so much higher than that which either you or I found in the other?

H. I. AARONSON: The sectioning technique probably introduced some errors into the single-crystal study. The significance of the present results lies principally in the diffusivity ratios.

D. LAZARUS: I am somewhat confused by your observation that the relative diffusion coefficients of Ag and Mg actually crossed. This does not seem consistent with your assumption that the cycle is controlled almost entirely by diffusion in one sublattice; in this case, diffusion should occur only if there is a greater tendency to form vacancies in the other sublattice. Such an effect was observed by Gupta in studying the Au-Cd system. When the diffusion coefficient is controlled by the sublattice vacancy concentration, the relative diffusivities tend to maintain a constant ratio with temperature. His result was reasonably consistent with McCombie's model. You seem to have an additional factor entering.

H. I. AARONSON: (1) The conclusion that vacancies formed on the Mg sublattice are responsible for virtually all diffusion in β-AgMg was reached by calculation. (2) Under this circumstance, Eq 15 shows that D_{Mg}/D_{Ag} can have any value in the range of $\frac{1}{2}$ to 2, depending upon the relative values of $\Delta H_{0_{21}}$, $\Delta H_{0_{22}}$ and $\Delta H_{0_{23}}$. Only if one of these activation enthalpies is appreciably less than the other two will D_{Mg}/D_{Ag} be nearly independent of temperature. If $\Delta H_{0_{21}}$ is slightly greater than $\Delta H_{0_{22}}$, however, the diffusivity ratio can be greater than unity at high temperatures because of the $2 \exp(-\Delta H_{0_{21}}/RT)$ term in the numerator, but less than unity at low temperatures because of the higher relative value now attained by exp $(-\Delta H_{0_{22}}/RT)$ and the pre-exponential factor of 2 in the denominator. Thus, no additional factor is needed to explain the present results.

Discussion of Chapter 15 (p 225)
by R. J. Borg

P. G. SHEWMON: The elastic modulus E for any metal decreases with rising temperature. Are you saying that the change in $d \ln D/d(1/T)$ with temperature stems from a change in d^2E/dT^2 with temperature, as in Zener's theory of D_0 and ΔH?

R. J. BORG: Yes; that is right. The magnetic effect is completely compatible with the change in elastic properties occurring in the same temperature region. In other words, using the elementary Zener model, one can combine Young's modulus and the diffusion data in a way that eliminates the non-Arrhenius behavior.

P. G. SHEWMON: If what you say is true, a d^2E/dT^2 of the opposite sign might appear in the region of the Curie temperature for some alloy and one might see an enhancement below the Curie temperature instead of a retardation in D. Is there any alloy system in which you think this might occur, or are there any measurements that might indicate this?

R. J. BORG: Yes, if the model is strictly true, I suppose that D might increase rather than decrease below T_c. I do not however know, offhand, of any such systems.

S. J. ROTHMAN: These high-temperature elastic-constant measurements are very simple. Levitt and Martin from Watertown Arsenal have designed a beautiful apparatus for it. In effect they take a long rod and put a shoulder on it about 3 in. from one end, and then shoot sound waves through. They can keep their coupling at room temperature this way. They measure the difference in transit time between the reflection from the shoulder and the reflection from the end and calculate the elastic constants.

D. LAZARUS: I should like to note that in the work done by A. B. Kuper on β brass at the University of Illinois some years ago, we observed exactly the same correlation around the order-disorder transition. The nonlinear diffusional behavior was exactly mirrored in the temperature dependence of the elastic constants.

C. S. HARTLEY: V is sometimes included in this anomalous group, and it happens that there has been some work done in our laboratory on the elastic modulus of V up to about 1000 C. The temperature dependence is reasonably linear; there appear to be no breaks in the linearity.

Discussion of Chapter 16 (p 235)
by R. F. Peart

C. S. HARTLEY: This is some direct evidence about the existence or nonexistence of a crystallographic phase change of V. For the experiments that were reported earlier on Cb-V alloys, the lowest temperature was 1400 C, and if one observes diffusion couples of a system for which we know of a crystallographic phase change, like Mo-Ti or Cb-Ti, one sees a very sharp discrimination between the crystal structures formed on transformation. I just wanted to point out that in the instance of the Cb-V couples, when the diffusion zones were entirely examined, there was no evidence of anything like a crystal-structure change, or in fact nothing that indicated that it was anything but a continuous series of solid solutions. This is not conclusive evidence for the absence of a change in the electronic states, of course, but I think it does rule out a crystallographic phase change.

R. F. PEART: In addition to this metallographic evidence I think we can rule out a crystallographic phase change because of the absence of a discontinuity in the diffusion coefficient at the "transition" temperature.

A. D. LE CLAIRE: It is probably worth pointing out that there is evidence for electronic transitions in V. There is a small resistance anomaly at about 230 K. So, this metal has a propensity for electronic transitions, and there could be another one up in this temperature of 1350 C.

R. F. PEART: We have made some measurements on the resistivity of V up to 1500 C that showed some signs of a change in slope at 1300 to 1400 C. This result was not too reproducible, and we obviously need a more thorough investigation.

S. J. ROTHMAN: In plotting R_0/T against T, Fisher found anomalies in elastic constants of U at 40 K. There was no sign of the anomaly in the resistivity plot, but it showed up once he was looking for it. He found it best by plotting resistivity over temperature.

Discussion of Chapters 17 and 18 (p 247 and 253)
by J. Askill

S. J. ROTHMAN: I have several comments. First, your slide that compared the autoradiographic and sectioning values showed that the values obtained by autoradiography were invariably higher than the ones obtained by lathe sectioning.

Second, don't your results on single-crystal and polycrystalline Mo imply that the activation energy for grain-boundary diffusion in Mo is actually higher than that for volume diffusion?

Third, how do you account for the factor-of-two difference between your D's and those of Hagel?

J. ASKILL (Reading University, Reading, England): The autoradiographic results are consistently higher than the corresponding serial-sectioning ones, and the amount by which they are higher is found to be a function of the isotope used. For Co^{60} the amount is about 25%.

All the results given for self-diffusion in polycrystalline and single-crystal Mo were for volume diffusion. The higher diffusion coefficients and the small change in activation energy for the polycrystalline material could just be due to the different impurity content of the materials.

In the case of the Cr self-diffusion, again I would think that slight differences in the impurities in the Cr material could well give the difference between my data and Hagel's data.

F. R. WINSLOW: I would like to raise two points. First is the question of "tails" on a penetration plot. These could possibly be due to carry-over of isotope in a lathe-sectioned or a ground specimen. However, because we do see them on specimens sectioned by the anodizing and stripping technique, we believe they are real. We have electron-microscopic evidence for Ta, indicating little or no carry-over from one section to the next.

Discussion of Chapter 19 (p 261)
by J. F. Murdock

R. F. PEART: I would like to point out that if the Ti data are analyzed as two straight lines, then the intersection is approximately at 1250 C; and there are some data on electrical-resistivity measurements that show a cusp-like anomaly at approximately 1230 C in both iodide Ti and commercial Ti. This may be a coincidence; but it gives some weight to the possibility that, like the V results, these anomalies may be attributable to a change in the properties of the parent lattice.

C. S. HARTLEY: Before the dislocation idea is rejected, I wonder if it would not be of use to do some single-crystal experiments to compare the dislocation structure of material that had been cycled through the transformation temperature with that of material quenched from above the transition, and so on. Dislocations could enhance diffusion by permitting diffusion along the dislocation core, and vacancies could be emitted as the transformation dislocations anneal out. This would tend to give an internal-friction peak such as the one discussed by Dr. Rothman.

All the metals that seem to show the most anomalous results have in common the phase transformation; and there are other bcc materials, such as V, Ta, Cb, that have high solubilities for interstitials but don't exhibit the same kind of anomalous diffusion behavior.

S. J. ROTHMAN: The important structure in U, Ti or Zr is not the structure that you can see through a microscope at room temperature but the structure in the high-temperature phase. We have tried to think of ways of getting to this, but we have not succeeded. If you can think of a way of doing transmission electron microscopy on a thin film of a highly reactive metal at 900 C in the sort of a vacuum you get in a Siemens, please let me know!

D. LAZARUS: Offhand, it would appear that the calculated values of the two diffusion coefficients would be extremely sensitive to the way in which the fit is selected for the low-temperature end of the curve. Is there any way in which you can be less than arbitrary in choosing an optimal fit?

J. F. MURDOCK (Oak Ridge National Laboratory, Oak Ridge, Tenn.): To help the computer on its way, we needed to make some preliminary estimates of Q_A, Q_B, C_A and C_B. I drew a tangent to the experimental curve to the lowest temperature, and calculated the extrinsic region, the $D_0(C_A)$ and $Q(Q_A)$ value. Then subtracting this line from the experimental data, we obtained values for C_B and Q_B. After these four values were submitted to the computer, the program was untouched by human hands. This was the best solution we could find.

S. J. ROTHMAN: I have two very short comments. We have done the experiment of varying the time of diffusion of Co in γ-U from half an hour to an hour and a half. The D's were exactly the same. So the lifetime of whatever defect there is must be much longer than an hour, which is hard to believe for a vacancy.

I agree with Dr. Lazarus. We got the enormous variations in the high-temperature Q in the two-exponential fits for impurity diffusion in γ-U in just this way. The value of Q_2 given by the machine was always very close to the input estimate of Q_2.

G. J. DIENES: May I ask, on this same point of curve fitting, what happens if you take your derivative as a difference from experimental point to experimental point? Do you get a mess or does it look like a curve?

J. F. MURDOCK: We tried this and got a mess.

Discussion of Chapter 21 (p 275)
by R. H. Moore

D. GRAHAM: In your analysis of solute diffusion in β-Ti, which values of activation energy were used? The values proposed for the lower temperature range are more reliable than those at higher temperatures where the uncertainty in the calculated activation energy can be as large as ± 10 kcal.

R. H. MOORE (General Electric Co., Richland, Washington): The values for the activation energy in the low temperature range were used in this analysis.

D. N. BESHERS: Which volume are you applying; atomic volume of the pure metal or a partial molar volume in the solution?

R. H. Moore: The volumes used here were the atomic volumes of the pure solute element.

Discussion of Chapter 22 (p 283)
by I. I. Kovenskii*

G. R. LOVE (Oak Ridge National Laboratory, Oak Ridge, Tenn.):* I would like to suggest that Dr. Kovenskii's results may be part of a rather general class of observations and that curvature of this kind should not be particularly surprising. Several attempts to justify the Arrhenius relation for diffusion have been predicated upon absolute-rate theory. However, in any such justification there inevitably comes a point at which rigor must be abandoned and we must make some simplifying assumptions. Let us examine that derivation in a little greater detail.

We may write for any reaction

$$\bar{k} = \nu^* C^*$$

where $\bar{k}$ is the specific reaction rate, C^* is the concentration of "activated complexes" and ν^* is the rate of frequency of forward reaction. We may approximate ν^* by

$$\nu^* = \bar{v}/\delta$$

where $\bar{v}$ is the mean velocity of forward reaction and δ is a critical displacement along the reaction coordinate. From classical mechanics this becomes

$$\nu^* = (kT/2\pi m)^{\frac{1}{2}}/\delta$$

at an absolute temperature T for a complex of mass m.

Because the relative population in connected energy levels is inversely proportional to the energy difference between the levels, we may write

$$C^* = \exp\left(-\Delta G^*/kT\right)$$

* Paper by I. I. Kovenskii was presented by G. R. Love.

taking the population of reactant atoms to be unity, where ΔG^* is the energy difference between reactants and complexes at temperature T. To express this in terms of the zero-point (thermodynamic) free-energy difference we must include the ratios of the partition functions of activated complexes and reactants. For the particular case of diffusion, assigning all the energy in the complex to the diffusing atom. we may write

$$\bar{k} = \frac{1}{\delta} \left(\frac{kT}{2\pi m} \right)^{1/2} \frac{\Pi Z_c}{\Pi Z_r} \exp\left(-\Delta\epsilon_0/kT\right)$$

with adequate rigor to this point. Here, the Z's represent the several partition functions corresponding to rotational, vibrational and translational degrees of freedom in the complex and reactants. The ratio of products of partition functions can be calculated only by making some assumptions about the reactants and activated complexes. At this point either of two possible assumptions may be used.

The assumption thought to apply to most metallurgical systems, and first proposed by Wert and Zener, is that the number of degrees of freedom in the two states is the same but one vibrational degree of freedom in the reactants becomes a translational degree of freedom in the complex. Then the ratio of partition functions becomes

$$\frac{\Pi Z_c}{\Pi Z_r} = \frac{Z_{tr}}{Z_{vib}} = \frac{(2\pi mkT)^{1/2}\,\delta/h}{(kT/h\nu)} = \nu\delta\left(\frac{2\pi m}{kT}\right)^{1/2}$$

because the partition functions for all other degrees of freedom cancel identically. The reaction rate becomes the familiar

$$\bar{k} = \nu \exp\left(-\Delta\epsilon_0/kT\right)$$

where ν, the lattice vibration frequency, is essentially independent of temperature. Note that the assumption yielding this result is tantamount to the assumption that once an atom acquires the energy ΔG^* it will inevitably go all the way to the next equilibrium position.

An alternate assumption has been proposed by Eyring and found to be useful in a number of chemical reactions proceeding at moderate temperatures. If we assume the complex to have all the degrees of freedom of the reactants plus a translational degree of freedom toward completion of the reaction, the product of partition functions becomes

$$\Pi Z_c/\Pi Z_r = Z_{tr} = (2\pi mkT)^{1/2}\delta/h$$

and the reaction rate is given by

$$\bar{k} = (kT/h) \exp (-\Delta\epsilon_0/kT)$$

Qualitatively, this considers the particles to have at least metastable residence in the activated complex, such that all vibrational modes exist.

In general, experimental distinctions between these two expressions are very hard to observe because the exponential dependence on $1/T$ dominates the equation. Only when the activation energy, $\Delta\epsilon_0$, is very low or the range of experimental temperatures is very wide, can a linear tem-

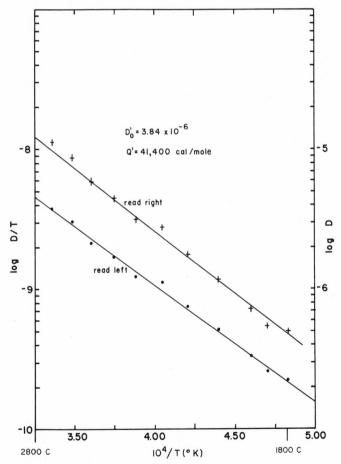

Fig. 2. Diffusivity of C in W versus temperature plotted both as log D versus $1/T$ and as log (D/T) versus $(1/T)$

perature dependence in the pre-exponential be observed. Such a temperature dependence is often observed in organic chemistry where activation
energies tend to be quite low. We may be observing this sort of dependence here, in part because the activation energies are rather low and in
part because Dr. Kovenskii's data span such a generous range in temperature. A first test of this hypothesis would be to construct the Arrhenius
plot in the form ln (D/T) versus $(1/T)$. As is evident in Fig. 2, 3 and 4,
this form of the plot does indeed yield a straight line even though more
conventional plotting yields a curve. The problem of resolution is pointed

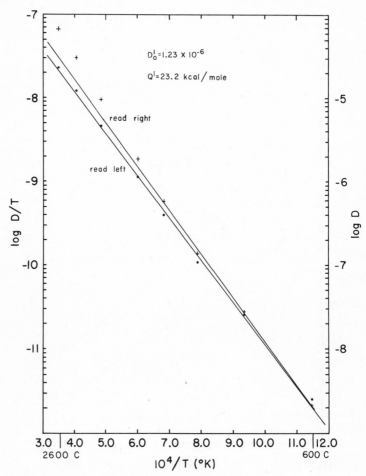

*Fig. 3 Diffusivity of C in Ta versus temperature plotted both as log D versus
1/T and as log (D/T) versus (1/T)*

up by the data for Ti, for which an equally good straight line may be drawn for either form of the equation.

A real physical distinction may exist between these two model descriptions of the diffusion process. In this same session we have seen computer simulations of crystals in which a local minimum in energy existed at the saddle-point configuration of a diffusion jump. Perhaps the presence, or the critical depth, of such a minimum is a prerequisite for a temperature-dependent pre-exponential. Thus the wide temperature range over which D_0 for self-diffusion in V is independent of temperature may indicate that

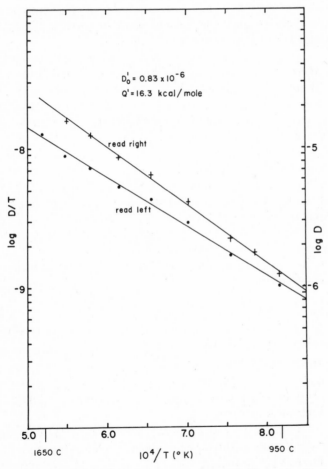

Fig. 4. Diffusivity of C in Ti versus temperature plotted both as log D versus 1/T and as log (D/T) versus (1/T)

the saddle point in V is really saddle-shaped—a true maximum along the reaction path.

I am suggesting, then, that the D_0 term in the conventional expression for the diffusivity of an appreciable number of systems may actually vary linearly with temperature. It may not be observed in many instances because of a combination of high activation energies and/or restricted temperature ranges for diffusion measurements. This certainly does not masquerade as any general explanation of curvature in Arrhenius plots; the curvature in the plots for diffusion of Zr and Cb in Zr is significantly greater than that predicted by this model, for example.

G. J. DIENES: Can you fit the diffusion data for C in Fe by this temperature dependence of the pre-exponentials? The range is comparable in temperature, but not in the number of cycles covered, to that of C in W. The data for C in Fe cover about 14 cycles.

G. R. LOVE: I have plotted the data for C in α-Fe in the following fashion. Wert's 1950 paper (1) reporting anelastic and internal-friction results did not give tabulated values, so I used the equation he reported for the temperature range of 0 to about 200 C and calculated points at 50 C intervals. I supplemented this with the data of Thomas and Leak (2). The results from more conventional measurements in the range of 500 to 865 C (3, 4) happily were tabulated. I then calculated the best least-squares straight line through the data over the combined temperature ranges for each way of plotting the data and calculated the standard deviation of the individual points from the derived curves. The conventional plot yielded $Q = 20.6$ kcal and σ, the deviation in ln D, equal to 0.094. The plot of ln D/T versus $1/T$ yielded $Q = 19.6$ kcal and $\sigma = 0.085$. On both plots, the highest-temperature data fell above the best straight line; it would appear that the experimental observations reflect at least this much curvature.

1   C. Wert, Phys Rev, **79,** 601 (1950)
2   W. R. Thomas and G. M. Leak, Phil Mag, **45,** 986 (1954)
3   J. T. Stanley, Trans AIME, **185,** 752 (1950)
4   R. P. Smith, Trans AIME, **224,** 105 (1962)

D. N. BESHERS: The activation energy for diffusion of C in Ta is about 38 kcal/mole, in contrast to the 23 or 24 reported here. This disagreement emphasizes the need for more studies of the diffusion of interstitials in bcc metals by classical methods.

L. S. DARKEN: In the paper you said there was 0.1% C. Is this much C soluble in all cases in the lower temperature range?

G. R. LOVE: Very probably.

Enhancement of Diffusion

Discussion of Chapter 23 (p 291)
by M. S. Wechsler

G. V. KIDSON: Because this conference is concerned primarily with unusual effects in bcc materials, I feel I should point out that the results of channeling experiments done on W are themselves anomalous. That is, in addition to the normal penetration a so-called supertail occurs.

M. S. WECHSLER: The origin of the "supertail" in W, which occurs in addition to the penetration (in excess of that observed for amorphous materials) attributed to channeling, has not been definitely established. However, the reader is referred to a recent, more complete description of the experimental results [Kornelsen, Brown, Davies, Domeij and Piercy, Phys Rev, **136,** A849 (1964)] and to a suggested explanation based on inelastic processes [Erginsoy, Phys Rev Letters, **12,** 366 (1964)].

R. J. BORG: Has anyone accurately measured the yields from these focusing collisions?

M. S. WECHSLER: Sputtering yields have been studied at a number of laboratories. In this country, Wehner and co-workers have investigated a wide variety of materials [J Appl Phys, **35,** 322 (1964); **35,** 1819 (1964); **33,** 1842 (1962); **32,** 365 (1961); **32,** 887 (1961); **31,** 2305 (1960) and Phys Rev, **112,** 1120 (1958); **102,** 690 (1956)], and Southern *et al.* have determined sputtering yields for 1- to 5-kev A ions on Cu, Si and Ge [J Appl Phys, **34,** 153 (1963)]. Also, Kistemaker and collaborators in Amsterdam have done sputtering-yield experiments on Cu [Physica, **30,** 144 (1964); J Appl Phys, **34,** 690 (1963)], and measurements in the USSR have been reported by Maskova, Molchanov and Odintsov [Soviet Phys–Solid State, **5,** 2516 (1964)]. A collection of papers in this field is found in the proceedings of the Sixième Conférence Internationale sur les Phénomènes d'Ionization dans les Gaz, Vol I and II, SERMA, Paris, 1963.

Discussion of Chapter 24 (p 317)
by A. C. Damask

C. ALTSTETTER (University of Illinois, Urbana, Ill.): I have two questions. First, you show that after the 19-day irradiation there wasn't enough C left at 150 C to give much precipitation as ε carbide. This indicates that the number of vacancies was about the same as the number of

C atoms. Does this vacancy content agree with other measurements of vacancy concentration?

Second, you varied the irradiation times to give a different defect concentration. Did you also do experiments with different C concentrations?

A. C. DAMASK: Monroe Wechsler pointed out in his talk that, because we don't know the magnitude of a physical property such as electrical resistivity associated with each defect in Fe, estimates of vacancy concentrations are no better than about a factor of two. Within this uncertainty there is agreement of vacancy content with C content. In answer to your second question, no, we did not vary the C content.

R. A. SWALIN (University of Minnesota, Minneapolis, Minn.): It would seem to me that you would have to change or vary the C content in order to disprove the idea that you have two C atoms in a vacancy. Did you perform any experiments of this type?

A. C. DAMASK: No, we did not change the C content, but we changed the irradiation dosage. During the course of these experiments we used 2-, 4-, 12- and 19-day irradiations. In each case the kinetics were bimolecular, and from analyses of these kinetics we could tell that the ratio of initial concentrations of vacancies and C atoms changed by the appropriate amounts. As shown in the internal-friction experiment, the 4-day irradiation does not go to completion. This indicates that the C atoms do saturate the vacancies, and the bimolecular kinetics of that reaction indicate that one C atom saturates one vacancy.

J. H. WESTBROOK: You have considered here essentially interactions within what you might call the matrix material. I would like to ask how you think the grain boundary might perturb this. The grain boundary can act as a sink for a vacancy. Also, Philips in this country and McLean in England have shown evidence by transmission electron microscopy of C segregation at the grain boundary. It seems to me this would affect some of this interpretation.

A. C. DAMASK: The probability of interaction depends upon the relative concentrations. If the concentration of a point defect, say the vacancy, is quite large, the mean free path to encounter one by a C atom during its migration is small compared with the path length to reach a grain boundary; the C atom may well encounter a large number of vacancies before it reaches the grain boundary.

J. H. WESTBROOK: Let me put the thing slightly differently. If we assume, for one reason or another, that there is a large segregation of C at the grain boundary, it may be quite effectively immobilized during the course of the experiments. Therefore, relative to Swalin's comment, perhaps it is not adequate to look at two different total analyzed C concentrations, and we must also consider how the C is initially distributed in the sample.

A. C. DAMASK: What you are suggesting is that the quench is not perfect.

J. H. WESTBROOK: Right.

A. C. DAMASK: I doubt if our quenches were perfect. They were usually monitored by an internal-friction measurement, and no two initial peaks were identical. When the C was quenched in the solid solution, I quite agree that some of it may well have not been quenched into interstitial positions but may have segregated initially, although internal friction and the electron micrographs suggest that very little segregation has occurred. We would not see this C in the kinetic interactions that we studied. This segregated C probably redissolves at a much higher temperature, and would perhaps precipitate during the formation of cementite; but if it is already segregated in grain boundaries, it is not going to migrate during the low-temperature migration at 50 C. As you recall from the figures, the curves are normalized and not dependent upon the initial concentration. The kinetics are from normalized data, and these are bimolecular with the correct migration energy. We conclude that the effects that we observe arise from the interstitial C not segregated at grain boundaries or in clusters.

J. MOTEFF (General Electric Co., Cincinnati, Ohio): In a recent report (TM 64-6-43) a homologous plot is made of an annealing step temperature found in Fe, W and Mo. A recovery peak at $0.31\ T_m$ occurs in each of these metals, and Ibragimov (see TM 64-6-43) has observed a recovery step in neutron-irradiated Fe at $0.31\ T_m$, which corresponds to the 295 C recovery step observed by Fujita and Damask. It seems quite possible that the defect that migrates at $0.31\ T_m$ in each of these metals is the vacancy.

Discussion of Chapter 25 (p 329)
by G. V. Kidson

H. I. AARONSON: Shewmon and Bechtold [Acta Met, **3,** 452 (1955)] have shown that O increases the rate of marker movement in diffusion couples of pure Mo and pure bcc Ti. Is this observation consistent with your mechanism of the effect of interstitial impurities on diffusion in bcc metals?

G. V. KIDSON: I am grateful to Dr. Aaronson for pointing out this work to me. Unfortunately, it is difficult to draw definitive conclusions about the significance of the results reported by Shewmon and Bechtold so far as their relevance to the present discussion is concerned. On the one hand it could be argued that the increase in marker movement in the impure Ti-Mo couple over that of the purer material reflects an increase in the diffusion coefficient of the Ti atoms and hence supports the impurity–vacancy–complex model. On the other hand, it is interesting to note that in the expression $x/t^{1/2} = B \exp(-A/RT)$ used by these authors to describe their results, the change in the ratio of marker movement x to annealing time t at constant temperature T appears to be contained entirely in the parameter B, with A remaining the same for both materials. It is recognized that the measured displacement x will be decreased by the formation of voids in the diffusion zone, due to supersaturation of vacancies on the Ti-rich side. It could be argued, therefore, that the impurities result in an increased density of dislocations, which, in turn, act as more effective sinks for the vacancies and hence increase the displacement measured. Unfortunately, no mention of void formation was made in their paper.

R. J. BORG: I would like to make one comment—the sort of a plea that I tried to enter yesterday. It seems to me we have some anomalous diffusion data in some bcc metals that are reproducible between laboratories and are very real, but we do not have a good physical and chemical characterization of most of these particular metals. For example, we don't have good high-temperature lattice parameters. We can continue doing diffusion experiments over and over again, and most of us here are set up to do just this, but in order to understand the "anomaly" we have to know more about the other physical properties of these materials. Thus, we should probably reserve judgment as to the ultimate cause of the non-Arrhenius behavior until auxiliary information is available.

G. V. KIDSON: I certainly agree with Dr. Borg that more fundamental information about the physical and chemical properties of both Zr and Ti is needed. One point that has not been discussed at this conference, but may well be relevant is that in many ways the behavior (particularly the mechanical behavior) of the low-temperature phases of these metals is unusual. This could reflect the fact that the "anomalies" are not unique to the bcc phases but are characteristic of the metals themselves.

S. J. ROTHMAN: I dismissed the dislocations in my talk yesterday, and now I should like to mention some of the things that I had to think about before I dismissed them. The point about Fisher's results that you didn't make quite clear is the presence of a possible memory effect. That is, if you take α-Zr up into the β, and you come down into the α again, you get back the same orientation, the same crystals exactly. This means that some sort of memory of the α phase is retained in the β phase; this is apparently analogous to Gruzin's "surfaces of internal division." The question really concerns whether these things anneal out, either at your pre-annealing temperature or at my pre-annealing temperature. It is hard to say whether they will anneal out or not, if the dislocations line up, say in boundary walls.

The other thing is that the great variation of diffusivity between self-diffusion and impurity diffusion can be explained on the basis of dislocations by use of the factor that was introduced by Mortlock and that includes, in effect, in the value of the excess diffusivity the segregation of the impurity to the dislocations. You can assume 100 to 1000 times more impurity in the dislocation than in the lattice. So, really, the dislocations look very much like a possibility.

Further, in some torsion-pendulum internal-friction work on U, reported from Yemelyanov's institute, a small peak above the β-γ transformation temperature was found. This peak, which is very distinct, is found only on heating and disappears after, say, half an hour at a temperature very close to the phase transformation. It could very easily be a dislocation type of peak. So, I would like to echo Kidson's remarks that dislocations don't look too likely, but they are certainly not something that can be dismissed right now.

G. V. KIDSON: I should point out that the published text of my paper was revised to some extent after the conference. The reconsideration of the dislocation model contained in it includes most of the points made by Dr. Rothman, and I am grateful to both Dr. Rothman and Dr. Fisher for the fruitful private discussions during the conference.

C. ALTSTETTER: What is the basis for choosing O to explain the effect? C and N also are easily absorbed.

G. V. KIDSON: The reasons for suggesting O as the impurity responsible for the effect are discussed in my original paper [Can J Phys, **41**, 1563 (1963)]. In addition to the points made there, it should perhaps be remembered that there is a very strong covalent bond between O and Zr in chemical compounds, and this could be of some significance here. I do not know if similar effects occur for C and N, but if they do, their substitution for O will not affect the general features of the model.

R. A. SWALIN: It would appear, in view of the unduly high binding energy needed to explain the effect, that the explanation for the phenomenon lies elsewhere.

G. V. KIDSON: Dr. Swalin has, of course, indicated the most serious difficulty of the O-vacancy model as originally proposed. Before rejecting the model however, one must consider the point I made in my reply to Dr. Altstetter regarding the possibility of a very strong covalent bond between the O and Zr atoms. The directionality and strength of such bonds could lead to considerably larger binding energies than those observed for the C-vacancy complexes in α-Fe, as discussed by Johnson and Damask for example. This is not to suggest, however, that I disagree with Dr. Swalin's point, and I have discussed this at more length in the main text of my paper.

F. R. Winslow (Oak Ridge National Laboratory, Oak Ridge, Tenn.): As long as the data by Federer and Lundy [Trans AIME, **227,** 592–97 (1963)] on Zr^{95} in β-Zr are being used as the "type" specimen for the "anomalous" metals, it should be pointed out that there is an error in the ORNL report that was corrected in the paper. The points at lower temperatures were affected by diffusion of the Cb^{95} daughter so the higher point of each set should be used. This correction makes the curvature more pronounced.

B. J. Shaw (Westinghouse Electric Corp., Pittsburgh, Pa.): I would like to comment on vacancy diffusion in bcc materials in general. Vacancy migration may consist of two stages rather than just one. As a nearest neighbor to a vacancy jumps into the vacant site, it will pass through two barriers. At the halfway stage, symmetrically between these two barriers in the [111] direction, there may be a saddle point or a metastable-equilibrium point. Is it possible that the two components on your Arrhenius plot might be made up first from jumps into the saddle site and then from jumps into equilibrium positions?

The depth of the potential wells involved in this process can, of course, change slightly with temperature.

G. V. Kidson: Dr. Shaw's conjecture is an interesting one. However, because the diffusing atoms must migrate many interatomic distances during the course of their total displacements, they must necessarily pass through both potential barriers many times. It would seem, therefore, that the measured activation energy would simply be the larger of the two. I personally feel it unlikely that a change in the depth of the potential wells of the magnitude necessary to account for the observations would occur.

Discussion of Chapter 26 (p 349)
by J. T. Stanley

A. C. Damask: I am a bit confused by the magnitude of the flux of this electron irradiation. If I understand correctly, the idea of this experiment was that if you have some fault within a crystal, the point defects created by irradiation could go to this fault and thereby create a precipitate nucleus. It would seem to me that you would want as many point defects produced by electrons as you had produced by the neutrons, and yet your dose of 2.2×10^{14} should not create more than 2.2×10^{14} single point defects such as interstitials, whereas your neutron dosage has created about 200 times that.

J. T. Stanley (Oak Ridge National Laboratory, Oak Ridge, Tenn.): No, I don't believe that is right. The cross section for the defect production by electrons is 90 barns compared with 3 barns for neutrons. (written reply) The electron irradiation dose on the original slide was in error and should have been 1.8×10^{16} electrons/cm². Although I was aware of this error before the meeting, it escaped my memory during the meeting. The number of defects introduced by the electron irradiation, therefore, would be approximately 2×10^{17} per cu cm.

D. Lazarus: Is there any damage remaining at room temperature after 2-mev-electron irradiation? I had thought that only close pairs were formed at this energy and that they would all be annealed well below room temperature.

J. T. Stanley: I think the experiments of Lucasson and Walker showed that there is something left after you irradiate at low temperature and warm up to room temperature, and I don't think the fraction of correlated recombination for a low-temperature irradiation would be different than that for a high-temperature irradiation.

Discussion of Chapter 27 (p 357)
by R. A. Johnson

B. J. Shaw: Before potential functions of the sort described by Johnson may be used for lattice calculations, complete stability of the lattice has to be demonstrated. His model must essentially be stable against small homogeneous deformations because the elastic constants are positive. However, his calculations involve movements of atoms, and therefore stability should be demonstrated for both large homogeneous and inhomogeneous deformations. For example, how does the model behave if a large enough homogeneous deformation is given to transform the lattice from bcc to fcc?

My second point concerns the use of the potential function. If only radial laws of force are used in these calculations, the Cauchy relations ($C_{12} = C_{44}$) must be obeyed. Initially the model utilizes a supplementary function outside the first- and second-nearest-neighbor shells, which serves to destroy these relations. It is not quite clear how this function is introduced into the lattice calculations.

Recently I performed some lattice calculations in the bcc transition metals by use of a radial law of force between the atoms in conjunction with a volume potential. The potential functions were adjusted to give the experimentally observed tensor elastic constants. Calculations performed on the vacancy migration show that there is usually a substantial minimum in energy for an atom halfway between two (vacant) lattice sites in the [111] direction. This configuration has been called a "coilion" (from the Greek *koilos* for hollow or vacancy and *iov* for traveler) and is in fact a vacancy analogue to a crowdion.

There would therefore appear to be a slight difference between the results of Johnson and myself, but I think he would agree that results of calculations depend to some extent upon the type of model used and how it is used.

R. A. JOHNSON: The model I have used is completely stable. The average bond energy per atom in the crystallite region has its minimum value in the bcc structure at the lattice constant I have used ($a = 2.86$ A). By use of the same potential, the fcc structure gives a local minimum in the average bond energy per atom. In addition, there is a constraint on the crystallite from the elastic region, and so even if the fcc structure gave the minimum bond energy per atom, the crystallite could not make the transformation.

Concerning the second point, I do not use only radial laws of force because I have a term in the energy that is linear in the volume change and a term that is quadratic in the volume change. The coefficient of the term linear in the volume change is a pressure that is given by $P = (C_{12} - C_{44})/2$ (see H. B. Huntington, in Solid State Physics, Vol 7, edited by F. Seitz and D. Turnbull, Academic Press, Inc., New York, 1958, p 234).

G. J. DIENES: Do you want to comment on the question concerning the shape of the vacancy migration barrier?

R. A. JOHNSON: Yes. I found a small local minimum in the energy at the midpoint configuration for vacancy migration, but it was only metastable by about 0.04 ev and would therefore have very little effect upon the migration process.

D. LAZARUS: In your model have you taken into account the Eshelby correction arising from the image term at the surface?

R. A. JOHNSON: Yes. I made the Eshelby correction for the volume expansion.

D. LAZARUS: What volume did you actually calculate for the relaxed vacancy? Did you find a large relaxation?

R. A. JOHNSON: The relaxations around the vacancy were quite small, for example, the eight nearest neighbors relaxed inward about 2.5% a (a = lattice constant), the six second nearest neighbors relaxed outward about 2.5% a, and the 12 third nearest neighbors moved inward about 0.5% a. The net local volume contraction was only 0.06 atomic volume.

D. N. BESHERS: Isn't that pressure on the outside equivalent to Shaw's volume potential?

R. A. JOHNSON: I don't know exactly how he set up his model, but I believe it should be, yes.

D. GRAHAM: I would like to mention a recent calculation by H. H. Grimes, Lewis Research Center, Cleveland, for this alternative configuration of a vacancy in the bcc lattice. By use of a Morse potential function with parameters for the Na lattice it was observed that the potential energy of the "split vacancy," where an ion is located at $\frac{1}{4}$, $\frac{1}{4}$, $\frac{1}{4}$ with half vacancies at 0, 0, 0 and $\frac{1}{2}$, $\frac{1}{2}$, $\frac{1}{2}$, was lower than that for the conventional vacancy configuration. The calculation is being re-examined in order to establish the conditions under which this configuration might be expected to occur.

R. A. JOHNSON: With such a soft metal as Na for which the ion cores are very far apart, I am not surprised that the midpoint configuration turned out to be stable. Also I would expect that the tetrahedral vacancy mentioned earlier, in which four of the nearest neighbors of a vacancy relax inward and four relax outward, is more likely to be stable in Na than in a harder metal like Fe. (The following note was added in proof. The energy for the tetrahedral vacancy configuration was calculated and was found to be more than 1 ev higher than that for the stable vacancy. Furthermore, the configuration was neither metastable nor a saddle point; that is, no configuration with that symmetry exists when one uses the Fe model in which all the forces on the atoms are zero.)

L. W. BARR: I wonder if you have considered running similar calculations for Na, because we have there the additional evidence from the mass effect. Your calculation might be able to distinguish between the split interstitial and the vacancy, both of which are possible on the evidence from the isotope effect.

R. A. JOHNSON: Yes, a similar calculation for Na could be carried out. The basic physical input into the calculations is the interatomic potential. I have not looked into the Na problem in detail, but I am aware that there are difficulties in arriving at a potential. In Fe the primary contribution to the elastic constants comes from the ion cores, whereas in Na it comes from the conduction electrons. A central two-body nearest-neighbor force would appear to be a more realistic description of the interaction of ion cores

S. J. ROTHMAN: My comment is that you fitted your potential to the elastic constants. Now elastic constants are measured by use of extremely small strains, say 10^{-6}. You are talking now about processes for which the strains are very much larger. I am disturbed by this because I am not sure how applicable such a potential really is.

R. A. JOHNSON: What you say is very true. With the assumption of a central two-body interatomic potential that extends through second neighbors, the elastic constants only give information about the slope and curvature of the potential at first- and second-nearest-neighbor distances. It is certainly quite an extrapolation to draw a smooth and reasonably shaped curve that satisfies the elastic constants. One really has a right to be disturbed about many aspects of such a model calculation as this. But a first-principle calculation obviously cannot be carried out, so models must be used if calculations are to be made. It makes good sense to start with as simple a model as makes any sense at all and add complexities until the model yields good results. There is clearly no guarantee that such a model exists, and when its simplicity is considered, the present model is doing amazingly well.

J. R. COST: I would like to mention briefly experimental quenching results concerning the energy of motion of vacancies in bcc metals. The temperature of the Zener internal-friction peak (at a constant frequency of applied stress) is decreased in the presence of excess vacancies as in quenching. In fcc and hcp alloys it has been possible to quench-in excess vacancies and then follow their decay by observing the return of the internal-friction peak to its equilibrium temperature. When this was tried for a bcc Fe–18 at. % V alloy by use of rapid water quenches from various temperatures up to 1100 C, it was not possible to demonstrate the presence of this peak shift and therefore of excess vacancies. The apparent interpretation of this negative result is that vacancies are annealing away very rapidly and thus have very low energy of motion. A rough calculation based on these results agrees with what you have indicated for bcc—the energy of motion is not more than one third or one fourth of the total self-diffusion energy.

P. G. SHEWMON: One semirelated comment: has anyone used models like this to calculate the energies of more extended defects, such as dislocations with different orientations at grain boundaries?

R. A. JOHNSON: I have considered doing dislocation calculations, but preliminary investigations indicate that they are considerably more difficult to perform than point-defect calculations. I will not attempt to carry them out until I have a better understanding of the approximations I have made in setting up fcc and bcc point-defect models. I understand, though, that R. Bullough at AERE in Harwell is using Born-Mayer-type interatomic forces in present work on an fcc dislocation calculation.

G. J. DIENES: The only other atomic calculation I know of is by Englert and Tompa [J Phys Chem Solids, 21, 306 (1961)]. The important conclusion was that as you get into the core of the dislocation, the elastic approximation becomes very bad. This was a two-dimensional calculation.

A. C. Damask: I would like to call attention to a paper published by T. S. Kê [Sci Sinica, **6,** 623 (1957)]. He studied the internal-friction peak associated with C in γ-Fe stabilized with Mn. From the magnitude of the internal friction as a function of C concentration, he proposed a model based on the association of C with lattice vacancies. Such an experiment may well be possible in α-Fe in which the height of the Snoek peak could be measured as a function of C concentration. At low concentrations, approaching the quenched-in vacancy concentration, the height of the peak may vary with the quench temperature, that is, the vacancy concentration, if the model proposed by Wagenblast and Damask [J Phys Chem Solids, **23,** 221 (1962)] that a C atom trapped by a vacancy no longer contributes to the Snoek peak, is the correct one.

Index